18.08

Inequalities

Inequalities

Proceedings of a Symposium Held at
Wright-Patterson Air Force Base, Ohio,
August 19–27, 1965

EDITED BY

OVED SHISHA

APPLIED MATHEMATICS RESEARCH LABORATORY
AEROSPACE RESEARCH LABORATORIES
WRIGHT-PATTERSON AIR FORCE BASE, OHIO

ACADEMIC PRESS   New York and London 1967

BPR'68

SPONSORED BY THE OFFICE OF AEROSPACE RESEARCH,
UNITED STATES AIR FORCE, WRIGHT-PATTERSON AIR
FORCE BASE, OHIO
CONTRACT NUMBER AF-33(615)-3050

ACADEMIC PRESS INC.
111 Fifth Avenue, New York, New York 10003

United Kingdom Edition published by
ACADEMIC PRESS INC. (LONDON) LTD.
Berkeley Square House, London W.1

LIBRARY OF CONGRESS CATALOG CARD NUMBER: 66-30102

PRINTED IN THE UNITED STATES OF AMERICA

Contributors

Numbers in parentheses refer to the pages on which the authors' contributions begin.

E. F. BECKENBACH, *Department of Mathematics, University of California, Los Angeles, California* (17, 37)

N. G. DE BRUIJN, *Technological University, Eindhoven, Netherlands* (57)

J. B. DIAZ, *Institute for Fluid Dynamics and Applied Mathematics, University of Maryland, College Park, Maryland, and U.S. Naval Ordnance Laboratory, White Oak, Silver Spring, Maryland* (73, 79)

KY FAN, *Department of Mathematics, University of California, Santa Barbara, California* (105)

AVNER FRIEDMAN, *Department of Mathematics, Northwestern University, Evanston, Illinois* (119)

R. P. GOSSELIN, *University of Connecticut, Storrs, Connecticut* (127)

SAMUEL KARLIN, *Department of Mathematics, Stanford University, Stanford, California* (137)

J. E. LITTLEWOOD, *Trinity College, Cambridge, England* (151)

MARVIN MARCUS, *Department of Mathematics, University of California, Santa Barbara, California* (163)

ALBERT W. MARSHALL, *Boeing Scientific Research Laboratories, Seattle, Washington* (177)

F. T. METCALF, *Institute for Fluid Dynamics and Applied Mathematics, University of Maryland, College Park, Maryland, and U.S. Naval Ordnance Laboratory, White Oak, Silver Spring, Maryland* (73, 79)

B. MOND, *Aerospace Research Laboratories, Wright-Patterson Air Force Base, Dayton, Ohio* (191, 293)

T. S. MOTZKIN, *Department of Mathematics, University of California, Los Angeles, California* (199, 205, 225)

INGRAM OLKIN, *Stanford University, Stanford, California and Boeing Scientific Research Laboratories, Seattle, Washington* (177)

L. E. PAYNE, *Department of Mathematics, Cornell University, Ithaca, New York* (241)

GEORGE PÓLYA, *Department of Mathematics, Stanford University, Stanford, California* (1)

FRANK PROSCHAN, *Boeing Scientific Research Laboratories, Seattle, Washington* (177)

I. J. SCHOENBERG, *Mathematics Research Center, U.S. Army, University of Wisconsin, Madison, Wisconsin* (255)

OVED SHISHA, *Aerospace Research Laboratories, Wright-Patterson Air Force Base, Dayton, Ohio* (191, 293)

OLGA TAUSSKY, *Department of Mathematics, California Institute of Technology, Pasadena, California* (309)

JOHN TODD, *Department of Mathematics, California Institute of Technology, Pasadena, California* (321)

ALEXANDER WEINSTEIN, *Institute for Fluid Dynamics and Applied Mathematics, University of Maryland, College Park, Maryland* (329)

Y. K. WONG, *Department of Mathematics, State University of New York at Albany, Albany, New York* (339)

ZVI ZIEGLER, *Department of Mathematics, Technion–Israel Institute of Technology, Haifa, Israel* (137)

Preface

This volume consists, essentially, of the one-hour lectures presented at the Symposium on Inequalities held at Wright-Patterson Air Force Base, Ohio, during August 19–27, 1965. The symposium was sponsored by Aerospace Research Laboratories, a component of the Office of Aerospace Research, United States Air Force.

The purpose of this symposium was to bring together mathematicians working in areas where inequalities play a basic role, so that they could not only present formal lectures, but also exchange ideas informally.

In addition to the one-hour lectures, the symposium also included 15-minute talks, as well as informal "workshops."

The papers in this volume are arranged in the alphabetic order of their authors' names. There is, however, one exception: the first paper in the book is Professor G. Pólya's lecture "Inequalities and the Principle of Nonsufficient Reason." It was the first lecture of the symposium and served as an introduction to it.

I would like to thank Aerospace Research Laboratories (ARL) and its commander at the time, Colonel Robert E. Fontana, for sponsoring this symposium. Thanks are due in particular to Lt. Colonel John V. Armitage, Director of the Applied Mathematics Research Laboratory of ARL, for his great interest in the symposium and his efforts in its behalf. I am also very grateful to Dr. Bertram Mond, Mr. J. Edwin Wilson, and Captain David E. Greene, all of ARL, for their devoted work, before and during the symposium.

Academic Press Inc., the publishers, have shown much interest in the symposium since the early planning stage; I am most thankful to them for this and for their continued efforts during the preparation of the volume for publication.

It is also a pleasure to take this opportunity to thank all the participants in the symposium for making it such an interesting and congenial affair.

It is hoped that this book, including such a wide range of topics, will benefit a large audience of professional mathematicians and graduate students working in a variety of fields in pure and applied mathematics.

Wright-Patterson Air Force Base, Ohio
July 1967   OVED SHISHA

Contents

Uncertainty Principles in Fourier Analysis
N. G. De Bruijn

Inequalities Complementary to Cauchy's Inequality for Sums of Real Numbers
J. B. Diaz and F. T. Metcalf

Variations of Wirtinger's Inequality
J. B. Diaz and F. T. Metcalf

Inequalities for the Sum of Two M-Matrices
Ky Fan

On Some Inequalities and Their Application to the Cauchy Problem
Avner Friedman

General Subadditive Functions
R. P. Gosselin

Chebyshevian Spline Functions
Samuel Karlin and Zvi Ziegler

Some New Inequalities and Unsolved Problems
J. E. Littlewood

Lengths of Tensors
Marvin Marcus

Monotonicity of Ratios of Means and Other Applications of Majorization
Albert W. Marshall, Ingram Olkin, and Frank Proschan

On Spline Functions
I. J. Schoenberg

Bounds on Differences of Means
O. Shisha and B. Mond

Positive-Definite Matrices
Olga Taussky

Inequalities of Chebyshev, Zolotareff, Cauer, and W. B. Jordan
John Todd

On the New Maximum-Minimum Theory of Eigenvalues

Alexander Weinstein

Generalizations of Ostrowski's Inequality for Matrices with Dominant Principal Diagonal

Y. K. Wong

Inequalities and the Principle of Nonsufficient Reason

GEORGE PÓLYA
Department of Mathematics
Stanford University
Stanford, California

I begin with a statement that will surprise nobody in this audience: Inequalities play a role in most branches of mathematics and have widely different applications. An introductory talk such as this should survey at least parts of the existing material; it should find connections between inequalities that belong to different branches, and point out promising spots where there is a chance to do some interesting work. I shall try to do a little in these directions by emphasizing heuristic considerations. The name of the "heuristic principle" that will serve us as a sort of 'leitmotiv' is included in the title of this talk.

I may be excused if I take many of my examples from my own work: I know, naturally, the heuristic background of these examples more intimately. The following text has profited by conversations I had before, during, and after the Symposium. I wish to thank here especially my friend and colleague, Professor Max Schiffer.

1. The Principle of Nonsufficient Reason

The term "principle of sufficient reason" originates with Leibnitz, but the principle itself was essentially known long before him, in some form. Leibnitz stated it in various forms; here is a short one: "Nihil est sine ratione." That is, "There is nothing without reason."

The term "principle of nonsufficient reason" (NSR) was used in certain discussions on the theory of probability [4, p. 41]. I am not able to tell where or when it was initiated, or even to give an authoritative formulation of it; I take it to be a particular case of Leibnitz's principle which he himself has repeatedly stated. Here is a short formulation: "There is no difference without reason." Here is a more elaborate one: "Where there is no sufficient reason to distinguish there can be no distinction."

Passages to the same effect can be found, as I have just said, on several pages of Leibnitz's works, but I found only one such passage, extracted from his manuscripts and posthumously printed, which explicitly refers to

1

mathematical matters.[1] Freely condensed in a few words, we could state it so: "No difference in the condition, no difference in the solution." I wish to reformulate it freely, but carefully: "Where there is no difference between the unknowns in the [determining] condition there can be no difference between the values of the unknowns satisfying the condition."[2] I think that this passage must be interpreted in two different ways according as we do, or do not, take into account the word "determining" originally written, but afterwards deleted, by Leibnitz. Yet we will be in a better position to discuss this later, after some examples.

2. Examples

Let us consider four quite elementary problems.

(I) *Determine n positive numbers* $x_1, x_2, \ldots, x_n$ *of which the sum s is given,*

$$x_1 + x_2 + \cdots + x_n = s,$$

so that their product $x_1 x_2 \cdots x_n$ *becomes a maximum.*

There is no difference between the unknowns $x_1, x_2, \ldots, x_n$ in the condition. In fact, the condition is "fully symmetric" in the n unknowns: Any permutation of the unknowns leaves the condition unchanged. And, in fact, NSR is vindicated in the present case: The maximum in question is attained if and only if all unknowns have the same value, that is when

$$x_k = \frac{s}{n} \quad \text{for} \quad k = 1, 2, \ldots, n.$$

If we change the proposed problem by considering the minimum of that product instead of its maximum, NSR is still vindicated in a way: There is no minimum, there is no solution, and, there being none, the solution can make no distinction between the unknowns. If we change the proposed problem more by considering the minimum of that product *and* nonnegative real values of the unknowns, then NSR fails: the trivial minimum 0 is attained when some of the unknowns, but not all, are equal to 0, and so there must be a difference between the values of the unknowns in the solution.

---

[1] "Cum omnia ab una parte se habent ut ab alia parte in datis [determinantibus], ⟨tunc⟩ etiam in quaesitis seu consequentibus omnia se eodem modo habitura utrinque. Quia nulla potest reddi ratio diversitatis, quae utique ex datis petenda est." See [*1*, p. 519]. "If everything in the [determining] data is just so in one case as in the other, then also in the unknowns or the consequences everything will be the same in both cases. Since no reason can be given for the difference which in any case must be derived from the data." The square brackets [ ] enclose a word deleted by Leibnitz, the pointed brackets ⟨ ⟩ a word added later.

[2] For the usage of the term "condition" see [7, Vol. 1, pp. 119–120].

(II) *Find the numbers x and y satisfying the system of two equations*

$$x + y = 3, \qquad xy = 2.$$

Here NSR strikingly fails: There are two solutions,

$$\text{either} \qquad x = 1, \quad y = 2, \qquad \text{or} \qquad x = 2, \quad y = 1,$$

but the unknowns x and y do not get the same value in either although the condition is fully symmetric with respect to them.[3]

(III) *Find the numbers x, y, and z satisfying the system of three equations*

$$x^2 + 2y^2 + 4z^2 + 3(yz + zx + xy) = 16,$$
$$4x^2 + y^2 + 2z^2 + 3(yz + zx + xy) = 16,$$
$$2x^2 + 4y^2 + z^2 + 3(yz + zx + xy) = 16.$$

The condition is symmetric with respect to the unknowns x, y, and z in the following sense: Any one of these unknowns can be substituted for any other by a suitable cyclic permutation which leaves the condition expressed by the system of three equations unchanged.[4]

The three equations proposed imply that

$$x^2 = y^2 = z^2$$

and hence we can easily derive all eight solutions [values of (x, y, z) satisfying the system]. There are two solutions

$$(1, 1, 1) \qquad \text{and} \qquad (-1, -1, -1)$$

that attribute the same value to x, y, and z. Yet this is only a "partial success" for NSR: There are other solutions, namely all the six remaining solutions

$$(-2, 2, 2) \qquad (2, -2, 2) \qquad (2, 2, -2)$$
$$(2, -2, -2) \qquad (-2, 2, -2) \qquad (-2, -2, 2)$$

which do not attribute the same value to all three unknowns.

(IV) *In a tetrahedron, given L, the sum of the lengths of four edges forming a skew quadrilateral, find the maximum of the volume of the tetrahedron.*

---

[3] This example is easily generalized: Consider n unknowns of which the n elementary symmetric functions are given; cf. [7, Vol. 2, p. 161].

[4] More generally, the condition of a problem is called *symmetric with respect to a certain subset S* of the unknowns if there is a group of permutations of the unknowns that leaves the condition unchanged and is transitive with respect to the subset S, that is, contains permutations mapping any element of S onto any other element of S. We shall frequently refer to this definition in the sequel.

The two edges of the tetrahedron that do not belong to the skew quadrilateral with perimeter L are opposite edges (having no common vertex); let us call them "free" edges, and let us call the four other edges, belonging to the quadrilateral, "connected" edges. The condition of the proposed problem is symmetric with respect to the four connected edges; it is also symmetric with respect to the two free edges, but it is by no means symmetric with respect to all six edges. The solution is easily obtained (by "partial variation," see [6, Vol. 1, p. 128]) and vindicates NSR: When the maximum of the volume is attained, all four connected edges are of the same length $L/4$, also both free edges are of the same length (namely, $\sqrt{3}L/6$) and two faces contiguous to the same free edge are perpendicular to each other.

3. Restatement: The Principle of Symmetry

As we have said in Sec. 1, the sentence "No difference in the condition, no difference in the solution" is capable of two interpretations between which Leibnitz was apparently hesitating. By the examples of the foregoing section and the definition stated in footnote 4, we are led almost unavoidably to the following two statements:

I. *Unknowns with respect to which the condition is symmetric must obtain the same value in the solution, if the solution is unique.*

II. *Unknowns with respect to which the condition is symmetric may be expected to obtain the same value in the solution.*

Statement I is sufficiently clear and general (and there is not much need to reformulate it in logical jargon). Its proof is obvious: Let x_α and x_β be two of those unknowns with respect to which the condition is symmetric. Then there is a permutation of the unknowns leaving the condition unchanged that substitutes x_α for x_β. As there is a unique solution, that is, just one system of values for the unknowns satisfying the condition, x_α must obtain the same value as x_β.[5]

Statement II has no mathematical meaning, and it has no intention to have one: it is heuristic advice. We follow this advice if we devote appropriate attention to two possibilities: First, that there may be unknowns with respect to which the condition is symmetric, and second, that such unknowns may get the same value in the solution.[6]

I am going to survey a few classes of inequalities in paying due attention to these two possibilities.

[5] Cf. [6, Vol. 1, pp. 187–188, Ex. 41].
[6] Cf. [7, Vol. 2, pp. 160–164, Ex. 15.21–15.40].

In the following, I retain the abbreviation NSR for statement II. If the reader prefers, he may read NSR also as "the principle of symmetry" or "the heuristic principle of symmetry." This principle expresses an expectation which may or may not be vindicated by the outcome. More precisely there are three cases; all three presuppose that the problem in question has solutions (at least one solution). Unknowns with respect to which the condition is symmetric may obtain the same value

(a) in all solutions, or
(b) in no solution, or
(c) in some solutions, but not in all solutions.

In case (a), NSR (the principle of symmetry) is vindicated, in (b) it fails, and in (c) we shall say it is "partially vindicated." [Case (c) is illustrated by example (III) of Sec. 2; for a more important illustration see Sec. 6]. I think that it is instructive to compare these cases; they certainly challenge the problem-solver who naturally tries to foresee which case will present itself eventually.

4. Symmetric Functions

Many of the best known and most useful elementary inequalities result from appropriate particular cases of the following general problem:

Let $f(x_1, x_2, \ldots, x_n)$ and $g(x_1, x_2, \ldots, x_n)$ be symmetric functions, homogeneous of the same degree and positive for all positive values of the variables $x_1, x_2, \ldots, x_n$. Find the maximum of the ratio

$$\frac{f(x_1, x_2, \ldots, x_n)}{g(x_1, x_2, \ldots, x_n)}.$$

And just in those well-known, useful cases, the solution of this problem fully vindicates NSR: The maximum is attained if and only if

$$x_1 = x_2 = \cdots = x_n.$$

Thus, the inequality between the arithmetic and geometric means results from the particular case where

$$f = x_1 x_2 \cdots x_n, \qquad g = (x_1 + x_2 + \cdots + x_n)^n.$$

Further cases are listed in [3, p. 109].

5. Symmetric Functionals

The isoperimetric problem requires to find the minimum of $L^2 A^{-1}$ where L denotes the perimeter and A the area of a simple closed plane curve. If the isoperimetric problem is restricted to polygons with n sides considered as particular curves, it is symmetric with respect to the n sides and to the n angles of the polygon. Hence NSR suggests that all sides, and also all angles, should be equal. In fact, this suggestion is fully confirmed: The minimum of L^2A^{-1} is attained if and only if the polygon with n sides is regular.

If the isoperimetric problem is taken unrestrictedly so that all simple closed plane curves are admitted, NSR, interpreted in an appropriate extension, suggests that each point of the curve should be situated in the same way with respect to the whole curve, and, especially, that the curvature of the curve should be the same at each of its points. In fact, this suggestion is fully confirmed: The minimum of L^2A^{-1} is attained if and only if the curve is a circle.

In passing from polygons with n sides to general closed curves, we have enlarged the scope of the principle of nonsufficient reason, or heuristic principle of symmetry. Let us try to see a little more clearly in what sense this scope can be reasonably enlarged.

The area A and the perimeter L are functionals of a simple closed plane curve which "depend in the same way on each point (on each element) of the curve." Let us call functionals of this nature "symmetric functionals."[7]

A similarity transformation of the curve (enlargement in the proportion of 1 to c, say) affects A and L in a simple, obvious way (changes A into c^2A and L into cL). Hence we may call A and L "homogeneous functionals," A of degree 2, L of degree 1.

The terminology introduced may help us to see more clearly the analogy between certain simple and other much less simple mathematical facts. For the sake of concreteness let us compare two inequalities: the inequality between the arithmetic and geometric means and the isoperimetric inequality. We express the essential facts by the two following lines:

$$n \leqq \frac{x_1 + x_2 + \cdots + x_n}{(x_1 x_2 \cdots x_n)^{1/n}} < \infty, \tag{1}$$

$$4\pi \leqq \frac{L^2}{A} < \infty. \tag{2}$$

---

[7] The analogy to symmetric functions of n variables is weak in a respect which, however, is irrelevant when seen from our standpoint based on the definition of footnote 4: When we take the curve as a polygon with n vertices (x_1, y_1), (x_2, y_2), ..., (x_n, y_n), the expressions for A and L in terms of the coordinates of the vertices are not left invariant by all $n!$ permutations of the n vertices, that is, by the whole symmetric group, but only by one of its cyclic subgroups—this subgroup, however, is transitive.

In case (1) we consider the ratio of two symmetric functions which are homogeneous of the same degree; in case (2) we consider the ratio of two symmetric functionals which are homogeneous of the same degree. In both cases, the ratio is homogeneous of degree 0. Hence, in case (1) the ratio depends only on the proportion $x_1 : x_2 : \cdots : x_n$; in case (2) the ratio depends only on the shape, not on the size or on the location, of the curve. In both cases, the upper bound of the quantity considered is unattainable, infinite, and the lower bound is attained if and only if there is perfect symmetry, that is, when all variables $x_1, x_2, \ldots, x_n$ obtain the same value and all points of the curve are contained in the same way in the curve.

6. Examples of Success

Besides A and L, there are several other functionals of a simple closed plane curve C which are homogeneous and "symmetric." Here is a list of the symbols and the names of some of the better explored functionals of this nature; D stands for the domain surrounded by the curve C:[8]

A, area of D;

L, perimeter of C;

I, polar moment of inertia of D with respect to the centroid of D which we conceive here as covered with matter of uniform surface density 1;

$\bar{r}$, outer conformal radius of C;

$\dot{r}$, maximum inner conformal radius of C;

P, torsional rigidity of D which is conceived now as the cross section of a uniform and isotropic elastic cylinder twisted around an axis perpendicular to D;

Λ, principal frequency of D conceived as the equilibrium position of a uniform and uniformly stretched elastic membrane fixed along the boundary C of D;

C, electrostatic capacity of D conceived as a thin plate, a conductor of electricity.

We can take any two of these eight functionals and ask whether there is between them an inequality analogous to the classical isoperimetric inequality between A and L. In most cases the answer is *yes* and can be proved. In some cases, where it is not yet fully proved, the answer *yes* can be reasonably conjectured. There is just one case in which we definitely know that the answer is *no*. The known results are condensed into the

---

[8] See [13, pp. 1–3] for first definitions, and later chapters for full details.

following compound statement (3) which needs a few additional explanations:

$$\dot{r}^4 \leqq \left(\frac{j}{\Lambda}\right)^4 \underset{(?)}{\leqq} \frac{2P}{\pi} \leqq \left(\frac{A}{\pi}\right)^2 \left\{ \begin{array}{c} \leqq \dfrac{2I}{\pi} \overset{(!)}{\leqq} \\[2mm] \leqq \dfrac{\pi C^4}{2} \underset{(?)}{\leqq} \end{array} \right\} \dot{r}^4 \leqq \left(\frac{L}{2\pi}\right)^4. \qquad (3)$$

The two inequalities in (3) which are marked by (?) under the sign $\leqq$ are only conjectural; further research is needed to decide whether the suggested relation between Λ and P is correct or not and the same holds for the relation between C and $\dot{r}$. There is a difference, however. The relations

$$\dot{r}^4 \leqq \frac{2P}{\pi}, \qquad \left(\frac{j}{\Lambda}\right)^2 \leqq \frac{A}{\pi}, \qquad (4)$$

where $j = 2.4048\ldots$ denotes the first positive zero of the Bessel function $\mathcal{J}_0(x)$, can be established independently of any conjecture. [They would follow from the conjectural relation between Λ and P in combination with others displayed in (3) and already proven.] Yet the relation between C and L (which depends on that between C and $\dot{r}$) remains to be elucidated.

There is no "isoperimetric inequality" between I and C: the quantity IC^{-4} has 0 as lower bound and ∞ as upper bound, and (3) tries to express this fact too.

The relation between I and $\dot{r}$ (the sign $\leqq$ is qualified by the sign (!) printed over it) is peculiar: the case of equality is attained if the curve is a circle, but it is also attained for infinitely many different shapes so that NSR is "partially vindicated" in the terminology explained at the end of Sec. 3.

In the other cases [five mentioned by (3) and two by (4)], NSR is fully vindicated: equality is attained by the circle and only by the circle.[9]

Observe that from the inequalities explicitly listed in (3) and (4) several others immediately follow. Thus, the classical isoperimetric inequality between A and L follows from three other inequalities: between A and I, I and $\dot{r}$, $\dot{r}$ and L. Hence, still more triumph for NSR.

Are the two conjectured inequalities listed in (3) [between Λ and P, and between C and $\dot{r}$] true? The success of the circle in so many analogous cases seems to make them more likely or, at any rate, more interesting.

By the way, this section has tried to illustrate that the survey of a chapter of mathematics (as the chapter on "isoperimetric inequalities") can be enlivened, and so benefit, by heuristic considerations.

---

[9] See [13] for all comments on (3) and (4); for an additional remark on the case of equality see also [10, pp. 436–439].

7. Examples of Failure

We have seen by now almost too many cases where NSR is successful. Let us then construct a case, with the functionals considered in the foregoing section, where NSR fails.

Of the eight functionals considered in Sec. 6, there are three that are clearly more "elementary" than the other five, namely A, L, and I. (The computation of these three involves only the evaluation of definite integrals whereas the computation of any one of the remaining five functionals depends on the solution of a partial differential equation.) Each of the three combinations

$$L^2 A^{-1}, \qquad A^{-1} I, \qquad I^{-1} L^4$$

has ∞ as least upper bound and attains its minimum for the circle and only for the circle [this fact is already contained in (3)]. Let us consider, then, the simplest homogeneous combination of degree 0 of all three functionals, $AL^2 I^{-1}$. Here is what is known at present about the bounds of this combination [9]:

$$16 < AL^2 I^{-1} < \infty \qquad \text{for all curves,} \tag{5a}$$

$$48 < AL^2 I^{-1} \underset{(?)}{\leq} 108 \qquad \text{for convex curves,} \tag{5b}$$

$$AL^2 I^{-1} = 8\pi^2 \qquad \text{for the circle.} \tag{5c}$$

It can be proved that $AL^2 I^{-1}$ has a finite upper bound for convex domains but it is just a conjecture [see the sign (?) under the sign $\leq$ in (5b)] that this bound is 108, the value attained by the equilateral triangle. The other bounds given by (5a) and (5b) (two lower bounds and one upper) are well-established and are best-possible, although unattainable, bounds. Altogether, there are four different bounds for the functional $AL^2 I^{-1}$ which is "symmetric" and depends only on the shape of the curve (as AL^{-2}), but the circle yields none of the four bounds (no lower and no upper bound) for all curves and for convex curves, since[10]

$$48 < 8\pi^2 < 108.$$

There are other combinations, homogeneous of degree 0, of three "symmetric" functionals chosen among those considered in Sec. 6, which behave analogously to $AL^2 I^{-1}$. Let us quote just one (see [8]):

$$0 < A^4 P^{-1} I^{-1} < \infty \qquad \text{for all curves,} \tag{6a}$$

$$27 < A^4 P^{-1} I^{-1} \underset{(?)}{\leq} 45 \qquad \text{for convex curves,} \tag{6b}$$

$$A^4 P^{-1} I^{-1} = 4\pi^2 \qquad \text{for the circle.} \tag{6c}$$

---

[10] In the strict sense laid down in Sec. 3, this failure of the circle has to be regarded as a failure of NSR only if the upper bound for convex figures is attained.

The facts are closely analogous to those of the foregoing case and the notation is the same. It is well established that $A^4P^{-1}I^{-1}$ has a finite upper bound for convex domains, but it is just a conjecture that this bound is 45, the value attained by the equilateral triangle. The other three bounds given for $A^4P^{-1}I^{-1}$ by (6a) and (6b) are well-established best-possible, but unattainable, bounds. None of the four bounds considered is attained by the circle since

$$27 < 4\pi^2 < 45.$$

We could have scarcely foreseen a priori that NSR would be more successful with the combinations of two than with three functionals.

8. A Heuristic Remark on Inequalities as Side Conditions in Extremum Problems

Each of the statements (5b) and (6b) has a conjectural half, and both conjectures attribute the maximum to the equilateral triangle among all convex figures. This peculiar agreement will be somewhat elucidated by the considerations of the present section.

(I) We start from a simple and useful type of problem which is widely known nowadays: *The point* (x, y, z) *is subject to n side conditions* (*linear inequalities*)

$$a_\nu x + b_\nu y + c_\nu z + d_\nu \leq 0 \qquad \text{for} \quad \nu = 1, 2, \ldots, n.$$

Find the maximum of the linear function $ax + by + cz$. (The numbers a_ν, b_ν, c_ν, d_ν, a, b, c are given; x, y, z, unknown.)

By the linear inequalities, the point (x, y, z) is restricted to a convex polyhedron P which we suppose finite and nondegenerate. It is easy to see that there must be a solution (x, y, z) coinciding with (and at which the desired maximum must be attained) one of the *vertices* of the polyhedron P. (There may be other solutions; the maximum may be reached also at points of P different from the vertices.)

That is, there is necessarily a solution (a way of attaining the extremum) such that the case of equality is attained in not less than a standard number, namely three, of side conditions.

(II) It is easy to extend the foregoing consideration to linear functions of n variables (to n dimensions). Can we extend it to more comprehensive classes of functions?

The following simple example can teach us some caution: *Find the extrema* (*maximum and minimum*) *of*

$$x^2 + y^2 + z^2 + w^2$$

where

$$w = 1 - x - y - z$$

under the side conditions

$$x \geq 0, \quad y \geq 0, \quad z \geq 0, \quad w \geq 0.$$

These side conditions restrict the point (x, y, z) to a closed tetrahedron with vertices

$$(0, 0, 0), \quad (1, 0, 0), \quad (0, 1, 0), \quad (0, 0, 1).$$

The desired maximum, which is 1, is assumed just at these four vertices, which conforms to the pattern (I). The minimum, however, which is $\frac{1}{4}$, is assumed, in conformity with NSR, only at the centroid $(\frac{1}{4}, \frac{1}{4}, \frac{1}{4})$ of the tetrahedron. And this centroid is an interior point; it attains the case of equality in none of the four side conditions.

This example may douse sanguine hopes: A very general extension of (I) which would be also simple seems now rather unlikely. And so it may be advisable to remain on the heuristic level. Without attempting a precise, but possibly complicated statement we just intend to pay due attention to the eventuality that an extremum sought in a domain limited by several side conditions may be attained on the boundary of the domain, on a sort of edge or at a corner, where the case of equality is reached in a "considerable number" of side conditions.

(III) Let us compare two situations, one elementary [cf. (II)], the other not so elementary:

$$1 \leq \frac{(x_1 + x_2 + \cdots + x_n)^2}{x^2 + x_2{}^2 + \cdots + x_n{}^2} \leq n, \tag{7}$$

$$\frac{1}{8} \leq \frac{\bar{r}}{L} \leq \frac{1}{2\pi}. \tag{8}$$

In situation (7) we consider the ratio of two symmetric functions of n variables, in situation (8) the ratio of two symmetric functionals of a simple closed curve C surrounding a plane domain D. In both situations the ratio considered is homogeneous of degree 0. In both situations we restrict the variability. In situation (7) we consider only nonnegative real values of the variables so that

$$x_1 \geq 0, \quad x_2 \geq 0, \ldots, x_n \geq 0. \tag{7a}$$

In situation (8) we consider only convex domains D so that in each point of the boundary curve C

$$\text{curvature} \geq 0. \tag{8a}$$

In fact, these restrictions are irrelevant for the upper bound which is attained in conformity with NSR in both situations. In situation (7) the upper bound is attained when

$$x_1 = x_2 = \cdots = x_n$$

and it is the same for all real values of the variables as in the subdomain of nonnegative values. In situation (8) the upper bound is attained when C is a circle and it is the same for all simple closed plane curves as for the subset of convex curves. (See [*12*, Vol. 2, p. 21, Ex. 124].)

Yet the restrictions of the variability stated above are essential for the lower bound. In situation (7) the lower bound is attained when just one of the unknowns is different from 0, for instance when

$$x_1 > 0, \qquad x_2 = x_3 = \cdots = x_n = 0$$

so that the case of equality is attained in all inequalities (7a) except one. In situation (8) the lower bound is attained when the convex curve C degenerates into a straight-line segment (regarded as doubly covered, so that L equals the length of the segment multiplied by 2; see [*11*]). Thus the case of equality in (8a) is attained at all but two points of the minimizing C (where the curvature does not exist or may be regarded as ∞).

(IV) We consider now a situation analogous to (8). We conceive the domain D as covered with matter of surface density 1, and we let I_1 and I_2 denote the moments of inertia of D about the principal axes of inertia through the centroid of D. (With the notation of Sec. 6, $I_1 + I_2 = I$.) We assume that $I_1 \leq I_2$. If we consider only convex domains D

$$6\sqrt{3} \leq \frac{A^2}{I_1} < \infty, \tag{9}$$

the lower bound is attained for the equilateral triangle and for no other convex figure.[11]

As in the situation (8), the minimizing figure is such that the case of equality in (8a) is attained at almost all points of its boundary; in fact, at all points except three.

(V) Let us return to the conjectures given in (5b) and (6b); both assert that the maximum of a certain functional of a convex curve is attained by the equilateral triangle. If we compare these conjectures with the facts discussed in this section, the conjectures appear, it seems to me, more understandable, perhaps more likely—at any rate more interesting.

We have discussed several situations which are similar in one respect: When the extremum is attained, the case of equality is also attained in "many" inequalities which are side conditions of the extremum problem. This was so in the cases here emphasized, but need not be so in other cases as we have already observed in subsection (II). The upper bounds in (7) and (8) (which are upper bounds also under restriction to $x_\nu \geq 0$ and to convex C, respectively) offer good illustrations.

---

[11] This follows easily from [*8*, pp. 114–115]. For establishing uniqueness, we need the remark that the only triangle for which $I_1 = I_2$ is the equilateral triangle.

9. Additional Examples

The remarks offered in the foregoing sections can be illustrated by many more examples and can be followed up in various directions. There remain more parallels to be drawn between seemingly unconnected facts, and more promising spots to point out where some intriguing problem waits for its solution. The variety of possibilities should be illustrated by just a few briefly treated examples.

(I) *Polygons.* Is NSR valid for polygons when it is valid for all closed curves? More explicitly: It is known that the minimum of a certain "symmetric" functional F which depends on the shape of a variable closed curve is attained by the circle (L^2A^{-1} is the principal example of such a functional). Is the minimum attained by the regular polygon when F is restricted to polygons with n sides?

The answer is *yes* when F is L^2A^{-1}, and this was essentially known to the ancient Greek geometers. The answer *yes* has been proved, at least for convex polygons, in the case when F is IA^{-2} [8, 9]. A little is known about the following five functionals:

$$\bar{r}^{-2}A, \quad \bar{r}^2A^{-1}, \quad P^{-1}A^2, \quad \Lambda^2A, \quad C^2A^{-1}.$$

Each of them is a minimum for the equilateral triangle if restricted to triangles, and also a minimum for the square if restricted to quadrilaterals (see [13, pp. 158–159]).

To go beyond these results in any one of the many possible directions seems to me a challenging but not an easy problem.

At any rate, this example has tried to illustrate how a heuristic principle can lead us to interesting problems.

(II) *Polyhedra.* Let S stand for the surface area of a closed surface of the topological type of the sphere and V for the volume of the region surrounded by the surface. The classical isoperimetric problem is concerned with L^2A^{-1} in the plane and with S^3V^{-2} in space. In the plane we have considered L^2A^{-1} for general curves and for polygons; analogously, we are going to distinguish two cases in space.

Considered for all closed surfaces, S^3V^{-2} attains its minimum for the sphere and only for the sphere. We can regard this fact as a success for NSR since we can regard S and V as "symmetric" functionals.

Now, let us consider the problem of the minimum of S^3V^{-2} for polyhedra with a given number f of faces. This problem seems to be symmetric with respect to the f faces, but symmetric also with respect to the vertices, with respect to the edges, with respect to the dihedral angles attached to the edges, and with respect to the face angles (ordinary angles contained in each face). Therefore, NSR induces us to expect that constituent parts of the same nature will be equal: all faces congruent, all edges of the same length, all dihedral angles equal, all face angles equal, all solid angles attached to the vertices congruent. In a word, NSR suggests "quantitative uniformity" and so it leads us to expect that the polyhedron with f faces minimizing S^3V^{-2} will be regular.

Yet this expectation fails conspicuously. In the first place, it fails for almost all values of f because a regular polyhedron exists only in five cases, for $f = 4$, 6, 8, 12, and 20. And it even fails in two out of these five cases: for $f = 8$ and $f = 20$, the polyhedron yielding the minimum of S^3V^{-2} is not regular. Thus NSR succeeds only in three cases: for $f = 4$, 6, and 12, S^3V^{-2} is minimized by the regular tetrahedron, the cube, and the regular dodecahedron, respectively.[12]

Yet even behind such a disastrous failure of NSR there may be hidden a grain of success. Certainly, NSR's suggestion of "quantitative uniformity" fails except in those three cases: $f = 4$, 6, and 12. For all values of f, however, there is, in fact, "qualitative uniformity" in one respect: It can be shown that just three edges start from each vertex of the minimizing polyhedron.[13] Now, this qualitative uniformity of the vertices renders the qualitative uniformity of the faces impossible: All faces cannot be surrounded by the same number of edges, except in the cases $f = 4$, 6, and 12 (this follows easily from Euler's theorem on polyhedra). Yet there is, possibly, "approximate qualitative uniformity" in the faces: According to an ingenious conjecture of Goldberg, two faces of the minimizing polyhedron which differ in the number of surrounding edges, cannot differ by more than one unit (except the cases $f = 11$ and $f = 13$, see [2]).

The aim of this example was to illustrate the flexibility of our heuristic principle.

(III) *Bounded analytic function.* An analytic function $f(z)$ of the complex variable z which is regular in the unit circle (for $|z| < 1$) can be expanded there in a power series:

$$f(z) = a_0 + a_1 z + a_2 z^2 + \cdots + a_n z^n + \cdots.$$

Landau [5, pp. 26–29] gave an elegant solution of the following problem: *Supposing that $f(z)$ is regular and $|f(z)| \leq 1$ for $|z| < 1$, find the maximum of $|a_0 + a_1 + a_2 + \cdots + a_n|$.*

We are here concerned with one feature of Landau's result: The function

---

[12] See [2]; an essential gap left in this remarkable paper of Goldberg was later filled by L. Fejes Tóth.

[13] This is, by the way, the reason why the regular octahedron and icosahedron are not minimizing polyhedra.

$f(z)$ that attains the desired maximum remains regular in the closed unit circle, for $|z| \leq 1$, and

$$|f(z)| = 1 \quad \text{for} \quad |z| = 1.$$

We may recognize in this fact an illustration of the heuristic considerations of Sec. 8. And we can find many similar illustrations in the theory of bounded analytic functions developed by Toeplitz, Carathéodory, Schur, Nevanlinna, and others. For instance, if the problem deals with analytic functions regular inside the unit circle and having there a nonnegative real part $[\Re f(z) \geq 0]$ we will find that the extremum is attained by a function $f(z)$ which remains meromorphic for $|z| \leq 1$. More precisely, it is regular with

$$\Re f(z) = 0$$

at almost all points of the boundary $|z| = 1$ and it has just a finite number of singular points on $|z| = 1$, which are all poles and where we can appropriately set

$$\Re f(z) = \infty.$$

Such behavior is closely analogous to that observed in Sec. 8, (III) and (IV).

The aim of this example was to illustrate the variety of problems accessible to the same heuristic considerations.

REFERENCES

[1] Couturat, L., "Opuscules et fragments inédits de Leibnitz." 1903.
[2] Goldberg, M., *Tohoku Math. J.* **40**, 226–236 (1935).
[3] Hardy, G. H., Littlewood, J. E., and Pólya, G., "Inequalities," 2nd ed. Cambridge Univ. Press, London and New York, 1953.
[4] Keynes, J. M., "A Treatise on Probability." 1921.
[5] Landau, E., "Darstellung und Begründung einiger neueren Ergebnisse der Funktionentheorie," 2nd ed. 1929.
[6] Pólya, G., "Mathematics and Plausible Reasoning." Princeton Univ. Press, Princeton, New Jersey, 1954.
[7] Pólya, G., "Mathematical Discovery." Wiley, New York, 1962/65.
[8] Pólya, G., *Comment. Math. Helv.* **29**, 112–119 (1955).
[9] Pólya, G., *Ann. Univ. Sci. Budapest. Eötvös Sect. Math.* **3–4**, 233–239 (1960–61).
[10] Pólya, G., "Modern Mathematics for the Engineer" (E. F. Beckenbach, ed.), 2nd series, pp. 420–441. McGraw-Hill, New York, 1961.
[11] Pólya, G., and Schiffer, M. M., *Compt. Rend.* **248**, 2837–2839 (1959).
[12] Pólya, G., and Szegö, G., "Aufgaben und Lehrsätze aus der Analysis," 3rd ed. Springer, Berlin, 1964.
[13] Pólya, G., and Szegö, G., "Isoperimetric Inequalities in Mathematical Physics." 1951.

Inequalities in the Differential Geometry of Surfaces*

E. F. BECKENBACH
Department of Mathematics
University of California
Los Angeles, California

1. Introduction

Geometric inequalities have a prominent place in complex-variable theory. Among the tools used in establishing these inequalities, convex functions and subharmonic functions are especially important.

In this chapter, it is shown that these same tools yield analogous results and other inequalities in the theory of surfaces.

2. Convex Functions

A continuous function $f(u)$, defined in an interval I, is said to be *convex* [15, 4] there if and only if

$$f(ta + (1 - t)b) \leq tf(a) + (1 - t)f(b) \tag{1}$$

for all a, b in I and for all t satisfying $0 \leq t \leq 1$. That is, $f(u)$ is convex if and only if the graph of $y = f(u)$ lies nowhere above any of its chords.

If the second derivative d^2f/du^2 exists throughout I, then $f(u)$ is convex there if and only if

$$\frac{d^2f}{du^2} \geq 0 \tag{2}$$

at each point of I.

The function $f(u)$ is said to be *concave* if and only if $-f(u)$ is convex.

3. Geodesic Parallels

If an analytic surface S is given in parametric representation,

$$S: \quad x_j = x_j(u, v), \quad j = 1, 2, 3,$$

* The preparation of this paper was sponsored in part by the National Science Foundation Grant GP-5279.

for (u, v) in a domain D, then the element of length ds and the element of area dA are given by

$$ds^2 = E\ du^2 + 2F\ du\ dv + G\ dv^2$$

and

$$dA = (EG - F^2)^{1/2}\ du\ dv,$$

respectively, where E, F, and G are the coefficients of the first fundamental differential form for S:

$$E = \sum_{j=1}^{3} \left(\frac{\partial x_j}{\partial u}\right)^2, \qquad F = \sum_{j=1}^{3} \frac{\partial x_j}{\partial u} \frac{\partial x_j}{\partial v}, \qquad G = \sum_{j=1}^{3} \left(\frac{\partial x_j}{\partial v}\right)^2.$$

Given a smooth curve C_0 on S, there exists a unique family of geodesics on S intersecting C_0 orthogonally. If segments of equal length s are measured along the geodesics from C_0, then the locus of their endpoints is an orthogonal trajectory C_s of the geodesics. Parameters u, v, called *geodesic parameters*, can then be chosen such that the coefficients of the first fundamental form satisfy

$$E = 1, \qquad F = 0, \qquad G = [\mu(u, v)]^2, \qquad \mu \geq 0, \tag{3}$$

so that we have

$$ds^2 = du^2 + \mu^2\ dv^2$$

and

$$dA = \mu\ du\ dv.$$

The curves $v = \text{constant} = v_0$ are the geodesics of length $u_1 - u_0$ between the points (u_0, v_0) and (u_1, v_0) on S, $u_0 < u_1$, while the curves $u = \text{constant}$ are the *geodesic parallels* C_s [13, p. 152]. The surface is said to be given in *geodesic representation*.

Singular points of the surface, or of the geodesic family, are points where $\mu = 0$. The remaining points, where $\mu > 0$, are *regular points*.

The Gaussian, or total, curvature K of S exists at all regular points of S. By a classical theorem of Gauss [13, p. 140], K is a function of E, F, and G, and their partial derivatives of the first and second orders. If (3) is satisfied, then the formula for K reduces [14; 13, p. 153] to

$$K = -\frac{1}{\mu} \frac{\partial^2 \mu}{\partial u^2}. \tag{4}$$

We shall say that S is a *surface of nonpositive Gaussian curvature* if and only if $K \leq 0$ at all regular points of S. It follows from (2) and (4) that *if S is given in geodesic representation for (u, v) in D, then S is a surface of non-*

positive Gaussian curvature if and only if the function $\mu(u, v_0)$ *is a convex function of* u *for each line segment* $u_0 < u < u_1$, $v = v_0$, *in* D [5].

Similarly, S is a surface of nonnegative Gaussian curvature if and only if $\mu(u, v_0)$ is a concave function of u for each line segment $u_0 < u < u_1$, $v = v_0$, in D.

In the neighborhood of a point where $K < 0$, a surface S lies on both sides of its tangent plane, as in the depressions between one's knuckles. Accordingly, a surface S of nonpositive Gaussian curvature is often called a *saddle surface*. In the neighborhood of a point where $K > 0$, a surface S lies entirely on one side of its tangent plane, as on the tops of one's knuckles. A visualization of the surfaces involved should make the following results intuitively more plausible.

Theorem 1. *Let the arcs* $C(u)$, $u_0 \leq u \leq u_1$, *of length* $l(u)$, *be arcs of geodesic parallels between geodesics* $v = v_0$ *and* $v = v_1$, $v_0 < v_1$, *on a surface* S *of nonpositive Gaussian curvature. Then the length* $l(u)$ *is a convex function of* u, *that is, of the geodesic length* $u - u_0$; $l(u)$ *is strictly convex if* S *is not a developable surface, and is linear if* S *is developable.*

Proof.   Since $\mu(u, c)$ is a convex function of u for $v_0 < c < v_1$, we have

$$\mu(ta + (1 - t)b, c) \leq t\mu(a, c) + (1 - t)\mu(b, c) \qquad (5)$$

for all a, b, c, and t satisfying $u_0 < a < b < u_1$, $v_0 < c < v_1$, and $0 < t < 1$. The sign of equality holds in (5) if and only if $\partial^2\mu/\partial u^2 \equiv 0$ on the line segment $u_0 < u < u_1$, $v = c$; that is, by (4), if and only if $K \equiv 0$ there. Hence

$$l(ta + (1 - t)b) = \int_{v_0}^{v_1} \mu(ta + (1 - t)b, v)\, dv$$

$$\leq \int_{v_0}^{v_1} [t\mu(a, v) + (1 - t)\mu(b, v)]\, dv$$

$$= tl(a) + (1 - t)l(b), \qquad (6)$$

so that $l(u)$ is convex. The sign of equality holds in (6) if and only if $K \equiv 0$ for $u_0 < u < u_1$, $v_0 < v < v_1$, and therefore, by analytic continuation, $K \equiv 0$ on S; that is, if and only if S is a developable surface.

It follows in particular that $l(u)$ has an interior maximum only if $l(u)$ is identically constant.

Theorem 2.   *Let the arcs* $C(u)$, $u_0 - W < u < u_0 + W$, *of length* $l(u)$, *be arcs of geodesic parallels between geodesics* $v = v_0$ *and* $v = v_1$, $v_0 < v_1$, *on an analytic surface* S *of nonpositive Gaussian curvature, and let* $A(w)$ *denote the* *area of the part of S enclosed by $v = v_0$, $C(u_0 + w)$, $v = v_1$, and $C(u_0 - w)$, $0 \leq w < W$. Then $A(w)$ is a convex function of w; $A(w)$ is strictly convex if S is not a developable surface, and is linear if S is developable.*

Proof. We have

$$A(w) = \int_{u_0 - w}^{u_0 + w} \int_{v_0}^{v_1} \mu(u, v) \, du \, dv = \int_{u_0 - w}^{u_0 + w} l(u) \, du,$$

whence

$$A'(w) = l(u_0 + w) + l(w_0 - w),$$
$$A''(w) = l'(u_0 + w) - l'(u_0 - w).$$

Since, by Theorem 1, $l(u)$ is convex, it follows that $l'(u)$ is monotonic nondecreasing, so that $A''(w) \geq 0$, the sign of equality holding if and only if $l'(u) = $ constant, that is, since

$$l''(u) = \int_{v_0}^{v_1} \frac{\partial^2 \mu(u, v)}{\partial u^2} \, dv,$$

if and only if S is developable. Hence $A(w)$ is strictly convex if S is not a developable surface, and is linear if S is developable.

4. Geodesic Circles

If equal lengths are laid off from a point P_0 of an analytic surface S along the geodesics in all directions through P_0 on S, then the locus of endpoints is an orthogonal trajectory of the geodesics. We take the geodesics for the curves $v = $ constant, and let u denote distances measured along the geodesics from P_0. The coordinate v can be adjusted to satisfy $v_1 = \theta_1$, for all θ_1, where θ_1 is the angle between the tangents at P_0 to the geodesics $v = 0$ and $v = v_1$. We then write r, θ for u, v, respectively. The parameters r, θ are called *geodesic polar coordinates*, with *pole* at P_0; the curve $r = r_0$ is a *geodesic circle* with *center* at P_0 and *geodesic radius* r_0 [13, p. 184].

Necessary and sufficient conditions for the above coordinate system are (3) and

$$\mu(0, \theta) = 0, \qquad \frac{\partial \mu}{dr}\bigg|_{r=0} = 1. \tag{7}$$

Methods similar to those of Sec. 3 can now be employed to establish the following result concerning the length,

$$l(r) = \int_0^{2\pi} \mu(r, \theta) \, d\theta,$$

of the circumference of geodesic circles on surfaces of nonpositive Gaussian curvature.

Theorem 3. *Let S be an analytic surface of nonpositive Gaussian curvature, and let $l(r)$ denote the length of the circumference of the geodesic circle $C(P_0, r)$ on S with fixed center P_0 and geodesic radius r. If $C(P_0, r)$ is on S for $0 \leq r \leq r_0$, then the function*

$$\phi_1(r) = l(r) - 2\pi r, \qquad 0 \leq r \leq r_0,$$

is a continuous monotonic nondecreasing convex function of r; $\phi_1(r) \equiv 0$ if S is a developable surface, but otherwise $\phi_1(r)$ is monotonic increasing and strictly convex. Further, the function

$$\psi_1(r) = l(r)/2\pi r, \qquad 0 < r \leq r_0,$$
$$\psi_1(0) = 1,$$

is a continuous monotonic nondecreasing function of r; $\psi_1(r) \equiv 1$ if S is a developable surface, but otherwise $\psi_1(r)$ is monotonic increasing.

As an immediate consequence of Theorem 3, we have the following result.

Corollary. *Under the hypothesis of Theorem 3, $l(r)$ is a monotonic increasing convex function of r and satisfies the inequality*

$$l(r) \geq 2\pi r;$$

$l(r)$ is strictly convex and satisfies the strict inequality for $r > 0$ on S if S is not a developable surface, and is linear and satisfies the equality if S is developable.

Similar results hold for the area,

$$A(r) = \int_0^r \int_0^{2\pi} \mu(\rho, \theta) \, d\rho \, d\theta,$$

of the geodesic circular disks bounded by $C(P_0, r)$. Namely, Theorem 3 remains valid if $\phi_1(r)$ and $\psi_1(r)$ are replaced, respectively, by

$$\phi_2(r) = A(r) - \pi r^2$$

and

$$\psi_2(r) = A(r)/\pi r^2, \qquad 0 < r \leq r_0,$$
$$\psi_2(0) = 1.$$

It follows as a corollary that $A(r)$ is a monotonic increasing strictly convex function of r and satisfies the inequality

$$A(r) \geq \pi r^2,$$

the sign of equality holding for $0 < r \leq r_0$ if and only if S is a developable surface.

Actually, the nonnegative functions $A(r)$ and $\phi_2(r) = A(r) - \pi r^2$ satisfy even stronger convexity conditions than those indicated above. For a nonnegative function $p(r)$, the convexity of $[p(r)]^{1/2}$ implies the convexity of $p(r)$, but the converse does not hold. We have the following result.

Theorem 4. *Let S be an analytic surface of nonpositive Gaussian curvature, and let $A(r)$ denote the area of the geodesic circular disk $D(P_0, r)$ on S, with fixed center P_0 and with geodesic radius r. If $D(P_0, r)$ is on S for $0 \leq r \leq r_0$, then*

$$f(r) = [A(r)]^{1/2}, \qquad 0 \leq r \leq r_0,$$

is a continuous monotonic increasing convex function of r; $f(r)$ is linear if S is developable, but otherwise $f(r)$ is strictly convex. Further, the function

$$[\phi_2(r)]^{1/2} = [A(r) - \pi r^2]^{1/2}$$

is a continuous monotonic nondecreasing convex function of r; $[\phi_2(r)]^{1/2} \equiv 0$ if S is a developable surface, but otherwise $[\phi_2(r)]^{1/2}$ is monotonic increasing and strictly convex.

In Sec. 10 of this chapter, it is shown that the isoperimetric inequality

$$A \leq \frac{1}{4\pi} l^2$$

between area A and perimeter l characterizes surfaces S of nonpositive Gaussian curvature; that is, the inequality holds for all Jordan regions on S if and only if S is a surface of nonpositive Gaussian curvature. For geodesic circles on S, the methods of the present section can be applied to show that Theorem 3 remains valid when the functions

$$\phi_3(r) = \frac{1}{4\pi} [l(r)]^2 - A(r), \qquad 0 \leq r \leq r_0,$$

and

$$\psi_3(r) = \frac{(1/4\pi)[l(r)]^2}{A(r)}, \qquad 0 < r \leq r_0,$$

$$\psi_3(0) = 1,$$

are substituted for $\phi_1(r)$ and $\psi_1(r)$, respectively. From this it follows, in particular, that for geodesic circles on surfaces of nonpositive Gaussian curvature,

$$A(r) \leq \frac{1}{4\pi} [l(r)]^2.$$

5. Surfaces of Nonnegative Gaussian Curvature

The above results concerning surfaces of nonpositive Gaussian curvature hold in the large and are unaffected by singular points. Many rather analogous results hold for surfaces of nonnegative Gaussian curvature, but in general only on parts of S where there are no singular points of the surface or of the family of geodesics other than at the pole of geodesic polar coordinates. If there are no such singular points, then we shall say that S is *regular*.

Thus Theorems 1 and 2 and the results given above for the functions $\phi_j(r)$ and $\psi_j(r)$, $j = 1, 2, 3$, remain valid if we restrict S to being regular and interchange "nonpositive" and "nonnegative," "convex" and "concave," "nondecreasing" and "nonincreasing," and "increasing" and "decreasing."

It follows that on a regular analytic surface S of nonnegative Gaussian curvature the function $l(r)$ is concave and satisfies

$$l(r) \leq 2\pi r;$$

$l(r)$ is strictly concave and satisfies the strict inequality for $0 < r \leq r_0$ if S is not a developable surface. For a given pole P_0 on S, either $l(r)$ is monotonic increasing or there is an $r^* = r^*(S, P_0)$ such that $l(r)$ is monotonic increasing for $0 \leq r \leq r^*$ and monotonic decreasing for $r^* \leq r \leq r_0$.

The function $A(r)$ satisfies

$$A(r) \leq \pi r^2,$$

with strict inequality for $0 < r \leq r_0$ if S is not a developable surface. Further, either $A(r)$ is strictly convex or, for the above r^*, $A(r)$ is strictly convex for $0 \leq r \leq r^*$ and strictly concave for $r^* \leq r \leq r_0$.

On a sphere, for example, $l(r)$ is increasing and concave, and $A(r)$ is convex, until a hemisphere has been covered. Thereafter, $l(r)$ is decreasing but still concave, and $A(r)$ becomes concave, until the other hemisphere has been covered. At the point diametrically opposite the pole we encounter a singular point of the geodesic representation.

In all of the above results we have assumed either that the Gaussian curvature of S is nonpositive or that the Gaussian curvature of S is nonnegative. In most instances we have obtained, in the two cases, conclusions that are distinct except for the dividing class of developable surfaces. Thus by logical exclusion we obtain several characterizations of these classes of surfaces. For example, for a regular surface S we have

$$A(r) > \pi r^2, \qquad A(r) < \pi r^2, \qquad \text{or} \qquad A(r) = \pi r^2$$

for all poles P_0 on S and all $r > 0$ on S if and only if S is a surface of negative curvature, a surface of positive curvature, or a developable surface, respectively.

For the above results and other similar results, see [5].

6. Surfaces of Bounded Gaussian Curvature

The above results can be extended [12] to yield analogous results for surfaces of bounded Gaussian curvature, in particular for analytic surfaces S whose Gaussian curvature K satisfies $K \leq K_0$, where K_0 is a negative constant. Such a surface will be called a *sub-K_0 surface.*

The extension involves generalized convex functions [1, 7]. Let $\{F(x; \alpha, \beta)\}$ be a two-parameter family of real finite functions defined on an interval $a < x < b$, such that

(i) each $F(x; \alpha, \beta)$ is a continuous function of x;

(ii) there is a unique member of the family that, at arbitrary x_1, x_2 satisfying $a < x_1 < x_2 < b$, takes on arbitrary values y_1, y_2.

For example, $\{F(x; \alpha, \beta)\}$ might be $\{\alpha x + \beta\}$ or $\{x^2 + \alpha x + \beta\}$. Members of $\{F(x; \alpha, \beta)\}$ might be denoted simply by $F(x)$, not $F(x; \alpha, \beta)$, with individual members distinguished by subscripts. In particular, $F_{ij}(x)$ might denote the member satisfying

$$F_{ij}(x_i) = f(x_i), \qquad F_{ij}(x_j) = f(x_j), \qquad a < x_i < x_j < b,$$

for a given function $f(x)$.

Then $f(x)$ is called a *sub-$\{F(x; \alpha, \beta)\}$ function* if and only if

$$f(x) \leq F_{12}(x)$$

for all x_1, x_2, x satisfying $a < x_1 < x < x_2 < b$.

Now for $K_0 < 0$ let $\{F(x; \alpha, \beta)\}$ be the family of solutions of

$$F''(x) + K_0 F(x) = 0.$$

Then we can take

$$\{F(x; \alpha, \beta)\} = \{\alpha \cosh [(-K_0)^{1/2}x] + \beta \sinh [(-K_0)^{1/2}x]\}.$$

In this case, we shall say briefly that a sub-$\{F(x; \alpha, \beta)\}$ function is a *sub-K_0 function.*

If the Gaussian curvature K satisfies $K \equiv K_0$ on a surface S_0, we shall say that S_0 is a K_0-surface. On such a surface the circumference and area of a geodesic circle of radius r are given by

$$l_0(r) = \frac{2\pi}{(-K_0)^{1/2}} \sinh [(-K_0)^{1/2}r]$$

and

$$A_0(r) = \frac{2\pi}{-K_0} \{\cosh [(-K_0)^{1/2}r] - 1\},$$

respectively.

Let S be an analytic sub-K_0 surface and let $l(r)$ and $A(r)$ denote the circumference and area, respectively, of a geodesic circle of radius r on S. Then it can be shown, for example, that

$$l(r) - l_0(r) \quad \text{and} \quad A(r) - A_0(r)$$

are continuous nondecreasing sub-K_0 functions of r that equal 0 at $r = 0$; they are identically 0 if S is a K_0-surface, but otherwise they are strictly sub-K_0 functions. As a consequence, $l(r)$ and $A(r)$ satisfy

$$l(r) \geq l_0(r) \quad \text{and} \quad A(r) \geq A_0(r)$$

and are monotonic nondecreasing sub-K_0 functions of r.

The isoperimetric inequality also extends to geodesic circles on these surfaces. Namely, the *isoperimetric function*

$$\frac{1}{4\pi} [l(r)]^2 + \frac{1}{4\pi} K_0 [A(r)]^2 - A(r)$$

has the same properties as those given above for the functions $l(r) - l_0(r)$ and $A(r) - A_0(r)$, and consequently we have

$$A(r) \leq \frac{1}{4\pi} [l(r)]^2 + \frac{1}{4\pi} [A(r)]^2,$$

with equality if and only if S is a K_0-surface.

7. Subharmonic Functions

Thus far we have seen how convex functions ("sublinear" functions) and generalized convex functions [sub-$\{F(x; \alpha, \beta)\}$ functions] can be applied in the study of certain classes of surfaces.

We shall now see how yet another generalization of the notion of convex function can be applied in differential geometry.

Linear functions $l(u)$ are characterized, in the class of functions continuous in an interval (a, b), by the mean-value property

$$l(u_0) = \tfrac{1}{2}[l(u_0 + h) + l(u_0 - h)]$$

holding for all u_0, h that satisfy $a < u_0 - h < u_0 + h < b$. In the same way, harmonic functions $h(u, v)$ are characterized, in the class of functions continuous in a domain D, by the mean-value property

$$h(u_0, v_0) = \frac{1}{2\pi} \int_0^{2\pi} h(u_0 + r \cos \theta, v_0 + r \sin \theta) \, d\theta$$

holding for all circular disks $(u-u_0)^2+(v-v_0)^2 \leq r^2$ in D. Similarly, linear functions $l(u)$ are characterized by

$$\Delta l(u) \equiv \frac{d^2l}{du^2} = 0,$$

and harmonic functions $h(u, v)$ by

$$\Delta h(u, v) \equiv \frac{\partial^2 h}{\partial u^2} + \frac{\partial^2 h}{\partial v^2} = 0.$$

As noted earlier, the graph of a continuous convex function $f(u)$ is dominated by its chords. In the same way, the graph of a continuous *subharmonic* function [see *17*] $g(u, v)$ is dominated, in any Dirichlet region R in its domain of definition, by the graph of the function that is harmonic in the interior of R, is continuous in R, and coincides with $g(u, v)$ on the boundary of R.

Thus continuous convex functions $f(u)$ are characterized by

$$f(u_0) \leq \tfrac{1}{2}[f(u_0+h)+f(u_0-h)],$$

and continuous subharmonic functions $g(u, v)$ are characterized by

$$g(u_0, v_0) \leq \frac{1}{2\pi} \int_0^{2\pi} g(u_0 + r \cos \theta, v_0 + r \sin \theta) \, d\theta.$$

Convex functions of class C'' are characterized by

$$\Delta f(u) \equiv d^2f/du^2 \geq 0,$$

and subharmonic functions of class C'' are characterized by

$$\Delta g(u, v) \equiv \frac{\partial^2 g}{\partial u^2} + \frac{\partial^2 g}{\partial v^2} \geq 0.$$

We shall have occasion to refer, directly or indirectly, to several properties of subharmonic functions. The first and perhaps most important of these is the fact that a subharmonic function $g(u, v)$ cannot take on a maximum value at any interior point of its domain of definition unless $g(u, v)$ is identically constant.

Next, if $g(u, v)$ is subharmonic in $(u-u_0)^2+(v-v_0)^2 \leq r^2$, then the circumference mean

$$\frac{1}{2\pi} \int_0^{2\pi} g(u_0 + \rho \cos \theta, v_0 + \rho \sin \theta) \, d\theta$$

is a nondecreasing function of ρ for $0 \leq \rho \leq r$. Consequently,

$$g(u_0, v_0) \leq \frac{1}{\pi r^2} \int_0^r \int_0^{2\pi} g(u_0 + \rho \cos \theta, v_0 + \rho \sin \theta) \rho \, d\rho \, d\theta$$

$$\leq \frac{1}{2\pi} \int_0^{2\pi} g(u_0 + r \cos \theta, v_0 + r \sin \theta) \, d\theta,$$

so that the area mean of a subharmonic function over a circular disk is dominated by its mean over the circumference of the circular boundary of the disk.

Let sg $\alpha = -1$ if $\alpha < 0$ and sg $\alpha = 1$ if $\alpha > 0$; let C_α, $\alpha \neq 0$, be the class of nonnegative functions $p(u, v)$ for which

$$\text{sg } \alpha[p(u, v)]^\alpha$$

is subharmonic; and let C_0 be the class of nonnegative functions $p(u, v)$ for which

$$\log p(u, v)$$

is subharmonic. Then for all real $\alpha < \beta$ we have $C_\alpha \subset C_\beta$.

If $p_1(u, v)$, $p_2(u, v), \ldots, p_n(u, v)$ are subharmonic functions for (u, v) in D, then for any $t > 1$ the function

$$\left\{ \sum_{j=1}^n [p_j(u, v)]^t \right\}^{1/t}$$

is subharmonic in D.

8. Harmonic Surfaces

Suppose a surface S has the property that it admits a representation

$$S: \quad x_j = x_j(u, v), \quad j = 1, 2, 3,$$

for $u^2 + v^2 \leq 1$, such that the functions $x_j(u, v)$ are harmonic for $u^2 + v^2 < 1$ and are continuous for $u^2 + v^2 \leq 1$.

Not all surfaces admit a representation in terms of harmonic functions, of course. In Sec. 11 we discuss one very important subclass of the class of surfaces S that do have this property. In the first place, the Gaussian curvature of such a surface must be nonpositive. This can be shown as follows: We have

$$K = \frac{eg - f^2}{EG - F^2},$$

where E, F, G, and e, f, g are the coefficients of the first and second fundamental differential forms, respectively, for S. Now, in vector notation,

$$eg - f^2 = [\mathbf{x}_{uu} \bullet (\mathbf{x}_u \times \mathbf{x}_v)][\mathbf{x}_{vv} \bullet (\mathbf{x}_u \times \mathbf{x}_v)] - [\mathbf{x}_{uv} \bullet (\mathbf{x}_u \times \mathbf{x}_v)]^2$$

and if the x_j are harmonic then

$$\mathbf{x}_{vv} = -\mathbf{x}_{uu} ,$$

so that in this case we have

$$eg - f^2 = -[\mathbf{x}_{uu} \cdot (\mathbf{x}_u \times \mathbf{x}_v)]^2 - [\mathbf{x}_{uv} \cdot (\mathbf{x}_u \times \mathbf{x}_v)]^2 \leq 0.$$

Since $EG - F^2$ cannot be negative, it follows that $K \leq 0$ wherever K is defined on S.

For S in the above representation, let $l(r)$ denote the length of the image on S of $u^2 + v^2 = r^2$. We shall show [see 3] that $l(r)$ is a nondecreasing function of r for $0 \leq r \leq 1$. Here the difficult and tricky point lies in establishing the result for $r \leq 1$, not just for $r < 1$.

For brevity, let us write $x_j(w)$, $w = u + iv$, in place of $x_j(u, v)$. For any r_0, $0 \leq r_0 < 1$, and for any $\epsilon > 0$, we can choose $\theta_0 < \theta_1 < \cdots < \theta_n$, with $\theta_n = \theta_0 + 2\pi$, such that

$$\sum_{k=1}^{n} \left\{ \sum_{j=1}^{3} [x_j(r_0 e^{i\theta_k}) - x_j(r_0 e^{i\theta_{k-1}})]^2 \right\}^{1/2} > l(r_0) - \epsilon.$$

Now consider the function

$$p(w) \equiv \sum_{k=1}^{n} \left\{ \sum_{j=1}^{3} [x_j(w e^{i\theta_k}) - x_j(w e^{i\theta_{k-1}})]^2 \right\}^{1/2}.$$

Using a remark made in Sec. 7, and the fact that the x_j are harmonic, we can show that $p(w)$ is subharmonic.

Hence for any r^*, $r_0 < r^* \leq 1$, $p(w)$ takes on its maximum in $|w| \leq r^*$ at some point $w = r^* e^{i\theta^*}$ on $|w| = r^*$. Then

$$l(r_0) - \epsilon < p(r_0) \leq p(r^* e^{i\theta^*}).$$

But $p(r^* e^{i\theta^*})$ is the length of a polygonal path inscribed around the image of $u^2 + v^2 = r^{*2}$ on S, so that

$$p(r^* e^{i\theta^*}) \leq l(r^*).$$

Hence

$$l(r_0) - \epsilon < l(r^*).$$

Letting $\epsilon \to 0$, we obtain

$$l(r_0) \leq l(r^*),$$

as desired.

In Sec. 10 we obtain an analogous result in a different context, but only for $0 \leq r < 1$. It would be interesting to determine whether or not this latter result holds also for $0 \leq r \leq 1$.

The above observation that $p(w)$ is subharmonic if the $x_j(u, v)$ are harmonic suggests the following result:

Theorem 5. *For functions $x_j(u, v)$, $j = 1, 2, 3$, that are continuous in a domain D, the distance function*

$$\mathfrak{M}(u, v; \mathbf{a}) \equiv \left\{ \sum_{j=1}^{3} [x_j(u, v) - a_j]^2 \right\}^{1/2}$$

is subharmonic for all real $\mathbf{a} \equiv (a_1, a_2, a_3)$ if and only if the $x_j(u, v)$ are harmonic.

Proof. If the $x_j(u, v)$ are harmonic, then since $x_j(u, v)$ and a_j are harmonic, $x_j(u, v) - a_j$ is harmonic and therefore subharmonic, $j = 1, 2, 3$. Hence, by an observation made in Sec. 7, $\mathfrak{M}(u, v; \mathbf{a})$ also is subharmonic.

Conversely, if $\mathfrak{M}(u, v; \mathbf{a})$ is subharmonic then $[\mathfrak{M}(u, v; \mathbf{a})]^2$ is subharmonic. Therefore, for each circular disk $(u_0, v_0; r)$ in D we have

$$\sum_{j=1}^{3} [x_j(u_0, v_0) - a_j]^2 \leq \frac{1}{2\pi} \int_0^{2\pi} \sum_{j=1}^{3} [x_j(u_0 + r \cos \theta, v_0 + r \sin \theta) - a_j]^2 \, d\theta,$$

whence

$$\sum_{j=1}^{3} [x_j(u_0, v_0)]^2 - \frac{1}{2\pi} \int_0^2 \sum_{j=1}^{3} [x_j(u_0 + r \cos \theta, v_0 + r \sin \theta)]^2 \, d\theta$$

$$+ 2 \sum_{j=1}^{3} a_j \left[\frac{1}{2\pi} \int_0^{2\pi} x_j(u_0 + r \cos \theta, v_0 + r \sin \theta) \, d\theta - x_j(u_0, v_0) \right] \leq 0.$$

With $(u_0, v_0; r)$ fixed, the left-hand member of this inequality is a non-constant linear function of the arbitrary real parameters a_j, $j = 1, 2, 3$, unless the coefficients of the a_j vanish. Therefore, for the inequality to hold for all real a_j these coefficients must vanish, so that

$$x_j(u_0, v_0) = \frac{1}{2\pi} \int_0^{2\pi} x_j(u_0 + r \cos \theta, v_0 + r \sin \theta) \, d\theta, \qquad j = 1, 2, 3,$$

for all $(u_0, v_0; r)$ in D. Therefore, by the converse of the Gauss mean-value theorem [16], the $x_j(u, v)$ are harmonic.

9. Isothermic Parameters and Functions of Class PL

A surface S is said to be given in terms of *isothermic parameters* (u, v) if and only if the coefficients E, F, G of the first fundamental form satisfy

$$E = G = \lambda(u, v), \qquad F = 0.$$

Such a representation is conformal, or angle-preserving, except at points where $\lambda(u, v) = 0$.

We shall see how subharmonic functions enter in two ways into the study of surfaces in isothermic representation.

The Gaussian curvature K of a surface S can be expressed in terms of E, F, and G and their partial derivatives of the first and second order. For an isothermic representation, the formula reduces simply to

$$K = -\frac{1}{2\lambda} \Delta \log \lambda.$$

Thus S is of nonpositive Gaussian curvature, $K \leq 0$, if and only if $\Delta \log \lambda \geq 0$, that is, if and only if $\log \lambda$ is subharmonic [11].

As mentioned in Sec. 7, it is a stronger restriction for a nonnegative function to have a subharmonic logarithm than it is for the function itself to be subharmonic.

Nonnegative functions having subharmonic logarithms are said [10] to be *of class PL*. This class has the following closure properties:

(i) It is closed under addition.
(ii) It is closed under multiplication.
(iii) It is closed under conformal transformations of the parameters.

In complex-variable theory, if $f(w)$ is analytic then $|f(w)|$ and $|f'(w)|$ are of class *PL*. The foregoing closure properties give the principle of the maximum its strength and are at the basis of geometric function theory. For surfaces given in isothermic representation, the function $[\lambda(u, v)]^{1/2}$ corresponds to the function $|f'(w)|$, for each gives the linear-deformation ratio between the domain and range of the respective mapping. Similarly, $\lambda(u, v)$ and $|f'(w)|^2$ give the area-deformation ratio in these two cases. It follows, in general, that insofar as the principle of the maximum and geometric function theory apply to $|f'(w)|$, there are analogous results concerning isothermic maps on surfaces of nonpositive Gaussian curvature.

As regards $|f(w)|$, we are naturally led to ask what corresponds in differential geometry to the fact that $|f(w)|$, or more generally $|f(w) - c|$ for an arbitrary complex constant c, is of class *PL*. Since for a fixed w, $|f(w) - c|$ represents the distance in the complex plane from c to the point $f(w)$, we wish accordingly to investigate the class of surfaces S and their representations for which

$$\mathfrak{M}(u, v; \mathbf{a}) \equiv \left\{ \sum_{j=1}^{3} [x_j(u, v) - a_j]^2 \right\}^{1/2}$$

is of class *PL*.

Suppose, then, that the functions $x_j(u, v), j = 1, 2, 3$, are continuous for (u, v) in a domain D, and that $\mathfrak{M}(u, v; \mathbf{a})$ is of class PL for each $\mathbf{a} = (a_1, a_2, a_3)$. By a remark made in Sec. 7, $\mathfrak{M}(u, v; \mathbf{a})$ also satisfies the weaker condition of being subharmonic. Therefore, by Theorem 5, the $x_j(u, v)$ are harmonic functions, $j = 1, 2, 3$.

A computation now gives

$$\Delta \log \mathfrak{M} = T/\mathfrak{M}^4,$$

where

$$T = \left[\sum_{j=1}^{3} \left(\frac{\partial x_j}{\partial u} \right)^2 + \sum_{j=1}^{3} \left(\frac{\partial x_j}{\partial v} \right)^2 \right] \left[\sum_{j=1}^{3} (x_j - a_j)^2 \right]$$
$$- 2 \left\{ \left[\sum_{j=1}^{3} (x_j - a_j) \frac{\partial x_j}{\partial u} \right]^2 + \left[\sum_{j=1}^{3} (x_j - a_j) \frac{\partial x_j}{\partial v} \right]^2 \right\}, \tag{8}$$

and we know that $T \geq 0$ since $\Delta \log \mathfrak{M} \geq 0$.

Consider a definite point (u_0, v_0) in D. Choose first, for $j = 1, 2, 3$,

$$a_j = x_j(u_0, v_0) - \frac{\partial x_j}{\partial u}\Big|_{(u, v) = (u_0, v_0)}.$$

Then $T \geq 0$ becomes

$$EG - E^2 - 2F^2 \geq 0. \tag{9}$$

Choose next, for $j = 1, 2, 3$,

$$a_j = x_j(u_0, v_0) - \frac{\partial x_j}{\partial v}\Big|_{(u, v) = (u_0, v_0)}.$$

This time $T \geq 0$ becomes

$$EG - G^2 - 2F^2 \geq 0. \tag{10}$$

Addition of (8) and (9) yields

$$-(E - G)^2 - 4F^2 \geq 0,$$

and consequently

$$E = G, \quad F = 0, \tag{11}$$

at (u_0, v_0). Since (u_0, v_0) is any definite point in D, it follows that (11) holds throughout D. Thus the surface

$$S: \quad x_j = x_j(u, v), \quad j = 1, 2, 3,$$

is given in isothermic representation.

We have now shown that if $\mathfrak{M}(u, v; \mathbf{a})$ is of class PL, then the coordinate functions are harmonic and the surface is given in isothermic representation.

Suppose, conversely, that the coordinate functions are harmonic and that the surface is given in isothermic representation. To show that $\mathfrak{M}(u, v; \mathbf{a})$ is of class PL, we need only to show that the function T, given by (8), satisfies $T \geq 0$.

At points where $\lambda = 0$, this is trivial since at such points we have

$$\frac{\partial x_j}{\partial u} = \frac{\partial x_j}{\partial v} = 0, \qquad j = 1, 2, 3.$$

At points where $\lambda \neq 0$, the vectors

$$\frac{\partial \mathbf{x}}{\partial u} \quad \text{and} \quad \frac{\partial \mathbf{x}}{\partial v}$$

are both nonnull. Further, since $F = 0$ they are perpendicular to each other. Let $\mathbf{n}$ denote the unit vector perpendicular to each of them. Then we can write

$$\mathbf{x} - \mathbf{a} = \alpha \frac{\partial \mathbf{x}}{\partial u} + \beta \frac{\partial \mathbf{x}}{\partial v} + \gamma \mathbf{n},$$

where α, β and γ are scalars. Therefore we have

$$(\mathbf{x} - \mathbf{a}) \cdot (\mathbf{x} - \mathbf{a}) = \alpha^2 \lambda + \beta^2 \lambda + \gamma^2,$$
$$(\mathbf{x} - \mathbf{a}) \cdot \partial \mathbf{x}/\partial u = \alpha \lambda,$$
$$(\mathbf{x} - \mathbf{a}) \cdot \partial \mathbf{x}/\partial v = \beta \lambda,$$

so that, by (8),

$$T = 2\lambda(\alpha^2 \lambda + \beta^2 \lambda + \gamma^2) - 2(\alpha^2 \lambda^2 + \beta^2 \lambda^2) = 2\lambda \gamma^2 \geq 0,$$

as desired.

According to a theorem of Weierstrass, a surface S given in isothermic representation is a minimal surface, or surface for which the mean curvature vanishes identically, if and only if the coordinate functions are harmonic. The above results concerning $\mathfrak{M}(u, v; \mathbf{a})$ can therefore be summarized as follows [10]:

Theorem 6. *For functions $x_j(u, v)$, $j = 1, 2, 3$, that are continuous in a domain D, the distance function*

$$\mathfrak{M}(u, v; \mathbf{a}) \equiv \left\{ \sum_{j=1}^{3} [x_j(u, v) - a_j]^2 \right\}^{1/2}$$

is of class PL for all real $\mathbf{a} \equiv (a_1, a_2, a_3)$ if and only if the $x_j(u, v)$ are the coordinate functions of a minimal surface in isothermic representation.

Thus minimal surfaces in isothermic representation are characterized by the distance function $\mathfrak{M}$ being of class PL, and surfaces of nonpositive Gaussian curvature in isothermic representation are characterized by the deformation-ratio function $\lambda^{1/2}$ being of class PL. Since the Gaussian curvature of a minimal surface must be nonpositive, both $\mathfrak{M}$ and $\lambda^{1/2}$ are of class PL for minimal surfaces in isothermic representation.

10. Applications of Functions of Class *PL*

For a surface S given in isothermic representation, the length of the image of $(u - u_0)^2 + (v - v_0)^2 = r^2$ is given by

$$l(r) = \int_0^{2\pi} [\lambda(u_0 + r \cos \theta, v_0 + r \sin \theta)]^{1/2} r \, d\theta,$$

and the area of the image of $(u - u_0)^2 + (v - v_0)^2 \leq r^2$ is given by

$$A(r) = \int_0^r \int_0^{2\pi} \lambda(u_0 + \rho \cos \theta, v_0 + \rho \sin \theta) \rho \, d\rho \, d\theta.$$

The isoperimetric inequality

$$A(r) \leq \frac{1}{4\pi} [l(r)]^2$$

can then be written in the form

$$\frac{1}{\pi r^2} \int_0^r \int_0^{2\pi} \lambda(u_0 + \rho \cos \theta, v_0 + \rho \sin \theta) \rho \, d\rho \, d\theta$$

$$\leq \left\{ \frac{1}{2\pi} \int_0^{2\pi} [\lambda(u_0 + r \cos \theta, v_0 + r \sin \theta)]^{1/2} \, d\theta \right\}^2. \tag{12}$$

This inequality is stronger than the inequality between the area mean and the circumference mean given in Sec. 7 since the right-hand side of (12) involves the circumference mean of order $\frac{1}{2}$, which is less than or equal to the corresponding mean of order 1. It turns out that (12) characterizes functions λ of class PL. The isoperimetric inequality can thus be shown to hold for every simply connected portion, bounded by an analytic curve, of a surface if and only if the surface is of nonpositive Gaussian curvature.

Notice in the above expression for $l(r)$ that for surfaces of nonpositive Gaussian curvature, the function $\lambda^{1/2}$ is of class PL, and also that r is of class PL. Therefore the product $\lambda^{1/2}r$ is of class PL and consequently $\lambda^{1/2}r$ is subharmonic. Then $l(r)$ is a nondecreasing function of r since the integral mean of a subharmonic function is a nondecreasing function of r. Notice also, however, that this argument does not extend to the boundary if the functions $x_j(u, v)$, $j = 1, 2, 3$, are given to be smooth in $u^2 + v^2 < 1$ and merely continuous in $u^2 + v^2 \leq 1$.

For functions of class PL, the lemma of Schwarz can be expressed as follows [10]:

Let $p(u, v)$ be ≤ 1 and of class PL in $r^2 = u^2 + v^2 < 1$. Let $p(0, 0) = 0$, and suppose that for a certain $\alpha > 0$, $p(u, v)/r^\alpha$ remains bounded in $0 < r < 1$. Then $p(u, v) \leq r^\alpha$. If the equality holds for any (u, v), $0 < u^2 + v^2 < 1$, then it holds identically.

For minimal surfaces, this becomes the following [10]:

Let

$$S: \quad x_j = x_j(u, v), \qquad j = 1, 2, 3, \quad u^2 + v^2 < 1,$$

be a minimal surface in isothermic representation, such that $(0, 0)$ is mapped on $(0, 0, 0)$. If S lies within the unit sphere, $\{\sum_{j=1}^{3} [x_j(u, v)]^2\}^{1/2} \leq 1$, then

$$\left\{ \sum_{j=1}^{3} [x_j(r \cos \theta, r \sin \theta)]^2 \right\}^{1/2} \leq r, \qquad 0 < r \leq 1,$$

and

$$\lambda_0^{1/2} \leq 1,$$

where $\lambda_0^{1/2}$ denotes the length-deformation ratio at the origin. The equalities hold if and only if S is a simply covered circular disk with unit radius.

The above result suggests an analogue of the lemma of Schwarz for surfaces of nonpositive curvature [2], in particular for the plane maps of complex-variable theory.

Let

$$S: \quad x_j = x_j(u, v), \qquad j = 1, 2, 3, \quad u^2 + v^2 < 1,$$

be a surface of nonpositive curvature in isothermic representation. If

$$\int_0^1 [\lambda(\rho \cos \theta, \rho \sin \theta)]^{1/2} \, d\rho \leq 1$$

for all θ, $0 \leq \theta < 2\pi$, then

$$\int_0^r [\lambda(\rho \cos \theta, \rho \sin \theta)]^{1/2} \, d\rho \leq r, \qquad 0 < r \leq 1$$

and

$$\lambda_0^{1/2} \leq 1.$$

The equalities hold if and only if $\lambda \equiv 1$, that is, if and only if S is a developable piece of surface and is a geodesic circular disk given in isometric representation.

The fact that the distance function is of class *PL* for minimal surfaces in isothermic representation also allows an extension [6, 9] of Jensen's formula to these surfaces and furnishes the foundation for an extension of the Nevanlinna theory of meromorphic functions of a complex variable. In this context, the fundamental theorem of algebra, for example—if suitably stated—admits of a precise extension to rational minimal surfaces [8].

REFERENCES

[1] Beckenbach, E. F., Generalized convex functions, *Bull. Amer. Math. Soc.* **43,** 363–371 (1937).

[2] Beckenbach, E. F., A relative of the lemma of Schwarz, *Bull. Amer. Math. Soc.* **44,** 698–707 (1938).

[3] Beckenbach, E. F., The stronger form of Cauchy's integral theorem, *Bull. Amer. Math. Soc..* **49,** 615–618 (1943).

[4] Beckenbach, E. F., Convex functions, *Bull. Amer. Math. Soc.* **54,** 439–460 (1948).

[5] Beckenbach, E. F., Some convexity properties of surfaces of negative curvature, *Amer. Math. Monthly* **55,** 285–301 (1948).

[6] Beckenbach, E. F., The second fundamental theorem for minimal surfaces, to appear.

[7] Beckenbach, E. F., and Bing, R. H., On generalized convex functions, *Trans. Amer. Math. Soc.* **58,** 220–230 (1945).

[8] Beckenbach, E. F., and Eng, F. H., Rational minimal surfaces, to appear.

[9] Beckenbach, E. F., and Hutchison, G. A., Meromorphic minimal surfaces, *Bull. Amer. Math. Soc.* **68,** 519–522 (1962).

[10] Beckenbach, E. F., and Radó, T., Subharmonic functions and minimal surfaces, *Trans. Amer. Math. Soc.* **35,** 648–661 (1933).

[11] Beckenbach, E. F., and Radó, T., Subharmonic functions and surfaces of negative curvature, *Trans. Amer. Math. Soc.* **35,** 662–674 (1933).

[12] Clement, P. A., Generalized convexity and surfaces of negative curvature, *Pacific J. Math.* **3,** 333–368 (1953).

[13] Graustein, W. C., "Differential Geometry," Macmillan, New York, 1935.

[14] Hadamard, J., Les surfaces á courbes opposées et leurs lignes géodésiques, *J. Math. Pures Appl.* **63,** 27–73 (1898).

[15] Jensen, J. L. W. V., Sur un nouvel et important théorème de la théorie des fonctions, *Acta Math.* **22,** 359–364 (1898–1899).

[16] Kellogg, O. D., "Foundations of Potential Theory," Springer, Berlin, 1929.

[17] Radó, T., "Subharmonic Functions," Springer, Berlin, 1937.

A "Workshop" on Minkowski's Inequality*

E. F. BECKENBACH
Department of Mathematics
University of California
Los Angeles, California

1. Introduction

An inequality $a \leq b$ between positive numbers can be expressed by stating that the ratio b/a is greater than or equal to 1 ($b/a \geq 1$) or that the difference $b - a$ is greater than or equal to 0 ($b - a \geq 0$). The left-hand members in these inequalities are of quite different sorts, however, for the former measures the relative magnitudes of b and a, while the latter measures the numerical difference of b and a.

The comments given above apply in particular to the classical inequalities of Hölder, Minkowski, Lyapunov, and so on [3, 5]. For example, for any positive numbers $(x) \equiv (x_1, x_2, \ldots, x_n)$, $n > 1$, and any positive weights $(\alpha) \equiv (\alpha_1, \alpha_2, \ldots, \alpha_n)$, $\sum_{i=1}^{n} \alpha_i = 1$, the harmonic mean, or mean of order -1, is

$$M_{-1}(x; \alpha) = \left(\sum_{i=1}^{n} \alpha_i x_i^{-1} \right)^{-1},$$

and the arithmetic mean, or mean of order 1, is

$$M_1(x; \alpha) = \sum_{i=1}^{n} \alpha_i x_i.$$

Between $M_{-1}(x; \alpha)$ and $M_1(x; \alpha)$ we have the well-known inequality

$$M_{-1}(x; \alpha) \leq M_1(x; \alpha), \tag{1}$$

which can be written as

$$\frac{M_1(x; \alpha)}{M_{-1}(x; \alpha)} \geq 1, \tag{2}$$

or as

$$M_1(x; \alpha) - M_{-1}(x; \alpha) \geq 0. \tag{3}$$

It is easy to give examples for which the left-hand member of (2) or (3) is arbitrarily large. If the ratio of the greatest to the least of the x_j is bounded, however, then the ratio in (2) is correspondingly bounded from

* The preparation of this paper was sponsored in part by the National Science Foundation Grant GP-5279.

above. Thus the inequality of Kantorovich [6], for values x_j satisfying $0 < A \leq x_j \leq B < \infty$, $j = 1, 2, \ldots, n$, is

$$\left(\sum_{i=1}^{n} \alpha_i x_i \right) \left(\sum_{i=1}^{n} \alpha_i x_i^{-1} \right) \leq \frac{(A+B)^2}{4AB} .$$

This can be written, perhaps more perspicuously, as

$$\frac{M_1(x; \alpha)}{M_{-1}(x; \alpha)} \leq \frac{M_1(\tilde{c}; \tilde{\alpha})}{M_{-1}(\tilde{c}; \tilde{\alpha})},$$

where $(\tilde{c}) = (A, B)$ and $(\tilde{\alpha}) = (\frac{1}{2}, \frac{1}{2})$.

The inequality of Kantorovich has been extensively generalized; see the list of references in [1]. For example, upper-bound inequalities analogous to that of Kantorovich have been given by Cargo and Shisha [4] for ratios of means of all orders, $M_s(x; \alpha)/M_r(x; \alpha)$, $r < s$, where

$$M_t(x; \alpha) = \left(\sum_{i=1}^{n} \alpha_i x_i^{t} \right)^{1/t}, \qquad t \neq 0,$$

$$M_0(x; \alpha) = \prod_{i=1}^{n} x_i^{\alpha_i},$$

and by Marshall and Olkin [7] for ratios involved in the inequalities of Lyapunov, Hölder, and Minkowski.

Shisha and Mond [9] have similarly given upper bounds for differences of means,

$$M_s(x; \alpha) - M_r(x; \alpha), \qquad r < s,$$

provided the x_j are suitably bounded.

In the other direction, the sign of equality holds in (1), and therefore in (2) and (3), if and only if all the x_j are equal. Accordingly, if the x_j are restricted in such a way that they cannot all be equal, then the lower bound 1 for the ratio in (2) and the lower bound 0 for the difference in (3) cannot be attained. Thus for positive numbers $(c, x) \equiv (c_1, c_2, \ldots, c_m, x_{m+1}, x_{m+2}, \ldots, x_n)$ in which the first m numbers are fixed, $0 < m < n$, and only the remaining $n - m$ allowed to vary, (2) can be replaced [1] by

$$\frac{M_1(c, x; \alpha)}{M_{-1}(c, x; \alpha)} \geq \frac{M_1(c, \tilde{c}; \alpha)}{M_{-1}(c, \tilde{c}; \alpha)}, \tag{4}$$

where $(c, \tilde{c}) = (c_1, c_2, \ldots, c_m, \tilde{c}_{m+1}, \tilde{c}_{m+2}, \ldots, \tilde{c}_n)$, with

$$\tilde{c}_j = \tilde{c} = \left(\frac{\sum_{i=1}^{m} \alpha_i c_i}{\sum_{i=1}^{m} \alpha_i c_i^{-1}} \right)^{1/2}, \qquad j = m+1, m+2, \ldots, n.$$

The sign of equality holds in (4) if and only if each $x_j = \bar{c}$, $j = m+1$, $m+2, \ldots, n$.

Lower-bound inequalities analogous to (4) hold [1] for ratios of means of all orders, $M_s(c, x; \alpha)/M_r(c, x; \alpha)$, $r < s$, and improved upper-bound inequalities hold for these same ratios provided the variables x_j are constrained to satisfy $0 < A \leq x_j \leq B < \infty$, $j = m+1$, $m+2, \ldots, n$.

Similar results hold [2] for the Hölder-inequality ratio

$$\frac{\left(\sum_{i=1}^{n} x_i^p\right)^{1/p} \left(\sum_{i=1}^{n} y_i^q\right)^{1/q}}{\sum_{i=1}^{n} x_i y_i}, \qquad \frac{1}{p} + \frac{1}{q} = 1, \tag{5}$$

when all of the y_j and some of the x_j are held fixed.

It is shown in Secs. 2 and 3, below, that the same sort of analysis as was employed in [1] and [2] to investigate mean-value *ratios* and the Hölder-inequality *ratio* can be applied to the Minkowski-inequality *difference*,

$$\left(\sum_{i=1}^{n} x_i^p\right)^{1/p} + \left(\sum_{i=1}^{n} y_i^p\right)^{1/p} - \left[\sum_{i=1}^{n} (x_i + y_i)^p\right]^{1/p}. \tag{6}$$

Namely, precise lower and upper bounds for this difference, and the conditions under which the bounds are attained when the x_j and y_j are constrained as indicated above, are established. The results include the classical Minkowski inequality as a special case.

In Sec. 4, applications of the same methods to other expressions, in particular to the Hölder-inequality difference,

$$\left(\sum_{i=1}^{n} x_i^p\right)^{1/p} \left(\sum_{i=1}^{n} y_i^q\right)^{1/q} - \sum_{i=1}^{n} x_i y_i, \qquad \frac{1}{p} + \frac{1}{q} = 1,$$

are indicated.

2. Extension of the Minkowski Inequality

Let positive numbers $(c_1, c_2, \ldots, c_m)$ and $(k_1, k_2, \ldots, k_n)$ be given, $0 < m < n$, and let p satisfy $p > 1$. For positive variables $(x) \equiv (x_{m+1}, x_{m+2}, \ldots, x_n)$, consider the function

$$f(x) = \left(\sum_{i=1}^{m} c_i^p + \sum_{i=m+1}^{n} x_i^p\right)^{1/p} - \left[\sum_{i=1}^{m} (c_i + k_i)^p + \sum_{i=m+1}^{n} (x_i + k_i)^p\right]^{1/p}. \tag{7}$$

A computation gives

$$\frac{\partial f}{\partial x_j} = \left(\sum_{i=1}^{m} c_i{}^p + \sum_{i=m+1}^{n} x_i{}^p \right)^{1/p-1} x_j{}^{p-1}$$

$$- \left[\sum_{i=1}^{m} (c_i + k_i)^p + \sum_{i=m+1}^{n} (x_i + k_i)^p \right]^{1/p-1} (x_j + k_j)^{p-1}$$

$$= \left(\frac{\sum_{i=1}^{m} c_i{}^p + \sum_{i=m+1}^{n} x_i{}^p}{x_j{}^p} \right)^{(1-p)/p}$$

$$- \left[\frac{\sum_{i=1}^{m} (c_i + k_i)^p + \sum_{i=m+1}^{n} (x_i + k_i)^p}{(x_j + k_j)^p} \right]^{(1-p)/p}, \tag{8}$$

so that $\partial f / \partial x_j = 0$ if and only if

$$\frac{(x_j + k_j)^p}{x_j{}^p} = \frac{\sum_{i=1}^{m} (c_i + k_i)^p + \sum_{i=m+1}^{n} (x_i + k_i)^p}{\sum_{i=1}^{m} c_i{}^p + \sum_{i=m+1}^{n} x_i{}^p}. \tag{9}$$

By the theory of proportions, (9) is equivalent to

$$\frac{(x_j + k_j)^p}{x_j{}^p} = \frac{\sum_{i=1}^{m} (c_i + k_i)^p + \sum_{\substack{i=m+1 \\ i \neq j}}^{n} (x_i + k_i)^p}{\sum_{i=1}^{m} c_i{}^p + \sum_{\substack{i=m+1 \\ i \neq j}}^{n} x_i{}^p}, \tag{10}$$

whence

$$\frac{x_j}{k_j} = \frac{\left(\sum_{i=1}^{m} c_i{}^p + \sum_{\substack{i=m+1 \\ i \neq j}}^{n} x_i{}^p \right)^{1/p}}{\left[\sum_{i=1}^{m} (c_i + k_i)^p + \sum_{\substack{i=m+1 \\ i \neq j}}^{n} (x_i + k_i)^p \right]^{1/p} - \left(\sum_{i=1}^{m} c_i{}^p + \sum_{\substack{i=m+1 \\ i \neq j}}^{n} x_i{}^p \right)^{1/p}}. \tag{11}$$

In the same way, by the theory of proportions, we see from (9) that the *system* of equations

$$\frac{\partial f}{\partial x_j} = 0, \qquad j = m+1, m+2, \ldots, n,$$

has the unique solution

$$\frac{x_j}{k_j} = \bar{c}, \qquad j = m+1, m+2, \ldots, n,$$

where

$$\bar{c} = \frac{\left(\sum\limits_{i=1}^{m} c_i{}^p\right)^{1/p}}{\left[\sum\limits_{i=1}^{m}(c_i + k_i)^p\right]^{1/p} - \left(\sum\limits_{i=1}^{m} c_i{}^p\right)^{1/p}}. \qquad (12)$$

Thus there is precisely one horizontal tangent hyperplane to the hyper-surface

$$S: \quad y = f(x)$$

in the $(x_{m+1}, x_{m+2}, \ldots, x_n, y)$-space, and this occurs at the point $(\tilde{c}, f(\tilde{c}))$ on S at which

$$x_j = \bar{c}k_j = \tilde{c}_j, \qquad j = m+1, m+2, \ldots, n.$$

We shall show that y has a minimum value, namely $f(\tilde{c})$, on S, and that this value is assumed only at $(x) = (\tilde{c})$.

For any numbers A and B satisfying the inequalities

$$0 < A < \bar{c} < B < \infty, \qquad (13)$$

consider the $(n-m)$-dimensional rectangular parallelepiped I_{AB} determined by the inequalities

$$Ak_j \leq x_j \leq Bk_j, \qquad j = m+1, m+2, \ldots, n. \qquad (14)$$

Let L be a ray extending perpendicularly from one of the coordinate hyperplanes and intersecting I_{AB}; then L is determined by

$$x_j > 0, \qquad x_i = x_{i0}, \qquad Ak_i \leq x_{i0} \leq Bk_i, \qquad i \neq j,$$

with x_j varying, $0 < x_j < \infty$, for some fixed j, $m+1 \leq j \leq n$, and with $x_i = x_{i0}$ fixed, $Ak_i \leq x_{i0} \leq Bk_i$, for all $i \neq j$.

By (11), we have $\partial f / \partial x_j = 0$ at just one point P_0 on L, namely at the point of L at which

$$x_j = x_{j0}$$
$$= \frac{\left(\sum\limits_{i=1}^{m} c_i{}^p + \sum\limits_{\substack{i=m+1 \\ i \neq j}}^{n} x_{i0}^p\right)^{1/p} k_j}{\left[\sum\limits_{i=1}^{m}(c_i + k_i)^p + \sum\limits_{\substack{i=m+1 \\ i \neq j}}^{n}(x_{i0} + k_i)^p\right]^{1/p} - \left(\sum\limits_{i=1}^{m} c_i{}^p + \sum\limits_{\substack{i=m+1 \\ i \neq j}}^{n} x_{i0}^p\right)^{1/p}}.$$

$$(15)$$

We can show that P_0 is an interior point of the segment

$$L_{AB} = L \cap I_{AB},$$

that is, that

$$Ak_j < x_{j0} < Bk_j, \tag{16}$$

as follows.

The inequality

$$Ak_j < x_{j0} \tag{17}$$

is equivalent to

$$\left(\frac{A+1}{A}\right)^p > \left(\frac{x_{j0} + k_j}{x_{j0}}\right)^p. \tag{18}$$

To establish (18), we note first that by (13) we have

$$\left(\frac{A+1}{A}\right)^p > \left(\frac{\bar{c}+1}{\bar{c}}\right)^p,$$

and from (12) we obtain

$$\left(\frac{\bar{c}+1}{\bar{c}}\right)^p = \frac{\sum\limits_{i=1}^{m}(c_i + k_i)^p}{\sum\limits_{i=1}^{m} c_i{}^p} \, ;$$

hence we have

$$\left(\frac{A+1}{A}\right)^p > \frac{\sum\limits_{i=1}^{m}(c_i + k_i)^p}{\sum\limits_{i=1}^{m} c_i{}^p}. \tag{19}$$

Next, from the inequality

$$Ak_i \leq x_{i0}, \qquad i = m+1, m+2, \ldots, n, \qquad i \neq j,$$

we obtain

$$\left(\frac{A+1}{A}\right)^p \geq \frac{(x_{i0} + k_i)^p}{x_{i0}^p}, \qquad i = m+1, m+2, \ldots, n, \quad i \neq j,$$

so that

$$\left(\frac{A+1}{A}\right)^p \geq \frac{\sum\limits_{\substack{i=m+1 \\ i \neq j}}^{n}(x_{i0} + k_i)^p}{\sum\limits_{\substack{i=m+1 \\ i \neq j}}^{n} x_{i0}^p}. \tag{20}$$

Again, from either (10) or (15), we have

$$\frac{(x_{j0} + k_j)^p}{x_{j0}^p} = \frac{\sum\limits_{i=1}^{m} (c_i + k_i)^p + \sum\limits_{\substack{i=m+1 \\ i \neq j}}^{n} (x_{i0} + k_i)^p}{\sum\limits_{i=1}^{m} c_i^{\,p} + \sum\limits_{\substack{i=m+1 \\ i \neq j}}^{n} x_{i0}^p}. \tag{21}$$

Now from (19)–(21) we obtain (18) and therefore (17). Similarly, we can show that

$$x_{j0} < Bk_j.$$

Hence the inequalities (16) are valid, as desired.

Noting from (8) that

$$\lim_{x_j \to 0^+} \frac{\partial f}{\partial x_j} < 0, \qquad \lim_{x_j \to +\infty} \frac{\partial f}{\partial x_j} = 0^+,$$

we see that on L, f is a strictly decreasing function of x_j for $0 < x_j \leq x_{j0}$, and a strictly increasing function of x_j for $x_{j0} \leq x_j < \infty$. By (16), then, on the line segment L_{AB} the function f assumes its maximum value only at one or both endpoints, and its minimum value only at an interior point, of L_{AB}.

The following observations are immediate consequences of the behavior, as determined above, of the function f on the ray L.

(a) The function f assumes its maximum value on I_{AB} at one or more of the vertices (extreme points) of I_{AB}, and at no other points of I_{AB}.

(b) The function f assumes its minimum value on I_{AB} at no boundary point of I_{AB}.

(c) Both the maximum value of f on I_{AB}, and the minimum value of f on the boundary of I_{AB}, increase steadily as $A \to 0$, $0 < A < \bar{c}$, and as $B \to \infty$, $\bar{c} < B < \infty$.

Since there must be a horizontal tangent hyperplane at any interior minimum point of the function f on S, and since there is just one point $(\bar{c}, f(\bar{c}))$ of S at which there is a horizontal tangent hyperplane, it therefore follows from observation (b) that on I_{AB} the function f has a unique minimum, namely at $(x) = (\bar{c})$.

For $p < 1$, $p \neq 0$, the above discussion still applies, *mutatis mutandis*. Now, however, we have

$$\lim_{x_j \to 0^+} \frac{\partial f}{\partial x_j} = +\infty, \qquad \lim_{x_j \to +\infty} \frac{\partial f}{\partial x_j} = 0^-,$$

and hence on I_{AB} the function f has a unique maximum at $(x) = (\bar{c})$.

Letting $A \to 0$, $0 < A < \bar{c}$, and $B \to \infty$, $\bar{c} < B < \infty$, by (7) we therefore have the following result.

Theorem 1. *Let positive numbers* $(c_1, c_2, \ldots, c_m)$ *and* $(k_1, k_2, \ldots, k_n)$ *be given,* $0 < m < n$. *Then for* $p > 1$, *the inequality*

$$\left(\sum_{i=1}^{m} c_i{}^p + \sum_{i=m+1}^{n} x_i{}^p \right)^{1/p} - \left[\sum_{i=1}^{m} (c_i + k_i)^p + \sum_{i=m+1}^{n} (x_i + k_i)^p \right]^{1/p}$$

$$\geq \left(\sum_{i=1}^{'m} c_i{}^p + \sum_{i=m+1}^{n} \tilde{c}_i{}^p \right)^{1/p} - \left[\sum_{i=1}^{m} (c_i + k_i)^p + \sum_{i=m+1}^{n} (\tilde{c}_i + k_i)^p \right]^{1/p},$$

$$(22)$$

where

$$\tilde{c}_i = \bar{c} k_i, \qquad i = m+1, m+2, \ldots, n,$$

with

$$\bar{c} = \frac{\left(\sum\limits_{i=1}^{m} c_i{}^p \right)^{1/p}}{\left[\sum\limits_{i=1}^{m} (c_i + k_i)^p \right]^{1/p} - \left(\sum\limits_{i=1}^{m} c_i{}^p \right)^{1/p}}, \qquad (23)$$

holds for all positive $(x_{m+1}, x_{m+2}, \ldots, x_n)$, *with equality if and only if*

$$x_i = \tilde{c}_i, \qquad i = m+1, m+2, \ldots, n. \qquad (24)$$

For $p < 1$, $p \neq 0$, *the inequality sign is reversed in* (22), *again with equality if and only if* (x) *satisfies* (24).

For $m = 1$, (23) reduces to

$$\bar{c} = c_1/k_1,$$

and the right-hand side of (22) becomes

$$-\left(\sum_{i=1}^{n} k_i{}^p \right)^{1/p}.$$

Then (22) reduces to Minkowski's inequality:

For given positive c_1 *and* $(k_1, k_2, \ldots, k_n)$, *we have*

$$\left(c_1{}^p + \sum_{i=2}^{n} x_i{}^p \right)^{1/p} + \left(\sum_{i=1}^{n} k_i{}^p \right)^{1/p} \geq \left[(c_1 + k_1)^p + \sum_{i=2}^{n} (x_i + k_i)^p \right]^{1/p}$$

$$(25)$$

for all $p > 1$ *and for all positive* $(x_2, x_3, \ldots, x_n)$, *with equality if and only if*

$$x_j = (c_1/k_1)k_j, \qquad j = 2, 3, \ldots, n. \qquad (26)$$

For $p < 1$, $p \neq 0$, *the sign of inequality is reversed in* (25), *again with equality if and only if* (x) *satisfies* (26).

For $m > 1$, the right-hand side of (22) is greater than or equal to

$$-\left(\sum_{i=1}^{n} k_i{}^p\right)^{1/p},$$

that is,

$$\left(\sum_{i=1}^{m} c_i{}^p + \sum_{i=m+1}^{n} \tilde{c}_i{}^p\right)^{1/p} - \left[\sum_{i=1}^{m} (c_i + k_i)^p + \sum_{i=m+1}^{n} (\tilde{c}_i + k_i)^p\right]^{1/p}$$

$$\geq -\left(\sum_{i=1}^{n} k_i{}^p\right)^{1/p}, \tag{27}$$

if $p > 1$, with equality if and only if

$$c_j = \tilde{c} k_j, \qquad j = 1, 2, \ldots, m.$$

This follows, with a change of notation, from the case $m = 1$, which was discussed in the preceding paragraph. [As usual, the sign of inequality is reversed in (27) if $p < 1$, $p \neq 0$.] Hence, except when the given $(c_1, c_2, \ldots, c_m)$ is proportional to $(k_1, k_2, \ldots, k_m)$, (22) is stronger than Minkowski's inequality.

3. Kantorovich Inequalities

For given A, B satisfying $0 < A < B < \infty$, and for $p > 1$, we shall now investigate the maximum value of the function (7) for $0 \leq m < n$, subject to the constraints

$$A \leq x_j \leq B, \qquad j = m+1, m+2, \ldots, n. \tag{28}$$

Note that we no longer assume that $m > 0$ but only that $m \geq 0$; that is, we do not assume that there actually must be any given values c_j. Note further that A, B are not now assumed to satisfy (13), and that the constraints in (28) differ from those in (14) in that the factors k_j do not appear in (28).

Without loss of generality, by rearranging the subscripts as necessary, we henceforth assume that

$$k_{m+1} \leq k_{m+2} \leq \cdots \leq k_n. \tag{29}$$

Let us use K_{AB} to denote the hypercube determined by (28).

We recall from Sec. 2 that on the ray $x_j > 0$, $x_i = x_{i0} = \text{const.} > 0$, $i \neq j$, the function $f(x)$ decreases steadily to a minimum value as x_j increases from 0 to some $x_{j0} > 0$, and then increases steadily as x_j increases from x_{j0} to ∞. Accordingly, in and on the closed and bounded hypercube K_{AB}, the function $f(x)$ takes on its maximum value only at one or more of the vertices, where the $x_j = A$ or B, $j = m+1, m+2, \ldots, n$.

In a combinatorial search for such maximizing vertices $(x_{m+1}, x_{m+2}, \ldots, x_n)$, in considering vertices with h components $x_j = B$ and the remaining $n - m - h$ components $x_j = A$, $0 \leq h \leq n - m$, it is sufficient to consider only those $x_j = B$ that correspond to the least k's, namely to the values $k_{m+1}, k_{m+2}, \ldots, k_{m+h}$, and thus to evaluate only the $n - m + 1$ expressions

$$\varphi(h) = \left[\sum_{i=1}^{m} c_i{}^p + hB^p + (n - m - h)A^p \right]^{1/p}$$
$$- \left[\sum_{i=1}^{m} (c_i + k_i)^p + \sum_{i=m+1}^{m+h} (B + k_i)^p + \sum_{i=m+h+1}^{n} (A + k_i)^p \right]^{1/p}. \tag{30}$$

This observation is a simple consequence of the fact that the function given by $y = x^p$, $p > 1$, is an increasing convex function of x, $x > 0$, since the inequalities

$$k_i \leq k_{i+j} \qquad \text{and} \qquad A < B$$

imply

$$(B + k_i)^p + (A + k_{i+j})^p < (B + k_{i+j})^p + (A + k_i)^p.$$

For $p < 1$, $p \neq 0$, the argument is similar, but now on the ray $x_j > 0$, $x_i = x_{i0} = \text{const.} > 0$, $i \neq j$, $f(x)$ first increases steadily and then decreases steadily, whence we conclude that, in and on the hypercube K_{AB}, $f(x)$ attains its minimum value only at certain vertices. At such minimizing vertices, components of value $x_j = A$, rather than $x_j = B$, are associated with the least values k_j; the reasons for this are different for $0 < p < 1$ and for $p < 0$, but the conclusion is the same in both cases.

We shall show analytically that the extremizing integer $h = h_0$ either is unique or is unique to within being an arbitrary one of two specific consecutive integers. Accordingly, we have the following result.

Theorem 2. *Let positive $(c_1, c_2, \ldots, c_m)$ and $(k_1, k_2, \ldots, k_n)$ be given, $0 \leq m < n$, with $k_{m+1} \leq k_{m+2} \leq \cdots \leq k_n$. Let A, B satisfy $0 < A < B < \infty$, and consider $(x_{m+1}, x_{m+2}, \ldots, x_n)$ constrained by $A \leq x_j \leq B$, $j = m + 1$, $m + 2, \ldots, n$. Then for any $p > 1$ there is an integer h_0, $0 \leq h_0 \leq n - m$, either unique or unique to within being an arbitrary one of two specific consecutive integers, such that*

$$\left(\sum_{i=1}^{m} c_i{}^p + \sum_{i=m+1}^{n} x_i{}^p \right)^{1/p} - \left[\sum_{i=1}^{m} (c_i + k_i)^p + \sum_{i=m+1}^{n} (x_i + k_i)^p \right]^{1/p}$$
$$\leq \left[\sum_{i=1}^{m} c_i{}^p + h_0 B^p + (n - m - h_0)A^p \right]^{1/p}$$
$$- \left[\sum_{i=1}^{m} (c_i + k_i)^p + \sum_{i=m+1}^{m+h_0} (B + k_i)^p + \sum_{i=m+h_0+1}^{n} (A + k_i)^p \right]^{1/p}, \tag{31}$$

with equality if and only if h_0 components x_j, corresponding to values k_{m+1}, $k_{m+2}, \ldots, k_{m+h_0}$, satisfy $x_j = B$, with the remaining $x_j = A$. For $p < 1$, $p \neq 0$, the sign of inequality is reversed in (31), with A and B interchanged both in the inequality and in the conditions for equality.

Any combinatorial search for the extremizing integer (or for the two alternative extremizing integers) h_0 can be further expedited by the fact, established below, that in the set of values $0, 1, \ldots, n - m$ there is no interior $h \neq h_0$ at which there is a relative extreme value of $\varphi(h)$. Thus, for $p > 1$, if the integers h_1, h_2 satisfy $0 \leq h_1 < h_2 \leq n - m$, and if $\varphi(h_1) < \varphi(h_2)$, then $h_0 > h_1$; but if $\varphi(h_1) > \varphi(h_2)$, then $h_0 < h_2$.

For an analytic approach to the determination of h_0, we proceed, for $p > 1$, as follows. The function $\varphi(h)$ is given by (30) only for the integral values $h = 0, 1, \ldots, n - m$. Now for all real values h, $0 \leq h \leq n - m$, the definition

$$\varphi(h) = [\alpha(h)]^{1/p} - [\beta(h)]^{1/p}, \tag{32}$$

where

$$\alpha(h) = \sum_{i=1}^{m} c_i^p + hB^p + (n - m - h)A^p,,$$

$$\beta(h) = \sum_{i=1}^{m} (c_i + k_i)^p + \sum_{i=m+1}^{m+[h]} (B + k_i)^p + \sum_{i=m+[h]+1}^{n} (A + k_i)^p$$
$$+ (h - [h])[(B + k_{m+[h]+1})^p - (A + k_{m+[h]+1})^p],$$

and where $[h]$ denotes the greatest integer not greater than h, subsumes (30) and extends $\varphi(h)$ continuously to the entire interval.

For $h \neq [h]$, that is, for h not an integer, in $0 \leq h \leq n - m$, a computation yields

$$p \frac{d\varphi}{dh} = [\alpha(h)]^{1/p-1}(B^p - A^p) - [\beta(h)]^{1/p-1}[(B + k_{m+[h]+1})^p$$

$$- (A + k_{m+[h]+1})^p]. \tag{33}$$

Relative to (33), for $0 \leq h \leq n - m$, let us study the function

$$Q(h) = [\alpha(h)](B^p - A^p)^{p/(1-p)}$$
$$- [\beta(h)][(B + k_{m+[h]+1})^p - (A + k_{m+[h]+1})^p]^{p/(1-p)}. \tag{34}$$

A further computation gives

$$\frac{dQ(h)}{dh} = (B^p - A^p)^{1/(1-p)} - [(B + k_{m+[h]+1})^p$$

$$- (A + k_{m+[h]+1})^p]^{1/(1-p)}$$

for $h \neq [h]$. Since $p > 1$, it follows that

$$\frac{dQ}{dh} > 0, \qquad h \neq [h]. \tag{35}$$

From (34), we obtain

$$Q(j^+) = [\alpha(j)](B^p - A^p)^{p/(1-p)} \\ - [\beta(j)][(B + k_{m+j+1})^p - (A + k_{m+j+1})^p]^{p/(1-p)}$$

for $j = 0, 1, \ldots, n - m - 1$, and

$$Q(j^-) = [\alpha(j)](B^p - A^p)^{p/(1-p)} - [\beta(j)][(B + k_{m+j})^p - (A + k_{m+j})^p]^{p/(1-p)}$$

for $j = 1, 2, \ldots, n - m$. Therefore we have

$$Q(j^+) - Q(j^-) = \beta(j)\{[(B + k_{m+j})^p - (A + k_{m+j})^p]^{p/(1-p)} \\ - [(B + k_{m+j+1})^p - (A + k_{m+j+1})^p]^{p/(1-p)}\}$$

for $j = 1, 2, \ldots, n - m - 1$. Again since $p > 1$, we accordingly have

$$Q(j^+) - Q(j^-) \geq 0, \qquad j = 1, 2, \ldots, n - m - 1.$$

Adjoining the definitions

$$Q(0^-) = -\infty, \qquad Q((n - m)^+) = +\infty, \tag{36}$$

we now have

$$Q(j^+) - Q(j^-) \geq 0 \tag{37}$$

for all integers $j = 0, 1, \ldots, n - m$.

It follows from (35)–(37) that, for $0^- \leq h \leq (n - m)^+$, $Q(h)$ is strictly increasing from $Q(0^-) = -\infty$ to $Q((n - m)^+) = +\infty$, being continuous at nonintegral h and having nonnegative jumps at integral h. Therefore there is a unique h^*, $0 \leq h^* \leq n - m$, that is either (i) a nonintegral solution of $Q(h) = 0$ or (ii) an integer for which $Q(h^-) \leq 0$ and $Q(h^+) \geq 0$. Because of the possibility (ii), we shall use quotation marks in stating that h^* is a "solution" of the equation $Q(h) = 0$.

For $0 < h < h^*$, we have $Q(h) < 0$, so that, by (34),

$$[\alpha(h)](B^p - A^p)^{p/(1-p)} < [\beta(h)][(B + k_{m+[h]+1})^p - (A + k_{m+[h]+1})^p]^{p/(1-p)}.$$

Since $p > 1$, we therefore have

$$[\alpha(h)]^{1/p-1}(B^p - A^p) - [\beta(h)]^{1/p-1}[(B + k_{m+[h]+1})^p - (A + k_{m+[h]+1})^p] > 0$$

for $0 < h < h^*$. Hence, by (33) and (37) it follows that $\varphi(h)$ is a strictly increasing function for $0 \leq h \leq h^*$. Similarly, we have $Q(h) > 0$ for $h^* < h < n - m$, so that $\varphi(h)$ is a strictly decreasing function for $h^* \leq h \leq n - m$.

It thus follows that, in $0 \leq h \leq n - m$, $\varphi(h)$ has a unique maximum value at $h = h^*$.

For $p < 1$, $p \neq 0$, the analysis is similar, *mutatis mutandis*, with the roles of the lesser value A and the greater value B interchanged. The function $\varphi(h)$ now has a unique minimum value at $h = h^*$.

We thus have the following result.

Theorem 3. *Let positive $(c_1, c_2, \ldots, c_m)$ and $(k_1, k_2, \ldots, k_n)$ be given, $0 \leq m < n$, with $k_{m+1} \leq k_{m+2} \leq \cdots \leq k_n$. Let A, B satisfy $0 < A < B < \infty$, and consider $(x_{m+1}, x_{m+2}, \ldots, x_n)$ constrained by $A \leq x_j \leq B, j = m + 1$, $m + 2, \ldots, n$. Then for any $p > 1$,*

$$\left(\sum_{i=1}^{m} c_i{}^p + \sum_{i=m+1}^{n} x_i{}^p \right)^{1/p} - \left[\sum_{i=1}^{m} (c_i + k_i)^p + \sum_{i=m+1}^{n} (x_i + k_i)^p \right]^{1/p}$$

$$\leq \left[\sum_{i=1}^{m} c_i{}^p + h^* B^p + (n - m - h^*) A^p \right]^{1/p}$$

$$- \left\{ \sum_{i=1}^{m} (c_i + k_i)^p + \sum_{i=m+1}^{m+[h^*]} (B + k_i)^p + \sum_{i=m+[h^*]+1}^{n} (A + k_i)^p \right.$$

$$\left. + (h^* - [h^*])[(B + k_{m+[h^*]+1})^p - (A + k_{m+[h^*]+1})^p] \right\}^{1/p}, \quad (38)$$

where $[h^*]$ denotes the greatest integer not greater than h^*, and h^* is the unique "solution" of the equation

$$Q(h) = 0, \qquad 0^- \leq h \leq (n - m)^+,$$

in which

$$Q(0^-) = -\infty, \qquad Q((n - m)^+) = +\infty,$$

and otherwise

$$Q(h) = \left[\sum_{i=1}^{m} c_i{}^p + h B^p + (n - m - h) A^p \right] (B^p - A^p)^{p/(1-p)}$$

$$- \left\{ \sum_{i=1}^{m} (c_i + k_i)^p + \sum_{i=m+1}^{m+[h]} (B + k_i)^p + \sum_{i=m+[h]+1}^{n} (A + k_i)^p \right.$$

$$\left. + (h - [h])[(B + k_{m+[h]+1})^p - (A + k_{m+[h]+1})^p] \right\}$$

$$\times [(B + k_{m+[h]+1})^p - (A + k_{m+[h]+1})^p]^{p/(1-p)}, \qquad 0 \leq h \leq n - m.$$

$$(39)$$

The sign of equality holds in (38) if and only if h^* is an integer and h^* components x_j, corresponding to values $k_{m+1}, k_{m+2}, \ldots, k_{m+h^*}$, satisfy $x_j = B$, *with the remaining x_j satisfying $x_j = A$. For $p < 1$, $p \neq 0$, the sign of in-equality is reversed in (38), with A and B interchanged in (38), in (39), and in the conditions for the sign of equality to hold in (38).*

The h_0 of Theorem 2 is equal to the h^* of Theorem 3 if h^* is an integer; otherwise, h_0 is one or both of the two integers nearest h^*. Thus, if $h^* = [h^*]$, then $h_0 = h^*$; but if $h^* \neq [h^*]$, then $h_0 = [h^*]$, $[h^*] + 1$, or both, according as $\varphi([h^*]) > \varphi([h^*] + 1)$, $\varphi([h^*]) < \varphi([h^*] + 1)$, or $\varphi([h^*]) = \varphi([h^*] + 1)$.

4. Other Inequalities

Consider the Hölder-inequality difference,

$$\left(\sum_{i=1}^n x_i{}^p\right)^{1/p}\left(\sum_{i=1}^n y_i{}^q\right)^{1/q} - \sum_{i=1}^n x_i y_i, \qquad \frac{1}{p} + \frac{1}{q} = 1,$$

and ratio,

$$\frac{\left(\sum_{i=1}^n x_i{}^p\right)^{1/p}\left(\sum_{i=1}^n y_i{}^q\right)^{1/q}}{\sum_{i=1}^n x_i y_i}, \qquad \frac{1}{p} + \frac{1}{q} = 1,$$

and the Minkowski-inequality difference,

$$\left(\sum_{i=1}^n x_i{}^p\right)^{1/p} + \left(\sum_{i=1}^n y_i{}^p\right)^{1/p} - \left[\sum_{i=1}^n (x_i + y_i)^p\right]^{1/p}, \qquad p \neq 0,$$

and ratio,

$$\frac{\left(\sum_{i=1}^n x_i{}^p\right)^{1/p} + \left(\sum_{i=1}^n y_i{}^p\right)^{1/p}}{\left[\sum_{i=1}^n (x_i + y_i)^p\right]^{1/p}}, \qquad p \neq 0.$$

For vectors $(c_1, c_2, \ldots, c_m, x_{m+1}, x_{m+2}, \ldots, x_n)$ and $(k_1, k_2, \ldots, k_n)$, in which only the x_j are considered as variables, the foregoing expressions become, respectively,

$$\left(\sum_{i=1}^m c_i{}^p + \sum_{i=m+1}^n x_i{}^p\right)^{1/p}\left(\sum_{i=1}^n k_i{}^q\right)^{1/q} - \sum_{i=1}^m c_i k_i - \sum_{i=m+1}^n x_i k_i, \qquad (40)$$

$$\frac{\left(\sum_{i=1}^m c_i{}^p + \sum_{i=m+1}^n x_i{}^p\right)^{1/p}\left(\sum_{i=1}^n k_i{}^q\right)^{1/q}}{\sum_{i=1}^m c_i k_i + \sum_{i=m+1}^n x_i k_i}, \qquad (41)$$

$$\left(\sum_{i=1}^{m} c_i{}^p + \sum_{i=m+1}^{n} x_i{}^p\right)^{1/p} + \left(\sum_{i=1}^{n} k_i{}^p\right)^{1/p}$$
$$- \left[\sum_{i=1}^{m} (c_i + k_i)^p + \sum_{i=m+1}^{n} (x_i + k_i)^p\right]^{1/p},$$

(42)

$$\frac{\left(\sum_{i=1}^{m} c_i{}^p + \sum_{i=m+1}^{n} x_i{}^p\right)^{1/p} + \left(\sum_{i=1}^{n} k_i{}^p\right)^{1/p}}{\left[\sum_{i=1}^{m} (c_i + k_i)^p + \sum_{i=m+1}^{n} (x_i + k_i)^p\right]^{1/p}} \cdot$$

(43)

In (40), $-\sum_{i=1}^{m} c_i k_i$ is a constant addend; in (41), $(\sum_{i=1}^{n} k_i{}^q)^{1/q}$ is a constant factor; and in (42), $(\sum_{i=1}^{n} k_i{}^p)^{1/p}$ is a constant addend. There is no such constant addend or factor in (43). The constant addends and factor can be omitted in analyzing the expressions (40)–(42). Accordingly, we are concerned with the four functions

$$f_1(x) = \left(\sum_{i=1}^{m} c_i{}^p + \sum_{i=m+1}^{n} x_i{}^p\right)^{1/p} \left(\sum_{i=1}^{n} k_i{}^q\right)^{1/q} - \sum_{i=m+1}^{n} x_i k_i,$$

$$f_2(x) = \frac{\left(\sum_{i=1}^{m} c_i{}^p + \sum_{i=m+1}^{n} x_i{}^p\right)^{1/p}}{\sum_{i=1}^{m} c_i k_i + \sum_{i=m+1}^{n} x_i k_i},$$

$$f_3(x) = \left(\sum_{i=1}^{m} c_i{}^p + \sum_{i=m+1}^{n} x_i{}^p\right)^{1/p} - \left[\sum_{i=1}^{m} (c_i + k_i)^p + \sum_{i=m+1}^{n} (x_i + k_i)^p\right]^{1/p},$$

$$f_4(x) = \frac{\left(\sum_{i=1}^{m} c_i{}^p + \sum_{i=m+1}^{n} x_i{}^p\right)^{1/p} + \left(\sum_{i=1}^{n} k_i{}^p\right)^{1/p}}{\left[\sum_{i=1}^{m} (c_i + k_i)^p + \sum_{i=m+1}^{n} (x_i + k_i)^p\right]^{1/p}} \cdot$$

Despite their considerable differences in appearance, the functions $f_1(x)$, $f_2(x)$, and $f_3(x)$ all have similar gross behavior, as given for the function $f_3(x)$ in Secs. 2 and 3, above. The analogous discussion for $f_2(x)$ is given in [2]. While the details are rather different in the three cases, the theory of proportions plays an essential role in each case.

As an exercise, one might verify the following statements concerning $f_1(x)$.

• The equation

$$\frac{\partial f_1}{\partial x_j} = 0$$

is satisfied if and only if

$$\frac{x_j{}^p}{k_j{}^q} = \frac{\sum\limits_{i=1}^{m} c_i{}^p + \sum\limits_{\substack{i=m+1 \\ i \neq j}}^{n} x_i{}^p}{\sum\limits_{i=1}^{m} k_i{}^q + \sum\limits_{\substack{i=m+1 \\ i \neq j}}^{n} k_i{}^q}.$$

- The system of equations

$$\frac{\partial f_1}{\partial x_j} = 0, \qquad j = m+1,\ m+2,\ \ldots,\ n,$$

is satisfied if and only if

$$\frac{x_j{}^p}{k_j{}^q} = \frac{\sum\limits_{i=1}^{m} c_i{}^p}{\sum\limits_{i=1}^{m} k_i{}^q} = \bar{c}.$$

- For any A, B satisfying $0 < A < \bar{c} < B < \infty$, and for j fixed, $m+1 \leq j \leq n$, let L denote the ray

$$x_j > 0, \qquad x_i = x_{i0} = \text{const.} > 0, \qquad A k_i{}^q \leq x_{i0}^p \leq B k_i{}^q, \qquad i \neq j.$$

Then on L, the coordinate $x_j = x_{j0}$ of the point at which the relation $\partial f_1 / \partial x_j = 0$ holds satisfies the inequalities

$$A k_j{}^q \leq x_{j0}^p \leq B k_j{}^q.$$

- Let I_{AB} denote the rectangular parallelepiped determined by

$$A k_j{}^q \leq x_j{}^p \leq B k_j{}^q, \qquad j = m+1,\ m+2,\ \ldots,\ n.$$

For $p > 1$, the function $f_1(x)$ satisfies the conditions (a), (b), and (c) listed in Sec. 2. For $p < 1$, $p \neq 0$, $f_1(x)$ satisfies the same conditions, but with "maximum" and "minimum" interchanged, and with "increase" replaced by "decrease."

- **Theorem 4.** *Let positive numbers* $(c_1, c_2, \ldots, c_m)$ *and* $(k_1, k_2, \ldots, k_n)$ *be given, $0 < m < n$, and let p, q satisfy $1/p + 1/q = 1$. Then for $p > 1$, the inequality*

$$\left(\sum_{i=1}^{m} c_i{}^p + \sum_{i=m+1}^{n} x_i{}^p \right)^{1/p} \left(\sum_{i=1}^{n} k_i{}^q \right)^{1/q} - \sum_{i=m+1}^{n} x_i k_i$$

$$\geq \left(\sum_{i=1}^{m} c_i{}^p + \sum_{i=m+1}^{n} \tilde{c}_i{}^p \right)^{1/p} \left(\sum_{i=1}^{n} k_i{}^q \right)^{1/q} - \sum_{i=m+1}^{n} \tilde{c}_i k_i, \qquad (44)$$

where

$$\tilde{c}_i{}^p = \bar{c}k_i{}^q, \qquad i = m+1, m+2, \ldots, n,$$

with

$$\bar{c} = \frac{\sum\limits_{i=1}^{m} c_i{}^p}{\sum\limits_{i=1}^{m} k_i{}^q},$$

holds for all positive $(x_{m+1}, x_{m+2}, \ldots, x_n)$, *with equality if and only if*

$$x_i = \tilde{c}_i, \qquad i = m+1, m+2, \ldots, n. \tag{45}$$

For $p < 1$, $p \neq 0$, *the inequality sign is reversed in* (44), *again with equality if and only if* (x) *satisfies* (45).

• For $m = 1$, (44) *reduces to Hölder's inequality:*
For given positive c_1 *and* $(k_1, k_2, \ldots, k_n)$, *we have*

$$\left(c_1{}^p + \sum_{i=2}^{n} x_i{}^p\right)^{1/p} \left(\sum_{i=1}^{n} k_i{}^q\right)^{1/q} \geq c_1 k_1 + \sum_{i=2}^{n} x_i k_i \tag{46}$$

for all $p > 1$ *and for all positive* $(x_2, x_3, \ldots, x_n)$, *with equality if and only if*

$$x_i{}^p = \frac{c_1{}^p}{k_1{}^q} k_i{}^q, \qquad i = 2, 3, \ldots, n. \tag{47}$$

For $p < 1$, $p \neq 0$, *the sign of inequality is reversed in* (46), *again with equality if and only if* (x) *satisfies* (47).

• For $m > 1$, the inequality (44) is stronger than Hölder's inequality except when the given $(c_1{}^p, c_2{}^p, \ldots, c_m{}^p)$ is proportional to $(k_1{}^q, k_2{}^q, \ldots, k_m{}^q)$.

• If subscripts are arranged so that the inequalities (29) are satisfied, and if $p > 1$, then the function

$$f(h) = \left[\sum_{i=1}^{m} c_i{}^p + hB^p + (n - m - h)A^p\right]^{1/p} \left(\sum_{i=1}^{n} k_i{}^q\right)^{1/q}$$

$$- B \sum_{i=m+1}^{m+[h]} k_i - A \sum_{i=m+[h]+1}^{n} k_i - (h - [h])(B - A)k_{m+[h]+1},$$

$0 \leq h \leq n - m$, is concave for $j - 1 < h < j, j = 1, 2, \ldots, n - m$, and satisfies

$$\left.\frac{df}{dh}\right|_{h=j^+} - \left.\frac{df}{dh}\right|_{h=j^-} \leq 0$$

for $j = 1, 2, \ldots, n - m - 1$. Hence $f(h)$ is concave for $0 \leq h \leq n - m$.

• **Theorem 5.** *Let positive* $(c_1, c_2, \ldots, c_m)$ *and* $(k_1, k_2, \ldots, k_n)$ *be given,* $0 \leq m < n$, *with* $k_{m+1} \leq k_{m+2} \leq \cdots \leq k_n$, *and let* p, q *satisfy* $1/p + 1/q = 1$. *Let* A, B *satisfy* $0 < A < B < \infty$, *and consider* $(x_{m+1}, x_{m+2}, \ldots, x_n)$ *constrained by* $A \leq x_j \leq B$, $j = m+1, m+2, \ldots, n$. *Then for any* $p > 1$,

$$\left(\sum_{i=1}^{m} c_i{}^p + \sum_{i=m+1}^{n} x_i{}^p \right)^{1/p} \left(\sum_{i=1}^{n} k_i{}^q \right)^{1/q} - \sum_{i=m+1}^{n} x_i k_i$$

$$\leq \left[\sum_{i=1}^{m} c_i{}^p + h^* B^p + (n - m - h^*) A^p \right]^{1/p} \left(\sum_{i=1}^{n} k_i{}^q \right)^{1/q} - B \sum_{i=m+1}^{m+[h^*]} k_i$$

$$- A \sum_{i=m+[h^*]+1}^{n} k_i - (h^* - [h^*])(B - A) k_{m+[h^*]+1}, \tag{48}$$

where $[h^*]$ *denotes the greatest integer not greater than* h^*, *and* h^* *is the unique "solution" of the equation*

$$Q(h) = 0, \qquad 0^- \leq h \leq (n - m)^+,$$

in which

$$Q(0^-) = +\infty, \qquad Q((n - m)^+) = -\infty,$$

and otherwise

$$Q(h) = \frac{1}{p} \left[\sum_{i=1}^{m} c_i{}^p + h B^p + (n - m - h) A^p \right]^{1/p - 1}$$

$$\times (B^p - A^p) \left(\sum_{i=1}^{n} k_i{}^q \right)^{1/q} - (B - A) k_{m+[h]+1}, \tag{49}$$

$0 \leq h \leq n - m$. *The sign of equality holds in* (48) *if and only if* h^* *is an integer and* h^* *components* x_j, *corresponding to values* $k_{m+1}, k_{m+2}, \ldots, k_{m+h^*}$, *satisfy* $x_j = B$, *with the remaining* x_j *satisfying* $x_j = A$. *For* $p < 1$, $p \neq 0$, *the sign of inequality is reversed in* (48), *with* A *and* B *interchanged in* (48), *in* (49), *and in the conditions for the sign of equality to hold in* (48).

• If h^* is not an integer, then the maximum value of the left-hand member of (48) is equal to the value obtained by replacing h^* in the right-hand member of (48) either by $[h^*]$ or by $[h^*] + 1$, whichever yields the greater value, or by an arbitrary one of these if the values are equal.

The function $f_4(x)$, on the other hand, does not appear to lend itself as readily to the theory of proportions, and would seem to merit a separate study.

For mean-value functions, also, the ratio

$$f_5(x) = \frac{M_s(c, x; \alpha)}{M_r(c, x; \alpha)}, \qquad r < s,$$

can be treated [1] by an analysis similar to that given for $f_2(x)$ in Secs. 2 and 3, but seemingly the discussion of the difference,

$$f_6(x) = M_s(c, x; \alpha) - M_r(c, x; \alpha), \qquad r < s,$$

must be somewhat different. Perhaps the method of Shisha and Mond [9] for determining upper bounds in the case $m = 0$ can be adjusted to obtain both upper and lower bounds for the more general case $m \geq 0$.

The foregoing analysis can be extended to the treatment of vectors $(c_1, c_2, \ldots, c_m, x_{m+1}, x_{m+2}, \ldots, x_n)$ and $(y_1, y_2, \ldots, y_l, k_{l+1}, k_{l+2}, \ldots, k_n)$, in which some components of each vector are considered as being given and the rest allowed to vary.

Although we have restricted our attention to pairs of n-dimensional vectors, extensions might, of course, be given for any number of n-dimensional vectors, for infinite sums, and for integrals, paralleling the various contexts [3, 5] in which the classical inequalities are valid.

Many additional extensions of the results discussed above can be sought.

Separate bounds A_j, B_j (or separate ratios) rather than uniform bounds A, B (or a uniform ratio) for the variables might be considered.

Other inequalities, such as that of Lyapunov [7], might also be investigated in the case $m > 0$.

Matrix versions [8] of these results can also be examined.

REFERENCES

[1] Beckenbach, E. F., On the inequality of Kantorovich, *Amer. Math. Monthly* **71,** 606–619 (1964).
[2] Beckenbach, E. F., On Hölder's inequality, *J. Pure Appl. Math.* **15,** 21–29 (1966).
[3] Beckenbach, E. F., and Bellman, R., "Inequalities," 2nd revised printing, Springer, New York, 1965.
[4] Cargo, G. T., and Shisha, O., Bounds on ratios of means, *J. Res. Nat. Bur. Standards Sect. B* **66,** 169–170 (1962).
[5] Hardy, G. H., Littlewood, J. E., and Pólya, G., "Inequalities," 2nd ed. Cambridge Univ. Press, London and New York, 1952.
[6] Kantorovich, L. V., "Functional analysis and applied mathematics (C. D. Benster, transl., and G. E. Forsythe, ed.), *Nat. Bur. Standards, Rept. No. 1509,* 106–109 (1952).
[7] Marshall, A. W., and Olkin, I., Reversal of the Lyapunov, Hölder, and Minkowski inequalities and other extensions of the Kantorovich inequality, *J. Math. Anal. Appl.* **8,** 503–514 (1964).
[8] Mond, B., A matrix inequality including that of Kantorovich, *J. Math. Anal. Appl.* **13,** 49–52 (1966).
[9] Shisha, O., and Mond, B., Bounds on differences of means, these Proceedings.

Uncertainty Principles in Fourier Analysis

N. G. DE BRUIJN
Technological University
Eindhoven, Netherlands

1. Introduction

In this paper we consider some inequalities of the type of Heisenberg's uncertainty relation. Some of them will be formulated in terms of classical Fourier theory, others will be expressed in terms of a notion that will be called the *musical score* of a time function.

We shall consider a complex-valued function f of the real variable t, defined for $-\infty < t < \infty$. The variable t will be referred to as the *time*, and f will be called a *signal*. For the moment we shall assume that f belongs to L_2 [L_2 stands for $L_2(-\infty, \infty)$], whence Plancherel's theorem can be applied. We define the Fourier transform g of f by

$$g(\omega) = \int_{-\infty}^{\infty} e^{-2\pi i t \omega} f(t) \, dt, \tag{1.1}$$

where the integral has to be interpreted carefully as the limit in the mean of $\int_{-T}^{T}$ as $T \to \infty$. We shall write

$$g = \mathscr{F} f.$$

Plancherel's theorem states that f can be obtained from g in a similar way:

$$f(t) = \int_{-\infty}^{\infty} e^{2\pi i t \omega} g(\omega) \, d\omega, \tag{1.2}$$

and Parseval's theorem says that

$$\int_{-\infty}^{\infty} |f(t)|^2 \, dt = \int_{-\infty}^{\infty} |g(\omega)|^2 \, d\omega. \tag{1.3}$$

With the notation chosen here, the Heisenberg relation can be expressed as

$$\left[\int_{-\infty}^{\infty} (t-a)^2 |f(t)|^2 \, dt \right]^{1/2} \cdot \left[\int_{-\infty}^{\infty} (\omega-b)^2 |g(\omega)|^2 \, d\omega \right]^{1/2} \geq \|f\|/4\pi, \tag{1.4}$$

where, as usual, $\|f\|$ denotes $[\int_{-\infty}^{\infty} |f(t)|^2 \, dt]^{1/2}$.

57

Here a and b are arbitrary real numbers. The factors on the left-hand side of (1.4) can be called the *time spread* around the time a, and the *frequency spread* around the frequency b, respectively.

For convenience we shall only consider $a = b = 0$, from which the general case can be derived. This is achieved by introducing f^* and g^* instead of f and g, where

$$f^*(t) = f(t + a)\, e^{-2\pi i b t}, \quad g^*(\omega) = g(\omega + b)\, e^{2\pi i a \omega}, \tag{1.5}$$

where $g^* = \mathscr{F} f^*$. Now (1.4) reduces to

$$\left[\int_{-\infty}^{\infty} t^2 |f^*(t)|^2\, dt \right]^{1/2} \cdot \left[\int_{-\infty}^{\infty} \omega^2 |g^*(\omega)|^2\, d\omega \right]^{1/2} \geq \|f^*\|/4\pi.$$

So henceforth we shall consider the inequality

$$\left[\int_{-\infty}^{\infty} t^2 |f(t)|^2\, dt \right]^{1/2} \cdot \left[\int_{-\infty}^{\infty} \omega^2 |g(\omega)|^2\, d\omega \right]^{1/2} \geq \|f\|/4\pi, \tag{1.6}$$

where $g = \mathscr{F} f$. This was derived by Weyl ([6], Appendix 1) from the inequality

$$\int_{-\infty}^{\infty} |f(t)|^2\, dt \leq 4 \int_{-\infty}^{\infty} t^2 |f(t)|^2\, dt \cdot \int_{-\infty}^{\infty} |df(t)/dt|^2\, dt. \tag{1.7}$$

Equality in (1.6) and in (1.7) is attained if and only if f has the form $f(t) = A \exp(-\alpha t^2)$, where A and α are constants, $\alpha > 0$.

We deal with (1.6) in a different way in Sec. 2.

The uncertainty principle expresses, roughly speaking, that if a signal is confined to a small time interval, then its Fourier transform cannot be confined to a small frequency interval. A more detailed version of the uncertainty principle was given by Fuchs [2] and by Landau and Pollak [3]. These authors proved quantitative statements relating the percentage of the energy that lies in a given time interval (compared to the total energy $\|f\|^2$) to the percentage of the energy that lies in a given frequency interval. We shall not deal with this kind of work in this paper. Instead, we have an entirely different way (Sec. 2) of considering time and frequency simultaneously.

2. The Musical Score of a Signal

Usually we describe sound by a single function f, defined for $-\infty < t < \infty$, i.e. by a signal. For some applications it is natural to discuss mathematical and physical properties in terms of f itself, and for others it is more appropriate to speak in terms of its Fourier transform g. Between those extremes, however, there is a class of questions where it is desirable to consider time and frequency simultaneously.

For example, if f represents a piece of music, then the composer does not produce f itself; he does not even define it. He may try to prescribe the exact frequency and the exact time interval of a note (although the uncertainty principle says that he can never be completely successful in this effort), but he does not try to prescribe the phase. The composer does not deal with f; it is only the gramophone company which produces and sells an f. On the other hand, the composer certainly does not want to describe the Fourier transform. This Fourier transform is very useful for solving mathematical and physical problems, but it gives an absolutely unreadable picture of the given piece of music.

What the composer really does, or thinks he does, or should think he does, is something entirely different from describing either f or $\mathscr{F}f$. Instead, he constructs a function of two variables. The variables are the time and the frequency, the function describes the intensity of the sound. He describes the function by a complicated set of dots on score paper. His way of describing time is slightly different from what a mathematician would do, but certainly vertical lines denote constant time, and horizontal lines denote constant frequency.

We shall give a mathematical description of such an intensity function. In some respect our choice will be arbitrary and somewhat unrealistic (for example the fact that we use the future for the description of the present), but it has the advantage of being easy to handle and having several useful invariance and symmetry properties. It is essentially the same expression as the one for the phase-space distribution introduced in quantum mechanics by Wigner [7] and elaborated by Moyal [4]. Both in music and in quantum mechanics we have the situation of a function of a single variable, which appears to be a function of two variables as long as the observation is not too precise. The parallel between quantum mechanics and music can be carried a little further by comparing the composer to the classical physicist. The way the composer writes an isolated note as a dot, and thinks of it as being completely determined in time and frequency, is similar to the classical physicist's conception of a particle with well-determined position and momentum.

The possibility of describing energy density in the time-frequency plane by an expression which is essentially Wigner's, was pointed out by Ville [5].

In this paper's presentation we shall assume that our time functions are in L_2. The scope of the notion of the score is considerably wider, but presently we are dealing mainly with inequalities which are meaningless if f has infinite total energy. Therefore, not much is lost by assuming $f \in L_2$ in our present discussion.

If $f_1 \in L_2$, $f_2 \in L_2$, and if x, y are real numbers, then we define

$$H(x, y; f_1, f_2) = 2 \int_{-\infty}^{\infty} f_1(x+t)\overline{f_2(x-t)}e^{-4\pi i y t}\, dt. \qquad (2.1)$$

We shall call $H(x, y; f, f)$ the *energy density* of f at time x and frequency y. Considered as a function of x and y we call it the *musical score* of f, or *score* for short.

Of course we owe the reader some explanation for this definition. First we remark that (2.1) is related to

$$H(0, 0; f_1, f_2) = 2 \int_{-\infty}^{\infty} f_1(t)\overline{f_2(-t)}\, dt \qquad (2.2)$$

in the following way. If f_j^* is defined by

$$f_j^*(t) = f_j(t+x)e^{-2\pi i y t} \qquad (j = 1, 2)$$

[cf. (1.5)], then we have

$$H(x, y; f_1, f_2) = H(0, 0; f_1^*, f_2^*), \qquad (2.3)$$

and this is why we have the right to refer to $H(x, y; f_1, f_2)$ as something related to the moment x and the frequency y. The words "energy density" can be partly explained by formulas (2.4)–(2.6) which we mention without proof: If $-\infty \le p < q \le \infty$, and if both f and g $(=\mathscr{F}f)$ are in $L_1 \cap L_2$, then

$$\int_p^q dx \int_{-\infty}^{\infty} H(x, y; f, f)\, dy = \int_p^q |f(t)|^2\, dt, \qquad (2.4)$$

$$\int_p^q dy \int_{-\infty}^{\infty} H(x, y; f, f)\, dx = \int_p^q |g(\omega)|^2\, d\omega. \qquad (2.5)$$

If, moreover, f is what is called band-limited, i.e. if f has the form

$$f(t) = \int_c^d g(\omega)e^{2\pi i \omega t}\, d\omega,$$

with finite c and d $(c < d)$, then we have, for all p and q

$$\int_p^q dx \int_c^d H(x, y; f, f)\, dy = \int_p^q |f(t)|^2\, dt. \qquad (2.6)$$

On the other hand, there is also a serious objection against the name "energy density," namely the fact that $H(x, y; f, f)$ is not ≥ 0 for all f [for example, if $tf(t) > 0$ for all t, we have, by (2.2), $H(0, 0; f, f) < 0$]. But this objection does not hold against certain "moving averages" $H_{\alpha\beta}$, which we are introducing presently.

Let $\alpha > 0$, $\beta > 0$. We shall form the Gaussian average (often called Gauss transform, or Weierstrass transform, with slightly different notation)

$$H_{\alpha\beta}(x, y; f_1, f_2)$$

$$= (\alpha\beta)^{-1/2} \int_{-\infty}^{\infty} \int_{-\infty}^{\infty} \exp\left[-\frac{\pi}{\alpha}(x - \xi)^2 - \frac{\pi}{\beta}(y - \eta)^2 \right] H(\xi, \eta; f_1, f_2) \, d\xi \, d\eta.$$

$$(2.7)$$

This integral converges rapidly, since $|H(\xi, \eta; f_1, f_2)| \leq 2\|f_1\| \cdot \|f_2\|$, which follows from (2.1) by application of the Cauchy–Bunyakovski inequality.

From (2.7) we obtain by application of Fubini's theorem

$$H_{\alpha\beta}(x, y; f_1, f_2) = \alpha^{-1/2} \int_{-\infty}^{\infty} \int_{-\infty}^{\infty} \exp\left[-\frac{\pi}{4\alpha}(s + t - 2x)^2 \right.$$

$$\left. - \eta\beta(s - t)^2 - 2\pi i y(s - t) \right] f_1(s)\overline{f_2(t)} \, ds \, dt. \quad (2.8)$$

Owing to the strong convergence factors in (2.8), we can define $H_{\alpha\beta}$ in cases where the score itself does not exist, for example if f is a periodic function, or a delta function.

We can consider $H_{\alpha\beta}$ as a blurred picture of the score. It follows immediately from a well-known semigroup property of the Gauss transform, that if we make a blurred picture of $H_{\alpha\beta}$, with "blurring parameters" γ and δ, then what we obtain is $H_{\alpha+\gamma, \beta+\delta}$.

There is a simple relation between score and Fourier transform, which we mention without proof. The score of the Fourier transform of f is obtained by turning the score of f over $90°$, and the same thing holds for the blurred score (provided that we interchange the blurring parameters):

$$H_{\alpha\beta}(x, y; f_1, f_2) = H_{\beta\alpha}(y, -x; \mathscr{F}f_1, \mathscr{F}f_2). \quad (2.9)$$

This is a formula of Parseval type, and indeed, if $\alpha \to \infty$, $\beta \to \infty$, then (2.9) turns into the Parseval formula.

We finally emphasize that $H_{\alpha\beta}(x, y; f, f)$ is positive-definite if and only if $\alpha\beta > \frac{1}{4}$ (see Sec. 4). This means that if a physical experiment produces the value of $H_{\alpha\beta}(x, y; f, f)$, and if the nature of the experiment is such that it measures an amount of energy so that the result can never be negative, then the product of the blurring parameters α and β has to exceed $\frac{1}{4}$. This amounts to saying that if a measurement is very accurate in the sense that it needs the signal f in a small time interval only, then it cannot be very accurate about the frequencies in that signal.

3. The Heisenberg Inequality

We shall use the Hermite polynomials H_n with the following notation (see Erdélyi [1, p. 193])

$$H_n(t) = (-1)^n \exp(t^2) \left(\frac{d}{dt}\right)^n \exp(-t^2) \qquad (n = 0, 1, 2, \ldots). \quad (3.1)$$

For the corresponding orthogonal system on $L_2 = L_2(-\infty, \infty)$ we take

$$\psi_n(t) = (2^{n-1/2}n!)^{-1/2} H_n[(2\pi)^{1/2}t] \exp(-\pi t^2) \qquad (n = 0, 1, 2, \ldots),$$
$$(3.2)$$

whence $\psi_n(t)$ equals $n! \, C_n$ times the coefficient of w^n in the power series development of $\exp[\pi t^2 - 2\pi(t - w)^2]$, with

$$C_n = [2^{n-1/2}n! \, (2\pi)^n]^{-1/2}.$$

We have $(\psi_n, \psi_m) = \delta_{nm}$ $(n, m = 0, 1, 2, \ldots)$, where δ_{nm} is the Kronecker symbol, and the inner product is defined by $(f, g) = \int_{-\infty}^{\infty} f(t)\overline{g(t)} \, dt$.

It is well known that the ψ_m are eigenfunctions of the Fourier transform: $\mathscr{F}\psi_m = i^{-m}\psi_m$. Therefore, if $f \in L_2$, and $g = \mathscr{F}f$, then the Fourier coefficients of f and g are related by $(f, \psi_m) = (\mathscr{F}f, \mathscr{F}\psi_m) = i^m(g, \psi_m)$. This plays its role in the following theorem.

Theorem 3.1. *If* $f \in L_2(-\infty, \infty)$, $g = \mathscr{F}f$, $\gamma_m = (f, \psi_m)$, *then we have*

$$\int_{-\infty}^{\infty} t^2[|f(t)|^2 + |g(t)|^2] \, dt = (2\pi)^{-1} \sum_{m=0}^{\infty} |\gamma_m|^2(2m + 1). \quad (3.3)$$

Proof. It follows from the recurrence relation for the Hermite polynomials that for $m = 0, 1, 2, \ldots$

$$(4\pi)^{1/2}t\psi_m(t) = (m + 1)^{1/2}\psi_{m+1}(t) + m^{1/2}\psi_{m-1}(t)$$

[if we define $\psi_{-1}(t) = 0$]. Hence, putting $\gamma_{-1} = 0$,

$$(4\pi)^{1/2}[tf(t), \psi_m(t)] = (m + 1)^{1/2}\gamma_{m+1} + m^{1/2}\gamma_{m-1},$$
$$(4\pi)^{1/2}[tg(t), \psi_m(t)] = i^{-m-1}(m + 1)^{1/2}\gamma_{m+1} + i^{-m+1}m^{1/2}\gamma_{m-1}.$$

Applying Parseval's formula both to $tf(t)$ and $tg(t)$, we obtain that the left-hand side of (3.3) equals

$$(4\pi)^{-1} \left[2 \sum_{m=0}^{\infty} (m + 1)|\gamma_{m+1}|^2 + 2 \sum_{m=0}^{\infty} m|\gamma_{m-1}|^2 \right],$$

and this is equal to the right-hand side of (3.3).

Theorem 3.2. *If $f \in L_2(-\infty, \infty)$, $g = \mathscr{F}f$, then*

$$\int_{-\infty}^{\infty} t^2 |f(t)|^2 \, dt + \int_{-\infty}^{\infty} t^2 |g(t)|^2 \, dt \geq (2\pi)^{-1} \int_{-\infty}^{\infty} |f(t)|^2 \, dt,$$

with equality only if $f(t)$ is almost everywhere equal to a constant multiple of $\exp(-\pi t^2)$.

Proof. This follows directly from (3.3), since

$$\int_{-\infty}^{\infty} |f(t)|^2 \, dt = |\gamma_0|^2 + |\gamma_1|^2 + \cdots,$$

and since $\psi_0(t)$ is a multiple of $\exp(-\pi t^2)$.

From Theorem 3.2 we can derive Heisenberg's inequality as follows. We take some constant $p > 0$ and we consider the functions f_1, g_1 defined by

$$f_1(t) = p^{-1/2} f(t/p), \qquad g_1(t) = p^{1/2} g(tp) \tag{3.4}$$

(whence again $g_1 = \mathscr{F}f_1$), and we apply (3.3) to f_1, g_1. This leads to

$$p^2 \int_{-\infty}^{\infty} t^2 |f(t)|^2 \, dt + p^{-2} \int_{-\infty}^{\infty} t^2 |g(t)|^2 \, dt \geq (2\pi)^{-1} \int_{-\infty}^{\infty} |f(t)|^2 \, dt. \tag{3.5}$$

Taking, on the left, the minimum with respect to p, Heisenberg's inequality (1.6) follows at once.

We shall explore this idea a little further, by proving that if Heisenberg's inequality is almost an equality, then f is almost equal to one of the functions for which it is an exact equality.

Theorem 3.3. *Let $f \in L_2(-\infty, \infty)$, $g = \mathscr{F}f$, $\int_{-\infty}^{\infty} |f(t)|^2 \, dt = 1$. Assume that δ is a nonnegative number with the property that for every $c > 0$ and for every complex number λ with $|\lambda| = 1$ we have*

$$\left[\int_{-\infty}^{\infty} |f(t) - \lambda c^{-1/2} \psi_0(ct)|^2 \, dt \right]^{1/2} \geq \delta \tag{3.6}$$

[where $\psi_0(t) = 2^{1/4} \exp(-\pi t^2)$]. Then we have

$$\left[\int_{-\infty}^{\infty} t^2 |f(t)|^2 \, dt \right]^{1/2} \cdot \left[\int_{-\infty}^{\infty} \omega^2 |g(\omega)|^2 \, d\omega \right]^{1/2} \geq (4\pi)^{-1}[3 - 2(1 - \tfrac{1}{2}\delta^2)^2]. \tag{3.7}$$

Proof. We put

$$\int_{-\infty}^{\infty} t^2 |f(t)|^2 \, dt = A, \qquad \int_{-\infty}^{\infty} \omega^2 |g(\omega)|^2 \, d\omega = B.$$

From (3.3) it follows that

$$A + B \geq (2\pi)^{-1}[|\gamma_0|^2 + 3(|\gamma_1|^2 + |\gamma_2|^2 + \cdots)]$$
$$= (2\pi)^{-1}(3 - 2|\gamma_0|^2). \tag{3.8}$$

On the other hand we have, by (3.6), if $|\lambda| = 1$,

$$\delta^2 \leq \|f - \lambda\psi_0\|^2 = |\gamma_0 - \lambda|^2 + |\gamma_1|^2 + |\gamma_2|^2 + \cdots.$$

Taking λ such that $\lambda^{-1}\gamma_0 \geq 0$, $|\lambda| = 1$, we obtain

$$\delta^2 \leq (|\gamma_0| - 1)^2 + (1 - |\gamma_0|^2) = 2 - 2|\gamma_0|.$$

Hence, by (3.8),

$$A + B \geq (2\pi)^{-1}[3 - 2(1 - \tfrac{1}{2}\delta^2)^2].$$

If f, g satisfy the conditions of the theorem, then it is not difficult to show that also f_1, g_1 [defined by (3.4)] satisfy those conditions. Therefore

$$p^2 A + p^{-2} B \geq (2\pi)^{-1}[3 - 2(1 - \tfrac{1}{2}\delta^2)^2].$$

Choosing $p = A^{-1/4}B^{1/4}$, we infer (3.7).

As a corollary we mention:

Theorem 3.4. *If $f \in L_2(-\infty, \infty)$, $g = \mathscr{F}f$, $\int_{-\infty}^{\infty} |f(t)|^2 \, dt = 1$, and if f is odd* [i.e. $f(t) = f(-t)$ for all t], *then we have*

$$\left[\int_{-\infty}^{\infty} t^2 |f(t)|^2 \, dt \right]^{1/2} \cdot \left[\int_{-\infty}^{\infty} \omega^2 |g(\omega)|^2 \, d\omega \right]^{1/2} \geq 3/(4\pi).$$

Proof. Since f is odd, and $\psi_0(ct)$ is even, the inner product of $f(t)$ and $\psi_0(ct)$ vanishes for all c. Hence, the left-hand side of (3.6) equals $2^{1/2}$ (i.e. the length of the difference of two orthogonal unit vectors). Now taking $\delta = 2^{1/2}$, formula (3.7) gives the required result.

A further result is:

Theorem 3.5. *If the conditions of Theorem 3.3 hold, and if f is even, then*

$$\left[\int_{-\infty}^{\infty} t^2 |f(t)|^2 \, dt \right]^{1/2} \cdot \left[\int_{-\infty}^{\infty} \omega^2 |g(\omega)|^2 \, d\omega \right]^{1/2} \geq (4\pi)^{-1}[5 - 4(1 - \tfrac{1}{2}\delta^2)^2].$$

Proof. The following modification can now be made in the beginning of the proof of Theorem 3.3. Since f is even, and ψ_1 is odd, we have $\gamma_1 = 0$.

Hence (3.8) can be refined:

$$A + B = (2\pi)^{-1}[|\gamma_0|^2 + 5|\gamma_2|^2 + 7|\gamma_3|^2 + \cdots]$$
$$\geq (2\pi)^{-1}[|\gamma_0|^2 + 5(|\gamma_2|^2 + |\gamma_3|^2 + \cdots)]$$
$$\geq (2\pi)^{-1}(5 - 4|\gamma_0|^2).$$

The rest of the proof can be copied from Theorem 3.3.

4. Inequalities Concerning the Score

Before stating any inequality, we first remark that it is often sufficient to restrict the discussion of the blurred score $H_{\alpha\beta}$ [see (2.7) and (2.8)] to the case $\alpha = \beta$. For, the transformation (3.4) has a simple effect:

$$H_{\alpha\beta}(x, y; f, f) = H_{\gamma\delta}(u, v; f_1, f_1), \tag{4.1}$$

with $u = xp$, $v = y/p$, $\gamma = \alpha p^2$, $\beta = \delta p^{-2}$. Thus by taking $p = (\beta/\alpha)^{1/4}$ the general case is reduced to a case with equal parameters. The advantage of the case with equal parameters lies in the fact that it is especially adapted to the Hermite functions (with the normalization given in Sec. 2). For example, it can be shown that the score of ψ_m has complete rotational symmetry with respect to the origin of the score plane. And the following simple result will show its usefulness in the sequel.

Theorem 4.1. *If* $\alpha \geq 0$, *m, n* $= 0$, 1, 2, $\ldots$, *then*

$$H_{\alpha\alpha}(0, 0; \psi_m, \psi_n) = \delta_{mn}(\alpha + \tfrac{1}{2})^{-1}[(2\alpha - 1)/(2\alpha + 1)]^m.$$

Proof. From the definition of ψ_m (see the beginning of Sec. 3) it follows that $H_{\alpha\alpha}(0, 0; \psi_m, \psi_n)$ equals $C_m C_n m! n!$ times the coefficient of $w^m z^n$ in the power series development of $H_{\alpha\alpha}(0, 0; h_w, h_z)$, where

$$h_w(t) = \exp[\pi t^2 - 2\pi(t - w)^2], \qquad h_z(t) = \exp[\pi t^2 - 2\pi(t - z)^2].$$

If we express this $H_{\alpha\alpha}(0, 0; h_w, h_z)$ by means of (2.8), we get an integral of the type

$$\int_{-\infty}^{\infty} \int_{-\infty}^{\infty} \exp[-\pi Q(s, t) + 4\pi(sw + tz)] \, ds \, dt, \tag{4.2}$$

where Q is a binary quadratic form. The value of such an integral is

$$(\det Q)^{-1/2} \exp[\pi Q^{-1}(2s, 2w)],$$

where $\det Q$ stands for the determinant, and Q^{-1} for the inverse form. Explicit calculation leads to

$$H_{\alpha\alpha}(0, 0; h_w, h_z) = (\alpha + \tfrac{1}{2})^{-1/2} \exp[4\pi wz(2\alpha - 1)/(2\alpha + 1)].$$

If we expand this in powers of w and z the theorem follows in a few lines.

We can now settle the question whether $H_{\alpha\beta}(x, y; f, f)$ is positive-definite. (The words positive-definite refer to the dependence upon f. If x, y, α, β are given, we call $H_{\alpha\beta}(x, y; f, f)$ positive-definite if $H_{\alpha\beta}(x, y; f, f) > 0$ for all $f \in L_2(-\infty, \infty)$ unless f vanishes almost everywhere.)

Theorem 4.2. *Let* x, y, α, β *be real numbers,* $\alpha > 0$, $\beta > 0$. *Then* $H_{\alpha\beta}(x, y; f, f)$ *is positive-definite if and only if* $\alpha\beta > \frac{1}{4}$. *If* $\alpha\beta = \frac{1}{4}$, *it is semidefinite.*

Proof. Putting $f^*(t) = f(t + x) \exp(-2\pi i y t)$ we have [cf. (2.3)], for all ξ, η,

$$H(\xi + x, \eta + y; f, f) = H(\xi, \eta; f^*, f^*).$$

Hence by (2.7),

$$H_{\alpha\beta}(x, y; f, f) = H_{\alpha\beta}(0, 0; f^*, f^*),$$

and therefore it suffices to consider the case $x = y = 0$ from now on. Next, we remark that by (4.1) it suffices to consider the special case $\alpha = \beta$. So we only have to investigate whether $H_{\alpha\alpha}(0, 0; f, f)$ is definite.

Again putting $(f, \psi_m) = \gamma_m$, we have, by Theorem 4.1,

$$H_{\alpha\alpha}(0, 0; f, f) = \sum_{m=0}^{\infty} (\alpha + \tfrac{1}{2})^{-1}[(2\alpha - 1)/(2\alpha + 1)]^m |\gamma_m|^2.$$

If $\alpha > \frac{1}{2}$, the right-hand side is positive provided that at least one γ_m is nonzero. If $\alpha = \frac{1}{2}$, the right-hand side is ≥ 0 for all f, but $= 0$ as soon as $(f, \psi_0) = 0$. If $0 < \alpha < \frac{1}{2}$, we can have $H_{\alpha\alpha}(0, 0; f, f) < 0$, for example if $f = \psi_m$ and m is odd. This proves the theorem.

The fact that $H_{\alpha\beta}(x, y; f, f) \geq 0$ if $\alpha\beta \geq \frac{1}{4}$ can also be deduced directly from (2.8). Putting $2\beta - (2\alpha)^{-1} = \sigma$, expanding $\exp(\sigma st)$ in its power series, and interchanging summation and integration, we obtain

$$H_{\alpha\beta}(x, y; f, f) = \alpha^{-1/2} \sum_{k=0}^{\infty} (\sigma^k / k!) \left| \int_{-\infty}^{\infty} s^k \exp\left[-\frac{\pi}{4\alpha}(s^2 - 4xs + 2x^2) - \pi\beta s^2 - 2\pi i y s \right] ds \right|^2,$$

and this is ≥ 0 if $\sigma \geq 0$.

We next deal with some moments of H. For these we have inequalities expressing that the score cannot be concentrated upon a small neighborhood of a single point, and that is again something of the type of the uncertainty relation. The simplest case is

$$\int_{-\infty}^{\infty} \int_{-\infty}^{\infty} H(x, y; f, f)(x^2 + y^2) \, dx \, dy$$

$$\geq (2\pi)^{-1} \int_{-\infty}^{\infty} \int_{-\infty}^{\infty} H(x, y; f, f) \, dx \, dy. \tag{4.3}$$

This is the special case $k = 1$ of Theorem 4.4, but it is already equivalent to Theorem 3.2. For, we have

$$\int_{-\infty}^{\infty} H(x, y; f, f) \, dy = |f(x)|^2$$

for almost all x, whence

$$\int_{-\infty}^{\infty} \int_{-\infty}^{\infty} H(x, y; f, f) \, dx \, dy = \int_{-\infty}^{\infty} |f(x)|^2 \, dx, \tag{4.4}$$

$$\int_{-\infty}^{\infty} \int_{-\infty}^{\infty} H(x, y; f, f) x^2 \, dx \, dy = \int_{-\infty}^{\infty} x^2 |f(x)|^2 \, dx. \tag{4.5}$$

Using (2.9), we can derive from (4.5) that

$$\int_{-\infty}^{\infty} \int_{-\infty}^{\infty} H(x, y; f, f) y^2 \, dx \, dy = \int_{-\infty}^{\infty} y^2 |g(y)|^2 \, dy.$$

Thus the left-hand side of (4.3) is equal to the left-hand side in Theorem 3.2. The right-hand sides are equal according to (4.4), and so (4.3) is equivalent to the inequality in Theorem 3.2.

Our proof of the inequality for the kth moment of $H(x, y; f, f)$ will start from a result that is similar to Theorem 4.1:

Theorem 4.3. *Let, for $k, m = 0, 1, 2, \ldots$, the coefficient of $u^k v^m$ in the power series development of $(1 - u - v - uv)^{-1}$ be denoted by p_{km}. Then we have, for $k, m, n = 0, 1, 2, \ldots$,*

$$\int_{-\infty}^{\infty} \int_{-\infty}^{\infty} H(x, y; \psi_m, \psi_m)(x^2 + y^2)^k \, dx \, dy = \delta_{mn} k! (2\pi)^{-k} p_{mk}. \tag{4.6}$$

Proof. Using the method of proof of Theorem 4.3, and the functions h_w, h_z introduced there, we remark that the left-hand side of (4.6) equals $C_m C_n m! \, n!$ times the coefficient of $w^m z^n$ in the development of

$$\int_{-\infty}^{\infty} \int_{-\infty}^{\infty} H(x, y; h_w, h_z)(x^2 + y^2)^k \, dx \, dy. \tag{4.7}$$

We can evaluate $H(x, y; h_w, h_z)$ by means of (2.1). Integrating with respect to t, we obtain

$$H(x, y; h_w, h_z) =$$
$$2^{-1/2} \exp[-4\pi x(w + z) + 4\pi i y(w - z) - 2\pi(x^2 + y^2) - 4\pi wz].$$

It follows that $\int_{-\infty}^{\infty}\int_{-\infty}^{\infty} \exp[2\pi u(x^2 + y^2)]H(x, y; h_w, h_z)\, dx\, dy$ converges absolutely if $|u| < 1$, and that (4.6) equals $(2\pi)^{-k}k!$ times the coefficient of u^k in the power series expansion of that double integral. This double integral is of the type (4.2). Evaluation gives

$$\int_{-\infty}^{\infty} \int_{-\infty}^{\infty} \exp[2\pi u(x^2 + y^2)]H(x, y; h_w, h_z)\, dx\, dy$$
$$= 2^{-1/2}(1 - u)^{-1} \exp[4\pi wz(1 + u)/(1 - u)].$$

Hence the left-hand side of (4.6) equals $2^{-1/2}C_m C_n m!\, n!(2\pi)^{-k}k!$ times the coefficient of $w^m z^n u^k$ in the development of $(1 - u)^{-1} \exp[4\pi wz(1 + u)/(1 - u)]$. This coefficient vanishes if $m \neq n$; if $m = n$, it equals $(m!)^{-1}(4\pi)^m$ times the coefficient of u^k in the expansion of $(1 + u)^m(1 - u)^{-m-1}$. The latter coefficient is equal to the p_{km} defined in our theorem, for

$$\sum_{m=0}^{\infty} v^m(1 + u)^m(1 - u)^{-m-1} = (1 - u - v - uv)^{-1} = \sum_{m=0}^{\infty} v^m \sum_{k=0}^{\infty} p_{km} u^k.$$

Finally, since

$$2^{-1/2}C_m C_n m!\, n!(2\pi)^{-k}k!\, \delta_{mn}(m!)^{-1}(4\pi)^m p_{km} = \delta_{mn} k!(2\pi)^{-k} p_{km},$$

the theorem follows at once.

Theorem 4.4. *Let $f \in L_2$, $k = 0, 1, 2, \ldots$. Then we have*

$$\int_{-\infty}^{\infty} \int_{-\infty}^{\infty} H(x, y; f, f)(x^2 + y^2)^k\, dx\, dy \geq k!(2\pi)^{-k} \int_{-\infty}^{\infty} |f(t)|^2\, dt, \qquad (4.8)$$

where the left-hand side is to be interpreted as the limit of

$$\int_{-\infty}^{\infty} \int_{-\infty}^{\infty} H(x, y; f, f) \exp[-\pi\varepsilon(x^2 + y^2)](x^2 + y^2)^k\, dx\, dy, \qquad (4.9)$$

as ε tends to zero from the right.

If f is an odd function, and $k \geq 1$, then the constant $k!(2\pi)^{-k}$ on the right-hand side of (4.8) can be replaced by $3k!(2\pi)^{-k}$.

Proof. We first show that (4.9) is positive-definite (if k and ε are fixed, $0 < \varepsilon < 2$). It follows from Theorem 4.1 and (2.7) that

$$\int_{-\infty}^{\infty} \int_{-\infty}^{\infty} H(x, y; \psi_m, \psi_n) \exp[-\pi\varepsilon(x^2 + y^2)] \, dx \, dy$$
$$= \delta_{mn}(1 - \tfrac{1}{2}\varepsilon)^m(1 + \tfrac{1}{2}\varepsilon)^{-m-1} \qquad (\varepsilon > 0).$$

We can show that the kth derivative of $(1 - \tfrac{1}{2}\varepsilon)^m(1 + \tfrac{1}{2}\varepsilon)^{-m-1}$ has the sign of $(-1)^k$. It is the kth derivative (with respect to ε) of the coefficient of u^m in the development of $[1 - u + \tfrac{1}{2}\varepsilon(1 + u)]^{-1}$, that is, $(-1)^k$ times the coefficient of u^m in the development of

$$k! \, 2^{-k}(1 + u)^k[1 + \tfrac{1}{2}\varepsilon - (1 - \tfrac{1}{2}\varepsilon)u]^{-k-1},$$

and that coefficient is positive if $0 < \varepsilon < 2$. Therefore, if $c_{mk}(\varepsilon)$ is defined by

$$\int_{-\infty}^{\infty} \int_{-\infty}^{\infty} H(x, y; \psi_m, \psi_n) \exp[-\pi\varepsilon(x^2 + y^2)](x^2 + y^2)^k \, dx \, dy$$
$$= \delta_{mn}k!(2\pi)^{-k}c_{mk}(\varepsilon),$$

then $c_{mk}(\varepsilon) > 0$ if $0 < \varepsilon < 2$, $m = 0, 2, 1, \ldots$. It easily follows that (4.9) is positive-definite.

Applying the fact that (4.9) is positive-definite to $f - \sum_{m=0}^{M} \gamma_k \psi_k$ instead of f [with $\gamma_k = (f, \psi_k)$], we obtain that (4.9) is at least

$$k!(2\pi)^{-k} \sum_{m=0}^{M} c_{mk}(\varepsilon)|\gamma_m|^2.$$

As $c_{mk}(\varepsilon) \to p_{mk}$ [see (4.6)] if $\varepsilon \to 0$, it follows that the left-hand side of (4.8) (with the interpretation given in the theorem) is at least

$$k!(2\pi)^{-k} \sum_{m=0}^{M} p_{mk}|\gamma_m|^2.$$

Making $M \to \infty$ we obtain that it is at least

$$k!(2\pi)^{-k} \sum_{m=0}^{\infty} p_{mk}|\gamma_m|^2.$$

(Actually it is not difficult to show that the left-hand side of (4.8) is exactly equal to that sum.)

By the definition of p_{mk} (Theorem 4.3), we have $p_{00} = p_{10} = p_{20} = \cdots = 1$ and $p_{m+1,k+1} = p_{m,k} + p_{m,k+1} + p_{m+1,k}$. It follows that p_{mk} increases with

k as well as with m. In particular $p_{mk} \geq 1$ for all $m, k \geq 0$, and $p_{mk} \geq 3$ if $m \geq 1, k \geq 1$. Hence

$$\sum_{m=0}^{\infty} p_{mk} |\gamma_m|^2 \geq \sum_{m=0}^{\infty} |\gamma_m|^2 = \int_{-\infty}^{\infty} |f(t)|^2 \, dt.$$

If f is odd we have $\gamma_0 = 0$, whence, for $k \geq 1$,

$$\sum_{m=0}^{\infty} p_{mk} |\gamma_m|^2 \geq 3 \sum_{m=1}^{\infty} |\gamma_m|^2 = 3 \int_{-\infty}^{\infty} |f(t)|^2 \, dt.$$

Properly speaking, inequalities of the type (4.8) do not prove the impossibility of a very strong concentration of the score upon a small neighborhood of the origin. For example, if 99% of the energy lies very close to the origin, and the remaining 1% lies in a part of the xy plane where $(x^2 + y^2)^k$ is very large, then that 1% can make the left-hand side of (4.8) large.

This objection does not hold against the inequality

$$\int_{-\infty}^{\infty} \int_{-\infty}^{\infty} H(x, y; f, f) \left[1 - \exp\left(-\frac{\pi x^2}{\alpha} - \frac{\pi y^2}{\beta} \right) \right] dx \, dy$$

$$\geq [1 + 2(\alpha\beta)^{1/2}]^{-1} \int_{-\infty}^{\infty} |f(t)|^2 \, dt$$

(which holds for all $\alpha > 0, \beta > 0$). Using (2.7) and (4.4), we can derive this inequality from the following theorem.

Theorem 4.5.   *If $\alpha > 0, \beta > 0$, we have for all real values of x and y*

$$H_{\alpha\beta}(x, y; f, f) \leq [\tfrac{1}{2} + (\alpha\beta)^{1/2}]^{-1} \int_{-\infty}^{\infty} |f(t)|^2 \, dt. \qquad (4.10)$$

Proof.   As in the proof of Theorem 4.2, it suffices to specialize:

$$x = y = 0, \qquad \alpha = \beta > 0.$$

We have, if $\alpha > 0, m = 0, 1, 2, \ldots,$

$$|(\alpha + \tfrac{1}{2})^{-1}[(2\alpha - 1)/(2\alpha + 1)]^m| \leq (\alpha + \tfrac{1}{2})^{-1},$$

whence, by Theorem 4.1,

$$H_{\alpha\alpha}(0, 0; f, f) \leq \sum_{m=0}^{\infty} (\alpha + \tfrac{1}{2})^{-1} |\gamma_m|^2.$$

The theorem now follows from $\int_{-\infty}^{\infty} |f(t)|^2 \, dt = \sum_{m=0}^{\infty} |\gamma_m|^2$.

We briefly mention a second method for proving (4.10). If we put

$$K(s, t) = \alpha^{-1/2} \exp\left[-\frac{\pi(s + t)^2}{4\alpha} - \pi\beta(s - t)^2 \right],$$

then (4.10) can be considered, according to (2.8), as a statement concerning the largest positive eigenvalue of the symmetric integral equation

$$\int_{-\infty}^{\infty} K(s, t) f(t)\, dt = \lambda f(s).$$

It is not hard to show that

$$f_0(t) = \exp[-\pi t^2 (\beta/\alpha)^{1/2}]$$

is an eigenfunction, with eigenvalue $\lambda_0 = [\frac{1}{2} + (\alpha\beta)^{1/2}]^{-1}$. Taking into consideration that both $f_0(t) > 0$ and $K(s, t) \geq 0$ for all s and t, we know (in direct analogy to a theorem by Perron on symmetric matrices) that

$$\int_{-\infty}^{\infty} \int_{-\infty}^{\infty} K(s, t) f(s)\overline{f(t)}\, ds\, dt \leq \lambda_0 \int_{-\infty}^{\infty} |f(t)|^2\, dt \qquad (4.11)$$

for every $f \in L_2$. This is equivalent to (4.10).

A proof of (4.11) can be given in a few lines. We have

$$|f(s)\overline{f(t)}| \leq \frac{1}{2} \left\{ \frac{|f(s)|^2}{[f_0(s)]^2} + \frac{|f(t)|^2}{[f_0(t)]^2} \right\} f_0(s) f_0(t). \qquad (4.12)$$

Replacing in (4.11) the product $f(s)\overline{f(t)}$ by the right-hand side of (4.12), we obtain the right-hand side of (4.11).

REFERENCES

[1] Erdélyi, A. (ed.), "Higher Transcendental Functions," Vol. 2. McGraw-Hill, New York, 1953.

[2] Fuchs, W. H. J., On the magnitude of Fourier transforms, *Proc. Intern. Math. Congr., Amsterdam, 1954,* **2,** 106–107 (1954).

[3] Landau, H. J., and Pollak, H. O., Prolate spheroidal wave functions, Fourier analysis and uncertainty II, *Bell. System Tech. J.* **40,** 65–84 (1961).

[4] Moyal, J. E., Quantum mechanics as a statistical theory, *Proc. Cambridge Philos. Soc.* **45,** 99–124 (1949).

[5] Ville, J., Theory and applications of the notion of complex signal, Rept. T-92, The Rand Corp., Santa Monica, California, 1958.

[6] Weyl, H., "Theory of Groups and Quantum Mechanics," Dover, New York, 1950.

[7] Wigner, E., On the quantum correction for thermodynamic equilibrium, *Phys. Rev.* **40,** 749–759 (1932).

Inequalities Complementary to Cauchy's Inequality for Sums of Real Numbers*†

J. B. DIAZ and F. T. METCALF
Institute for Fluid Dynamics and Applied Mathematics
University of Maryland, College Park, Maryland
and
U.S. Naval Ordnance Laboratory
White Oak, Silver Spring, Maryland

Let a_k and b_k $(k=1, 2, \ldots, n)$ be real numbers. Cauchy's inequality [2; pages 373–374, Theorem 16] states that

$$\left(\sum_{k=1}^{n} a_k b_k\right)^2 \leq \sum_{k=1}^{n} a_k^2 \cdot \sum_{k=1}^{n} b_k^2.$$

This inequality may be regarded as giving an *upper* bound for the square of the scalar product, i.e., the number $(\sum_{k=1}^{n} a_k b_k)^2$, in terms of the two "squares of the lengths," $\sum_{k=1}^{n} a_k^2$ and $\sum_{k=1}^{n} b_k^2$.

Under certain circumstances (i.e., suitable hypotheses relative to the numbers a_k and b_k) there exist complementary inequalities to Cauchy's inequality; that is to say, inequalities which can be regarded as giving *lower* bounds for $(\sum_{k=1}^{n} a_k b_k)^2$ in terms of $\sum_{k=1}^{n} a_k^2$ and $\sum_{k=1}^{n} b_k^2$.

The purpose of the present note is to prove an inequality of this general "complementary" nature, which includes, as a special case, several other complementary inequalities appearing in the literature.

Section 1 discusses four inequalities (complementary to Cauchy's inequality) which occur in the literature. Section 2 presents a proof of a new inequality, which is also complementary to Cauchy's inequality, and which includes as special cases the previously known inequalities discussed in Section 1.

* The research of the authors was supported by the Air Force Office of Scientific Research, Grant AFOSR 400-64, and by the U.S. Naval Ordnance Laboratory, White Oak, Maryland; and in part by Grant AFOSR 1122-66 to the University of California, Riverside, which is the present address of the authors.

† The talk at the Symposium on Inequalities was given under the title "Four Inequalities in Search of Two Authors." The present note is based on our paper: Complementary inequalities I: Inequalities complementary to Cauchy's inequality for sums of real numbers, *J. Math. Anal. Appl.* **9**, 59–74, (1964).

Although attention is restricted here only to sums of real numbers, the same simple procedure also yields new complementary inequalities for definite integrals, self-adjoint operators in a Hilbert space, etc. (see the research announcement [3]).

1. The Four Known Complementary Inequalities

Let n be a positive integer. Suppose that the real numbers a_k, b_k, and γ_k ($k = 1, 2, \ldots, n$) satisfy the inequalities

$$0 < m_1 \leq a_k \leq M_1, \quad 0 < m_2 \leq b_k \leq M_2, \quad \text{and} \quad 0 < m \leq \gamma_k \leq M.$$

Further, let the numbers ξ_k ($k = 1, 2, \ldots, n$) be real. Then the following inequalities play a role in this paper:

$$\sum_{k=1}^{n} \gamma_k \cdot \sum_{k=1}^{n} \frac{1}{\gamma_k} \leq \frac{(M+m)^2}{4mM} \cdot n^2 \qquad \text{(Schweitzer [8])}, \tag{1}$$

$$\sum_{k=1}^{n} a_k^2 \cdot \sum_{k=1}^{n} b_k^2 \leq \frac{(M_1 M_2 + m_1 m_2)^2}{4 m_1 m_2 M_1 M_2} \left(\sum_{k=1}^{n} a_k b_k \right)^2 \qquad \text{(Pólya–Szegö [7])}, \tag{2}$$

$$\sum_{k=1}^{n} \gamma_k \xi_k^2 \cdot \sum_{k=1}^{n} \frac{\xi_k^2}{\gamma_k} \leq \frac{(M+m)^2}{4mM} \left(\sum_{k=1}^{n} \xi_k^2 \right)^2 \qquad \text{(Kantorovich [6])}, \tag{3}$$

and

$$\sum_{k=1}^{n} a_k^2 \xi_k^2 \cdot \sum_{k=1}^{n} b_k^2 \xi_k^2 \leq \frac{(M_1 M_2 + m_1 m_2)^2}{4 m_1 m_2 M_1 M_2} \left(\sum_{k=1}^{n} a_k b_k \xi_k^2 \right)^2$$

$$\text{(Greub–Rheinboldt [4])}. \tag{4}$$

Remark 1. It is clear that (4) implies the preceding three inequalities. Let $a_k^2 = \gamma_k$ and $b_k^2 = 1/\gamma_k$, together with $m_1 = m^{1/2}$, $M_1 = M^{1/2}$, $m_2 = M^{-1/2}$, and $M_2 = m^{-1/2}$ in result (4); this gives (3). Further, put $\xi_k = 1$ ($k = 1, 2, \ldots, n$) in (3); this yields (1). Lastly, put $\xi_k = 1$ ($k = 1, 2, \ldots, n$) in (4); this furnishes (2).

Remark 2. The relation of these inequalities to the Cauchy inequality is most clearly brought out by writing (4) in the form (when not all the numbers ξ_k are zero)

$$1 \leq \frac{\sum\limits_{k=1}^{n} a_k^2 \xi_k^2 \cdot \sum\limits_{k=1}^{n} b_k^2 \xi_k^2}{\left(\sum\limits_{k=1}^{n} a_k b_k \xi_k^2 \right)^2} \leq \frac{(M_1 M_2 + m_1 m_2)^2}{4 m_1 m_2 M_1 M_2}; \tag{5}$$

the left-hand inequality of (5), which is Cauchy's inequality, furnishes an upper bound for the square of the scalar product $\sum_{k=1}^{n} a_k\xi_k \cdot b_k\xi_k$, while the right-hand inequality of (5), which is inequality (4), gives a lower bound for the square of the same scalar product.

2. A Stronger Complementary Inequality

It will now be shown that the following inequality holds:

$$m_1M_1 \sum_{k=1}^{n} b_k{}^2\xi_k{}^2 + m_2M_2 \sum_{k=1}^{n} a_k{}^2\xi_k{}^2 \leq (M_1M_2 + m_1m_2) \sum_{k=1}^{n} a_kb_k\xi_k{}^2. \qquad (6)$$

Since

$$0 \leq \left[\left(m_1M_1 \sum_{k=1}^{n} b_k{}^2\xi_k{}^2 \right)^{1/2} - \left(m_2M_2 \sum_{k=1}^{n} a_k{}^2\xi_k{}^2 \right)^{1/2} \right]^2, \qquad (7)$$

one has that

$$2\left(m_1m_2M_1M_2 \sum_{k=1}^{n} a_k{}^2\xi_k{}^2 \cdot \sum_{k=1}^{n} b_k{}^2\xi_k{}^2 \right)^{1/2}$$

$$\leq m_1M_1 \sum_{k=1}^{n} b_k{}^2\xi_k{}^2 + m_2M_2 \sum_{k=1}^{n} a_k{}^2\xi_k{}^2, \qquad (8)$$

and hence the inequality (6) actually implies (4). The precise statement of the new inequality, including a discussion of exactly when equality holds, is contained in Theorem 1.

Theorem 1. *Let the real numbers a_k and b_k ($k = 1, 2, \ldots, n$) satisfy*

$$0 \leq m_1 \leq a_k \leq M_1 \qquad and \qquad 0 \leq m_2 \leq b_k \leq M_2. \qquad (9)$$

(In particular, one may choose $m_1 = \min_k a_k$, $M_1 = \max_k a_k$, and similarly for m_2 and M_2.) *Also, let ξ_k ($k = 1, 2, \ldots, n$) be real numbers. Then*

$$m_1M_1 \sum_{k=1}^{n} b_k{}^2\xi_k{}^2 + m_2M_2 \sum_{k=1}^{n} a_k{}^2\xi_k{}^2 \leq (M_1M_2 + m_1m_2) \sum_{k=1}^{n} a_kb_k\xi_k{}^2$$

$$\leq (M_1M_2 + m_1m_2) \left(\sum_{k=1}^{n} a_k{}^2\xi_k{}^2 \cdot \sum_{k=1}^{n} b_k{}^2\xi_k{}^2 \right)^{1/2}. \qquad (10)$$

If $0 < m_1$ and $0 < m_2$, then equality holds on the left if and only if, for each k such that $\xi_k \neq 0$, either $(a_k, b_k) = (m_1, M_2)$ or $(a_k, b_k) = (M_1, m_2)$, where the alternative may depend upon the particular value of k.

Proof.   The inequality on the right of (10) is clearly just the Cauchy inequality for finite sums, that is

$$\sum_{k=1}^{n} a_k\xi_k b_k\xi_k \leq \left(\sum_{k=1}^{n} a_k{}^2\xi_k{}^2 \cdot \sum_{k=1}^{n} b_k{}^2\xi_k{}^2 \right)^{1/2}.$$

Thus, only the left-hand inequality requires proof. To this end, note that it follows from (9) that

$$0 \leq M_2 a_k - m_1 b_k \quad \text{and} \quad 0 \leq M_1 b_k - m_2 a_k.$$

Hence,

$$0 \leq (M_2 a_k - m_1 b_k)(M_1 b_k - m_2 a_k) \tag{11}$$

for each $k = 1, 2, \ldots, n$. Thus, multiplying by ξ_k^2 and summing from $k = 1$ to $k = n$,

$$0 \leq \sum_{k=1}^{n} (M_2 a_k - m_1 b_k)(M_1 b_k - m_2 a_k)\xi_k^2; \tag{12}$$

which, upon expanding the product, gives the desired result. (Notice that what one is essentially doing is employing the identity

$$\sum_{k=1}^{n} (M_2 a_k - m_1 b_k)(M_1 b_k - m_2 a_k)\xi_k^2 = -m_1 M_1 \sum_{k=1}^{n} b_k^2 \xi_k^2 - m_2 M_2 \sum_{k=1}^{n} a_k^2 \xi_k^2$$

$$+ (M_1 M_2 + m_1 m_2) \sum_{k=1}^{n} a_k b_k \xi_k^2.)$$

Now consider the case of equality on the left-hand side of (10), under the additional assumption that $0 < m_1$ and $0 < m_2$. Clearly, equality holds in (12) if and only if equality holds in (11) for every k such that $\xi_k \neq 0$. But then either

$$M_2 a_k - m_1 b_k = 0 \tag{13}$$

or

$$M_1 b_k - m_2 a_k = 0. \tag{14}$$

If (13) holds for some k, then $a_k/m_1 = b_k/M_2$, where, from the hypotheses, $1 \leq a_k/m_1$ and $b_k/M_2 \leq 1$. Consequently, $a_k/m_1 = b_k/M_2 = 1$; that is, $a_k = m_1$ and $b_k = M_2$, which may be expressed in the form $(a_k, b_k) = (m_1, M_2)$. Similarly, if (14) holds, one is led to conclude that $a_k = M_1$ and $b_k = m_2$, that is $(a_k, b_k) = (M_1, m_2)$.

It is to be remarked that the condition for equality is (vacuously) satisfied in the extreme case when all the ξ_k's are zero.

The equality condition has been stated explicitly in the case when $0 < m_1$ and $0 < m_2$, only for convenience, because it is more informative than the following equality condition: if $0 \leq m_1$ and $0 \leq m_2$, then equality holds on the left-hand side of (10) if and only if, for every k such that $\xi_k \neq 0$, either (13) or (14) holds, where the choice of which actually holds, (13) or (14), depends upon k.

REFERENCES

[1] Beckenbach, E. F., and Bellman, R., "Inequalities." Springer, Berlin, 1961.
[2] Cauchy, A. L., "Cours d'analyse de l'École Royale Polytechnique," Ire partie. Analyse algébrique. Paris, 1821. (Œuvres complètes, IIe série, III.)
[3] Diaz, J. B., and Metcalf, F. T., Stronger forms of a class of inequalities of G. Pólya–G. Szegö, and L. V. Kantorovich. *Bull. Amer. Math. Soc.* **69**, 415–418 (1963).
[4] Greub, W., and Rheinboldt, W., On a generalization of an inequality of L. V. Kantorovich, *Proc. Amer. Math. Soc.* **10**, 407–415 (1959).
[5] Hardy, G. H., Littlewood, J. E., and Pólya, G., "Inequalities," Cambridge Univ. Press, London and New York, 1952.
[6] Kantorovich, L. V., Funktsionalnii analyz i prikladnaya matematika. *Usp. Mat. Nauk* **3**, 89–185 (1948), in particular pp. 142–144 [also translated from the Russian by C. D. Benster, *Nat. Bur. Standards Rept. No.* 1509 (*March 7, 1952*), in particular pp. 106–109].
[7] Pólya, G., and Szegö, G., "Aufgaben und Lehrsätze aus der Analysis," Vol. I. Springer, Berlin, 1925.
[8] Schweitzer, P., Egy egyenlötlenség az aritmetikai középértékröl (An inequality concerning the arithmetic mean), *Math. Phys. Lapok* **23**, 257–261 (1914).

Variations of Wirtinger's Inequality*

J. B. DIAZ and F. T. METCALF
Institute for Fluid Dynamics and Applied Mathematics
University of Maryland, College Park, Maryland
and
U.S. Naval Ordnance Laboratory
White Oak, Silver Spring, Maryland

1. Introduction

The present considerations arose from Chap. 7 of Hardy *et al.* [1]. Chapter 7 is entitled "Some applications of the calculus of variations," and contains proofs of several integral inequalities. These proofs are of various intermediate types, between the "elementary" and the "variational" proofs, depending upon the underlying amount of knowledge of "variational theory" which is required in each proof.

On p. 185 of Hardy *et al.* [1] there is an elementary proof, by Hans Lewy, of Wirtinger's inequality [see inequality (6.1) of Theorem 6 of Sec. 3 of this paper; notice that in the present paper attention is restricted to the class of continuously differentiable functions, rather than to the class of functions whose first derivatives are Lebesgue square-integrable]. What makes the proof in [1] elementary—and independent of the general theory of eigenvalues—is the explicit knowledge that the function sin x is an eigenfunction of the Euler–Lagrange equation of the corresponding "variational problem." The proof depends on an integral identity which involves the function sin x.

The same basic elementary idea is used here in Sec. 2 to derive some integral identities which are related to Wirtinger's inequality. In Sec. 3, which may be read independently of Sec. 2, an alternative way of deriving Wirtinger's inequality is given. This appears to be a simplification of the proof of Wirtinger's inequality given in [1] in that the integral identity involving sin x is not used in the main proof itself, but only in the proof of an auxiliary lemma [see (7.7.1) of p. 184 of [1], and Theorem I of Sec. 2

* This research was supported in part by the United States Air Force through the Air Force Office of Scientific Research Grant AFOSR 400-64; and in part by the U.S. Naval Ordnance Laboratory, White Oak, Maryland; and in part by Grant AFOSR 1122-66 to the University of California, Riverside, which is the present address of the authors.

of this paper, which is just a "translation" of (7.7.1) to an arbitrary interval $a \leq x \leq b$]. In other words, proofs of inequality (7.7.1) [1, p. 184] and of Wirtinger's inequality [1, p. 185] employ suitable integral identities involving sin x, whereas the argument given here in Sec. 3 shows that Wirtinger's inequality is actually a consequence of (7.7.1).

The bibliography lists recent papers containing integral inequalities which are closely connected to those occurring in the present paper.

2. Variations

The integral inequalities of this section are all based on the auxiliary Theorem I below, which is just a "translation," to an arbitrary interval $a \leq x \leq b$, of inequality (7.7.1) of p. 184 of Hardy *et al.* [1]. Since Theorem I underlies everything that follows, its proof will be presented in detail.

For the convenience of the reader, the flow chart shown in Fig. 1 illustrates the interrelationship of the various theorems of this section and reminds the reader, at a glance, of the special hypotheses made in each.

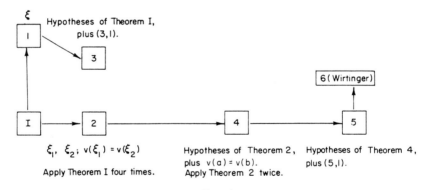

FIG. 1

Theorem I. *Let the real-valued function v be continuously differentiable on the finite closed interval $a \leq x \leq b$. Then*

$$\int_a^b [v(x) - v(a)]^2 \, dx \leq 4 \left(\frac{b-a}{\pi}\right)^2 \int_a^b [v'(x)]^2 dx, \qquad (I.1)$$

where, if $a = b$, equality always holds; while, if $a < b$, equality holds if and only if

$$v(x) = v(a) + B \sin\left(\frac{\pi}{2} \cdot \frac{x-a}{b-a}\right).$$

Also,

$$\int_a^b [v(x) - v(b)]^2\, dx \le 4\left(\frac{b-a}{\pi}\right)^2 \int_a^b [v'(x)]^2\, dx, \tag{I.2}$$

where if $a = b$, *equality always holds; while if* $a < b$, *equality holds if and only if*

$$v(x) = v(b) + B \sin\left(\frac{\pi}{2} \cdot \frac{b-x}{b-a}\right).$$

Proof. Suppose that $a < b$, since there is nothing to prove when $a = b$. Consider the inequality of (I.1). The starting point is the identity

$$\frac{d}{dx}\left\{2\left(\frac{b-a}{\pi}\right)[v(x) - v(a)]^2 \cot\left(\frac{\pi}{2} \cdot \frac{x-a}{b-a}\right)\right\}$$

$$= 4\left(\frac{b-a}{\pi}\right)[v(x) - v(a)]v'(x) \cot\left(\frac{\pi}{2} \cdot \frac{x-a}{b-a}\right)$$

$$- [v(x) - v(a)]^2 \left[1 + \cot^2\left(\frac{\pi}{2} \cdot \frac{x-a}{b-a}\right)\right].$$

Add and subtract $4[(b-a)/\pi]^2[v'(x)]^2$ to complete the square:

$$\frac{d}{dx}\left\{2\left(\frac{b-a}{\pi}\right)[v(x) - v(a)]^2 \cot\left(\frac{\pi}{2} \cdot \frac{x-a}{b-a}\right)\right\}$$

$$= 4\left(\frac{b-a}{\pi}\right)^2 [v'(x)]^2 - [v(x) - v(a)]^2$$

$$- \left\{2\left(\frac{b-a}{\pi}\right)v'(x) - [v(x) - v(a)] \cot\left(\frac{\pi}{2} \cdot \frac{x-a}{b-a}\right)\right\}^2.$$

This identity is valid on the interval $a < x \le b$. Hence, for each x in the same interval one has the inequality

$$\frac{d}{dx}\left\{2\left(\frac{b-a}{\pi}\right)[v(x) - v(a)]^2 \cot\left(\frac{\pi}{2} \cdot \frac{x-a}{b-a}\right)\right\}$$

$$\le 4\left(\frac{b-a}{\pi}\right)^2 [v'(x)]^2 - [v(x) - v(a)]^2,$$

with equality if and only if

$$v'(x) = \frac{\pi}{2(b-a)}[v(x) - v(a)] \cot\left(\frac{\pi}{2} \cdot \frac{x-a}{b-a}\right);$$

that is, if and only if

$$\frac{d}{dx}\left[\frac{v(x)-v(a)}{\sin\left(\frac{\pi}{2}\cdot\frac{x-a}{b-a}\right)}\right]$$

$$=\frac{v'(x)\sin\left(\frac{\pi}{2}\cdot\frac{x-a}{b-a}\right)-\frac{\pi}{2(b-a)}[v(x)-v(a)]\cos\left(\frac{\pi}{2}\cdot\frac{x-a}{b-a}\right)}{\sin^2\left(\frac{\pi}{2}\cdot\frac{x-a}{b-a}\right)}=0.$$

Further,

$$\lim_{x\to a+}[v(x)-v(a)]^2\cot\left(\frac{\pi}{2}\cdot\frac{x-a}{b-a}\right)=0,$$

and hence, by integration (first over the interval $a<a+\varepsilon\leq x\leq b$, and then letting ε tend to zero through positive values)

$$0=2\left(\frac{b-a}{\pi}\right)[v(b)-v(a)]^2\cot\left(\frac{\pi}{2}\right)$$

$$-2\left(\frac{b-a}{\pi}\right)\lim_{x\to a+}[v(x)-v(a)]^2\cot\left(\frac{\pi}{2}\cdot\frac{x-a}{b-a}\right)$$

$$\leq\int_a^b\left\{4\left(\frac{b-a}{\pi}\right)^2[v'(x)]^2-[v(x)-v(a)]^2\right\}dx,$$

with equality if and only if

$$\frac{d}{dx}\left[\frac{v(x)-v(a)}{\sin\left(\frac{\pi}{2}\cdot\frac{x-a}{b-a}\right)}\right]=0$$

for *every* x such that $a<x\leq b$; that is, if and only if

$$v(x)=v(a)+B\sin\left(\frac{\pi}{2}\cdot\frac{x-a}{b-a}\right),$$

where B is a constant.

The inequality (I.2) may be proved similarly, or else, it can be obtained by applying (I.1) to the auxiliary function w defined by $w(x)=v(b+a-x)$ on the interval $a\leq x\leq b$.

Remark 1. Putting $a=0$, $b=\pi/2$ in Theorem I, one obtains inequality (7.7.1) of [1] in the special case of continuously differentiable functions $v(x)$ which satisfy $v(0)=0$.

The integral inequalities (I.1) and (I.2) refer to the end numbers a and b, respectively, since $v(a)$ and $v(b)$ appear in these inequalities. There is a corresponding inequality involving an arbitrary intermediate number ξ, with $a \leq \xi \leq b$. This inequality is proved next.

Theorem 1. *Let the real-valued function v be continuously differentiable on the finite closed interval $a \leq x \leq b$. Let ξ be a real number such that $a \leq \xi \leq b$. Then*

$$\int_a^b [v(x) - v(\xi)]^2 \, dx \leq \frac{4}{\pi^2} \max[(\xi - a)^2, (b - \xi)^2] \int_a^b [v'(x)]^2 \, dx, \qquad (1.1)$$

where if $a = b$, equality always holds; while if $a < b$, equality holds when $\xi = a$, if and only if

$$v(x) = v(a) + B \sin\left(\frac{\pi}{2} \cdot \frac{x - a}{b - a}\right);$$

when $a < \xi < (a + b)/2$ or $(a + b)/2 < \xi < b$, if and only if $v(x) \equiv v(\xi)$; when $\xi = (a + b)/2$, if and only if

$$v(x) = v\left(\frac{a + b}{2}\right) + B \sin\left(\pi \cdot \frac{(a + b)/2 - x}{b - a}\right);$$

when $\xi = b$, if and only if

$$v(x) = v(b) + B \sin\left(\frac{\pi}{2} \cdot \frac{b - x}{b - a}\right);$$

for $a \leq x \leq b$.

Proof. If $\xi = a$, the desired inequality amounts to (I.1). If $\xi = b$, the desired inequality amounts to (I.2). Therefore, without loss, it will be assumed that $a < \xi < b$.

Now, from (I.2), applied to the subinterval $a \leq x \leq \xi$, one has

$$\int_a^\xi [v(x) - v(\xi)]^2 \, dx \leq 4 \left(\frac{\xi - a}{\pi}\right)^2 \int_a^\xi [v'(x)]^2 \, dx,$$

with equality if and only if

$$v(x) = v(\xi) + B_1 \sin\left(\frac{\pi}{2} \cdot \frac{\xi - x}{\xi - a}\right), \qquad \text{for all} \quad a \leq x \leq \xi. \qquad (1.2)$$

Also, from (I.1), applied to the subinterval $\xi \leq x \leq b$, one has

$$\int_\xi^b [v(x) - v(\xi)]^2 \, dx \leq 4 \left(\frac{b - \xi}{\pi}\right)^2 \int_\xi^b [v'(x)]^2 \, dx,$$

with equality if and only if

$$v(x) = v(\xi) + B_2 \sin\left(\frac{\pi}{2} \cdot \frac{x-\xi}{b-\xi}\right), \qquad \text{for all} \quad \xi \leq x \leq b. \qquad (1.3)$$

Adding the last two inequalities gives

$$\int_a^b [v(x) - v(\xi)]^2 \, dx$$

$$\leq \frac{4}{\pi^2} \left\{ (\xi - a)^2 \int_a^\xi [v'(x)]^2 \, dx + (b-\xi)^2 \int_\xi^b [v'(x)]^2 \, dx \right\},$$

which implies the desired inequality.

It only remains to discuss the equality conditions for $a < \xi < b$. Equality holds in (1.1) if and only if one has (1.2), (1.3), and

$$\left[(\xi - a)^2 \int_a^\xi + (b-\xi)^2 \int_\xi^b \right] [v'(x)]^2 \, dx$$

$$= \max[(\xi - a)^2, (b-\xi)^2] \int_a^b [v'(x)]^2 \, dx,$$

simultaneously. The last equality may be rewritten

$$\{(\xi - a)^2 - \max[(\xi - a)^2, (b-\xi)^2]\} \int_a^\xi [v'(x)]^2 \, dx$$

$$+ \{(b-\xi)^2 - \max[(\xi - a)^2, (b-\xi)^2]\} \int_\xi^b [v'(x)]^2 \, dx = 0,$$

and is equivalent to both

$$\{(\xi - a)^2 - \max[(\xi - a)^2, (b-\xi)^2]\} \int_a^\xi [v'(x)]^2 \, dx = 0 \qquad (1.4)$$

and

$$\{(b-\xi)^2 - \max[(\xi - a)^2, (b-\xi)^2]\} \int_\xi^b [v'(x)]^2 \, dx = 0. \qquad (1.5)$$

Thus, equality holds in (1.1) if and only if one has (1.2)–(1.5); that is to say, if and only if (1.2), (1.3),

$$\{(\xi - a)^2 - \max[(\xi - a)^2, (b-\xi)^2]\} B_1^2 = 0, \qquad (1.6)$$

and

$$\{(b-\xi)^2 - \max[(\xi - a)^2, (b-\xi)^2]\} B_2^2 = 0. \qquad (1.7)$$

Now, if (1.2) and (1.3) hold, and v is continuously differentiable at ξ, it must be true that

$$\frac{B_1}{\xi - a} = -\frac{B_2}{b - \xi}.$$

Hence, either $B_1 = B_2 = 0$, or both $B_1 \neq 0$ and $B_2 \neq 0$. Further, if $B_1 \neq 0$ and $B_2 \neq 0$, then equating to zero the expression within the braces in (1.6) gives

$$(\xi - a)^2 = \max[(\xi - a)^2, (b - \xi)^2];$$

whereas equating to zero the expression within the braces in (1.7) gives

$$(b - \xi)^2 = \max[(\xi - a)^2, (b - \xi)^2].$$

This means that $\xi = (a + b)/2$. These considerations imply the equality conditions in the theorem.

Remark 2. If $a < b$ and v' is not identically zero, the inequality (1.1) gives an upper bound for the ratio of the two definite integrals

$$\int_a^b [v(x) - v(\xi)]^2 \, dx \bigg/ \int_a^b [v'(x)]^2 \, dx;$$

namely,

$$\frac{4}{\pi^2} \max[(\xi - a)^2, (b - \xi)^2] = \frac{4}{\pi^2} \left[\frac{b - a}{2} + \left| \frac{a + b}{2} - \xi \right| \right]^2.$$

This upper bound has the minimum value $[(b - a)/\pi]^2$ when $\xi = (a + b)/2$.

The next theorem is concerned with *two* intermediate numbers, ξ_1 and ξ_2, where $a \leq \xi_1 \leq \xi_2 \leq b$; but such that, however, $v(\xi_1) = v(\xi_2)$.

Theorem 2. *Let the real-valued function v be continuously differentiable on the finite closed interval $a \leq x \leq b$. Let ξ_1 and ξ_2 be real numbers such that $a \leq \xi_1 \leq \xi_2 \leq b$ and $v(\xi_1) = v(\xi_2)$. Then*

$$\int_a^b [v(x) - v(\xi_1)]^2 \, dx$$

$$\leq \frac{4}{\pi^2} \max\left[(\xi_1 - a)^2, (b - \xi_2)^2, \left(\frac{\xi_2 - \xi_1}{2} \right)^2 \right] \int_a^b [v'(x)]^2 \, dx, \qquad (2.1)$$

where if $a = b$, equality always holds; while if $a < b$, equality holds

when $a < \xi_1 < \xi_2 < b$
$$\begin{cases} and\ \xi_1 = \dfrac{3a + b}{4},\ \xi_2 = \dfrac{a + 3b}{4}, \\[2ex] iff\ v(x) = v(\xi_1) + B \sin\left(2\pi \cdot \dfrac{(3a + b)/4 - x}{b - a}\right), \\[2ex] and\ either\ \xi_1 \neq \dfrac{3a + b}{4}\ or\ \xi_2 \neq \dfrac{a + 3b}{4}, \\[2ex] iff\ v(x) \equiv v(\xi_1); \end{cases}$$

when $a = \xi_1 < \xi_2 < b$
$$\begin{cases} and\ \xi_2 = \dfrac{a + 2b}{3}, \\[2ex] iff\ v(x) = v(\xi_1) + B \sin\left(\dfrac{3\pi}{2} \cdot \dfrac{(a + 2b)/3 - x}{b - a}\right), \\[2ex] and\ \xi_2 \neq \dfrac{a + 2b}{3}, \\[2ex] iff\ v(x) \equiv v(\xi_1); \end{cases}$$

when $a < \xi_1 < \xi_2 = b$
$$\begin{cases} and\ \xi_1 = \dfrac{2a + b}{3}, \\[2ex] iff\ v(x) = v(\xi_1) + B \sin\left(\dfrac{3\pi}{2} \cdot \dfrac{x - (2a + b)/3}{b - a}\right), \\[2ex] and\ \xi_1 \neq \dfrac{2a + b}{3}, \\[2ex] iff\ v(x) \equiv v(\xi_1); \end{cases}$$

when $a < \xi_1 = \xi_2 < b$
$$\begin{cases} and\ \xi_1 = \xi_2 = \dfrac{a + b}{2}, \\[2ex] iff\ v(x) = v(\xi_1) + B \sin\left(\pi \cdot \dfrac{(a + b)/2 - x}{b - a}\right), \\[2ex] and\ \xi_1 = \xi_2 \neq \dfrac{a + b}{2}, \\[2ex] iff\ v(x) \equiv v(\xi_1); \end{cases}$$

when $a = \xi_1 < \xi_2 = b$,   *iff* $v(x) = v(a) + B \sin\left(\pi \cdot \dfrac{x-a}{b-a}\right)$;

when $a < \xi_1 = \xi_2 = b$,   *iff* $v(x) = v(b) + B \sin\left(\dfrac{\pi}{2} \cdot \dfrac{b-x}{b-a}\right)$;

when $a = \xi_1 = \xi_2 < b$,   *iff* $v(x) = v(a) + B \sin\left(\dfrac{\pi}{2} \cdot \dfrac{x-a}{b-a}\right)$;

for $a \leq x \leq b$.

Proof. Suppose that $a < b$, since there is nothing to prove when $a = b$. The desired inequality follows from Theorem I, applied to the four subintervals

$$a \leq x \leq \xi_1, \quad \xi_1 \leq x \leq \frac{\xi_1+\xi_2}{2}, \quad \frac{\xi_1+\xi_2}{2} \leq x \leq \xi_2, \quad \text{and} \quad \xi_2 \leq x \leq b.$$

(i) From (I.2), applied to the subinterval $a \leq x \leq \xi_1$, one has

$$\int_a^{\xi_1} [v(x) - v(\xi_1)]^2 \, dx \leq 4\left(\frac{\xi_1-a}{\pi}\right)^2 \int_a^{\xi_1} [v'(x)]^2 \, dx; \tag{2.2}$$

where if $a = \xi_1$, equality always holds; while if $a < \xi_1$, equality holds if and only if

$$v(x) = v(\xi_1) + B_1 \sin\left(\frac{\pi}{2} \cdot \frac{\xi_1-x}{\xi_1-a}\right), \qquad \text{on} \quad a \leq x \leq \xi_1. \tag{2.2'}$$

(ii) From (I.1) applied to the subinterval $\xi_1 \leq x \leq (\xi_1+\xi_2)/2$, one has

$$\int_{\xi_1}^{(\xi_1+\xi_2)/2} [v(x) - v(\xi_1)]^2 \, dx \leq 4\left(\frac{\xi_2-\xi_1}{2\pi}\right)^2 \int_{\xi_1}^{(\xi_1+\xi_2)/2} [v'(x)]^2 \, dx; \tag{2.3}$$

where if $\xi_1 = \xi_2$, equality always holds; while if $\xi_1 < \xi_2$, equality holds if and only if

$$v(x) = v(\xi_1) + B_2 \sin\left(\pi \cdot \frac{x-\xi_1}{\xi_2-\xi_1}\right), \qquad \text{on} \quad \xi_1 \leq x \leq \frac{\xi_1+\xi_2}{2}. \tag{2.3'}$$

(iii) From (I.2) applied to the subinterval $(\xi_1+\xi_2)/2 \leq x \leq \xi_2$, one has

$$\int_{(\xi_1+\xi_2)/2}^{\xi_2} [v(x) - v(\xi_2)]^2 \, dx \leq 4\left(\frac{\xi_2-\xi_1}{2\pi}\right)^2 \int_{(\xi_1+\xi_2)/2}^{\xi_2} [v'(x)]^2 \, dx; \tag{2.4}$$

where if $\xi_1 = \xi_2$, equality always holds; while if $\xi_1 < \xi_2$, equality holds if and only if

$$v(x) = v(\xi_2) + B_3 \sin\left(\pi \cdot \frac{\xi_2-x}{\xi_2-\xi_1}\right), \qquad \text{on} \quad \frac{\xi_1+\xi_2}{2} \leq x \leq \xi_2. \tag{2.4'}$$

(iv)   From (I.1) applied to the subinterval $\xi_2 \leq x \leq b$, one has

$$\int_{\xi_2}^b [v(x) - v(\xi_2)]^2 \, dx \leq 4\left(\frac{b - \xi_2}{\pi}\right)^2 \int_{\xi_2}^b [v'(x)]^2 \, dx; \qquad (2.5)$$

where if $\xi_2 = b$, equality always holds; while if $\xi_2 < b$, equality holds if and only if

$$v(x) = v(\xi_2) + B_4 \sin\left(\frac{\pi}{2} \cdot \frac{x - \xi_2}{b - \xi_2}\right), \qquad \text{on} \quad \xi_2 \leq x \leq b. \qquad (2.5')$$

Adding the last four inequalities, one obtains, in an obvious notation, since $v(\xi_1) = v(\xi_2)$,

$$\int_a^b [v(x) - v(\xi_1)]^2 \, dx$$

$$\leq \frac{4}{\pi^2} \left\{ (\xi_1 - a)^2 \int_a^{\xi_1} + \left(\frac{\xi_2 - \xi_1}{2}\right)^2 \int_{\xi_1}^{\xi_2} + (b - \xi_2)^2 \int_{\xi_2}^b \right\} [v'(x)]^2 \, dx.$$

This implies the desired inequality.

It only remains to discuss the equality condition. Equality holds in (2.1) if and only if equality holds in (2.2)–(2.5), and

$$\left\{ (\xi_1 - a)^2 \int_a^{\xi_1} + \left(\frac{\xi_2 - \xi_1}{2}\right)^2 \int_{\xi_1}^{\xi_2} + (b - \xi_2)^2 \int_{\xi_2}^b \right\} [v'(x)]^2 \, dx$$

$$= \max\left[(\xi_1 - a)^2, \left(\frac{\xi_2 - \xi_1}{2}\right)^2, (b - \xi_2)^2 \right] \int_a^b [v'(x)]^2 \, dx,$$

simultaneously. This last equation is equivalent to the following three:

$$\left\{ \max\left[(\xi_1 - a)^2, \left(\frac{\xi_2 - \xi_1}{2}\right)^2, (b - \xi_2)^2 \right] - (\xi_1 - a)^2 \right\} \int_a^{\xi_1} [v'(x)]^2 \, dx = 0, \qquad (2.6)$$

$$\left\{ \max\left[(\xi_1 - a)^2, \left(\frac{\xi_2 - \xi_1}{2}\right)^2, (b - \xi_2)^2 \right] - \left(\frac{\xi_2 - \xi_1}{2}\right)^2 \right\} \int_{\xi_1}^{\xi_2} [v'(x)]^2 \, dx = 0, \qquad (2.7)$$

and

$$\left\{ \max\left[(\xi_1 - a)^2, \left(\frac{\xi_2 - \xi_1}{2}\right)^2, (b - \xi_2)^2 \right] - (b - \xi_2)^2 \right\} \int_{\xi_2}^b [v'(x)]^2 \, dx = 0. \qquad (2.8)$$

Thus, equality holds in (2.1) if and only if one has equality in (2.2)–(2.5), and one also has (2.6)–(2.8).

There are eight cases to consider, since $a \leq \xi_1 \leq \xi_2 \leq b$:

(1) $a < \xi_1 < \xi_2 < b$. Equality holds in (2.1) if and only if one has equality in (2.2)–(2.5), and one also has (2.6)–(2.8). That is to say, if and only if (2.2')–(2.5'), plus

$$\left\{ \max\left[(\xi_1 - a)^2, \left(\frac{\xi_2 - \xi_1}{2}\right)^2, (b - \xi_2)^2 \right] - (\xi_1 - a)^2 \right\} B_1{}^2 = 0, \quad (2.9)$$

$$\left\{ \max\left[(\xi_1 - a)^2, \left(\frac{\xi_2 - \xi_1}{2}\right)^2, (b - \xi_2)^2 \right] - \left(\frac{\xi_2 - \xi_1}{2}\right)^2 \right\} (B_2{}^2 + B_3{}^2) = 0,$$
$$(2.10)$$

and

$$\left\{ \max\left[(\xi_1 - a)^2, \left(\frac{\xi_2 - \xi_1}{2}\right)^2, (b - \xi_2)^2 \right] - (b - \xi_2)^2 \right\} B_4{}^2 = 0. \quad (2.11)$$

Now, if (2.2') and (2.3') hold, then since v is continuously differentiable at ξ_1, it must be true that

$$-\frac{1}{2} \cdot \frac{B_1}{\xi_1 - a} = \frac{B_2}{\xi_2 - \xi_1}.$$

If (2.3') and (2.4') hold, then since v is continuous at $(\xi_1 + \xi_2)/2$, it must be true that

$$B_2 = B_3.$$

If (2.4') and (2.5') hold, then since v is continuously differentiable at ξ_2, it must be true that

$$-\frac{B_3}{\xi_2 - \xi_1} = \frac{1}{2} \cdot \frac{B_4}{b - \xi_2}.$$

Hence, either $B_1 = B_2 = B_3 = B_4 = 0$, or $B_1 \neq 0$, $B_2 = B_3 \neq 0$, and $B_4 \neq 0$. Further, if $B_1 \neq 0$, $B_2 = B_3 \neq 0$, and $B_4 \neq 0$, upon equating to zero the expressions within the braces in (2.9)–(2.11) one obtains

$$\xi_1 - a = \frac{\xi_2 - \xi_1}{2}; \qquad \xi_1 - a = b - \xi_2; \qquad \text{and} \qquad \frac{\xi_2 - \xi_1}{2} = b - \xi_2.$$

In other words,

$$3\xi_1 - \xi_2 = 2a; \qquad \xi_1 + \xi_2 = a + b; \qquad \text{and} \qquad -\xi_1 + 3\xi_2 = 2b.$$

This means that

$$\xi_1 = \frac{3a + b}{4} \qquad \text{and} \qquad \xi_2 = \frac{a + 3b}{4}.$$

(2) $a = \xi_1 < \xi_2 < b$. Here equality always holds in (2.2), and (2.6) holds automatically. Hence, equality holds in (2.1) if and only if one has

equality in (2.3)–(2.5), and one also has (2.7) and (2.8). That is to say, if and only if (2.3′)–(2.5′), plus

$$\left\{\max\left[\left(\frac{\xi_2-\xi_1}{2}\right)^2,(b-\xi_2)^2\right]-\left(\frac{\xi_2-\xi_1}{2}\right)^2\right\}(B_2{}^2+B_3{}^2)=0 \quad (2.12)$$

and

$$\left\{\max\left[\left(\frac{\xi_2-\xi_1}{2}\right)^2,(b-\xi_2)^2\right]-(b-\xi_2)^2\right\}B_4{}^2=0. \quad (2.13)$$

Now, if (2.3′) and (2.4′) hold, then since v is continuous at $\frac{1}{2}(\xi_1+\xi_2)$, it must be true that

$$B_2=B_3.$$

On the other hand, if (2.4′) and (2.5′) hold, then since v is continuously differentiable at ξ_2, it must be true that

$$-\frac{B_3}{\xi_2-\xi_1}=\frac{1}{2}\cdot\frac{B_4}{b-\xi_2}.$$

Hence, either $B_2=B_3=B_4=0$, or both $B_2=B_3\neq0$ and $B_4\neq0$. Further, if $B_2=B_3\neq0$ and $B_4\neq0$, upon equating to zero the expressions within the braces in (2.12) and (2.13) one obtains

$$\frac{\xi_2-\xi_1}{2}=b-\xi_2;$$

this means that $\xi_2=(a+2b)/3$ (since $\xi_1=a$ in this case).

(3) $a<\xi_1<\xi_2=b$. This case is "symmetrical" to case (2), upon "interchanging" a and b, and ξ_1 and ξ_2.

(4) $a<\xi_1=\xi_2<b$. This is just Theorem 1, with $\xi=\xi_1=\xi_2$.

(5) $a=\xi_1<\xi_2=b$. Equality holds in (2.1) if and only if one has equality in (2.3), (2.4), and one also has (2.7); that is to say, if and only if (2.3′) and (2.4′), since (2.7) is automatically satisfied. Now, if (2.3′) and (2.4′) hold, then since v is continuous at $\frac{1}{2}(\xi_1+\xi_2)$, it must be true that

$$B_2=B_3.$$

(6) $a<\xi_1=\xi_2=b$. This amounts to (I.2) of Theorem I.

(7) $a=\xi_1=\xi_2<b$. This amounts to (I.1) of Theorem I.

(8) $a=\xi_1=\xi_2=b$. Equality always holds.

Remark 3. Since

$$b-a=(\xi_1-a)+\left(\frac{\xi_2-\xi_1}{2}\right)+\left(\frac{\xi_2-\xi_1}{2}\right)+(b-\xi_2),$$

it follows that

$$\max\left[\xi_1 - a, \ b - \xi_2, \frac{\xi_2 - \xi_1}{2}\right] \geq \tfrac{1}{4}(b - a),$$

with equality if and only if

$$\xi_1 - a = b - \xi_2 = \frac{\xi_2 - \xi_1}{2} = \tfrac{1}{4}(b - a),$$

that is, $\xi_1 = (3a + b)/4$ and $\xi_2 = (a + 3b)/4$. Therefore

$$\min_{\xi_1, \xi_2} \ \max\left[\xi_1 - a, \ b - \xi_2, \frac{\xi_2 - \xi_1}{2}\right] = \tfrac{1}{4}(b - a),$$

the minimum being attained only when $\xi_1 = (3a + b)/4$ and $\xi_2 = (a + 3b)/4$.

If $a < b$, and v' is not identically zero, the inequality (2.1) gives an upper bound for the ratio of the two definite integrals

$$\int_a^b [v(x) - v(\xi_1)]^2 \, dx \Big/ \int_a^b [v'(x)]^2 \, dx;$$

namely,

$$\frac{4}{\pi^2} \max\left[(\xi_1 - a)^2, \ (b - \xi_2)^2, \ \left(\frac{\xi_2 - \xi_1}{2}\right)^2\right]$$

$$= \frac{4}{\pi^2} \left\{\max\left[\xi_1 - a, \ b - \xi_2, \frac{\xi_2 - \xi_1}{2}\right]\right\}^2.$$

This upper bound has the minimum value $\tfrac{1}{4}[(b - a)/\pi]^2$ when $\xi_1 = (3a + b)/4$ and $\xi_2 = (a + 3b)/4$.

The next theorem is concerned with one intermediate number ξ, where $a \leq \xi \leq b$; but such that, however,

$$0 \leq (b - a)v^2(\xi) - 2v(\xi) \int_a^b v(x) \, dx.$$

Roughly speaking (put $a = 0$, $b = 2\pi$, and compare Theorem 6, Wirtinger's inequality), Theorem 2 uses half of the hypotheses of Wirtinger's inequality, namely, $v(0) = v(2\pi)$; while the hypothesis (3.1) of Theorem 3 is satisfied by the other half of the hypotheses of Wirtinger's inequality, namely, $\int_0^{2\pi} v(x) \, dx = 0$.

Theorem 3. *Let the real-valued function v be continuously differentiable on the finite closed interval $a \leq x \leq b$. Let ξ be a real number such that $a \leq \xi \leq b$ and*

$$0 \leq (b - a)v^2(\xi) - 2v(\xi) \int_a^b v(x) \, dx. \tag{3.1}$$

Then

$$\int_a^b v^2(x) \, dx \le \frac{4}{\pi^2} \max[(\xi - a)^2, (b - \xi)^2] \int_a^b [v'(x)]^2 \, dx, \qquad (3.2)$$

where if $a = b$, equality always holds; while if $a < b$, equality holds when $\xi = a$, if and only if

$$v(x) = v(a) + B \sin\left(\frac{\pi}{2} \cdot \frac{x - a}{b - a}\right), \qquad \text{where} \quad v(a)\left[B + \frac{\pi}{4}v(a)\right] = 0;$$

when $a < \xi < (a + b)/2$ or $(a + b)/2 < \xi < b$, if and only if $v(x) \equiv 0$; when $\xi = (a + b)/2$, if and only if

$$v(x) = B \sin\left(\pi \cdot \frac{(a + b)/2 - x}{b - a}\right);$$

when $\xi = b$, if and only if

$$v(x) = v(b) + B \sin\left(\frac{\pi}{2} \cdot \frac{b - x}{b - a}\right), \qquad \text{where} \quad v(b)\left[B + \frac{\pi}{4}v(b)\right] = 0;$$

for $a \le x \le b$.

Proof. Since

$$\int_a^b [v(x) - v(\xi)]^2 \, dx = \int_a^b v^2(x) \, dx - 2v(\xi) \int_a^b v(x) \, dx + v^2(\xi)(b - a),$$

the inequality (3.2) follows directly from Theorem 1 and the hypothesis (3.1).

It remains only to discuss the equality condition. Equality always holds if $a = b$; while, if $a < b$, equality holds if and only if equality holds both in Theorem 1 and in (3.1).

If $\xi = a$, equality holds if and only if

$$v(x) = v(a) + B \sin\left(\frac{\pi}{2} \cdot \frac{x - a}{b - a}\right) \qquad \text{and} \qquad (b - a)v^2(a) = 2v(a) \int_a^b v(x) \, dx;$$

that is, if and only if

$$v(x) = v(a) + B \sin\left(\frac{\pi}{2} \cdot \frac{x - a}{b - a}\right), \qquad \text{for} \quad a \le x \le b,$$

where

$$v(a)\left[B + \frac{\pi}{4}v(a)\right] = 0.$$

If $\xi = (a+b)/2$, equality holds if and only if

$$v(x) = v\left(\frac{a+b}{2}\right) + B \sin\left(\pi \cdot \frac{(a+b)/2 - x}{b-a}\right)$$

and

$$(b-a)v^2\left(\frac{a+b}{2}\right) = 2v\left(\frac{a+b}{2}\right)\int_a^b v(x)\,dx;$$

that is, if and only if

$$v(x) = B \sin\left(\pi \cdot \frac{(a+b)/2 - x}{b-a}\right), \qquad \text{for} \quad a \leq x \leq b.$$

If $\xi = b$, equality holds if and only if

$$v(x) = v(b) + B \sin\left(\frac{\pi}{2} \cdot \frac{b-x}{b-a}\right)$$

and

$$(b-a)v^2(b) = 2v(b)\int_a^b v(x)\,dx;$$

that is, if and only if

$$v(x) = v(b) + B \sin\left(\frac{\pi}{2} \cdot \frac{b-x}{b-a}\right), \qquad \text{for} \quad a \leq x \leq b,$$

where

$$v(b)\left[B + \frac{\pi}{4}v(b)\right] = 0.$$

If $a < \xi < (a+b)/2$ or $(a+b)/2 < \xi < b$, equality holds if and only if $v(x) \equiv v(\xi)$ and

$$(b-a)v^2(\xi) = 2v(\xi)\int_a^b v(x)\,dx;$$

that is, if and only if

$$v(x) \equiv 0, \qquad \text{for} \quad a \leq x \leq b.$$

Remark 4. The analog of Remark 2 holds. That is to say, if $a < b$, and v' is not identically zero, the inequality (3.2) gives an upper bound for the ratio of the two definite integrals,

$$\int_a^b [v(x)]^2\,dx \Big/ \int_a^b [v'(x)]^2\,dx.$$

This upper bound has the minimum value $[(b-a)/\pi]^2$ when $\xi=(a+b)/2$. This is of particular interest when $\int_a^b v(x)\,dx=0$, for then the condition (3.1) is satisfied for any ξ. This agrees with the fact that $\cos[\pi\cdot(x-a)/(b-a)]$ is a "second eigenfunction," with eigenvalue $\pi/(b-a)$, for the eigenvalue problem $v''+\lambda v=0$, where $v'(a)=v'(b)=0$; the restriction $\int_a^b v(x)\,dx=0$ expresses the orthogonality of v with respect to the first eigenfunction, which is identically one.

The next theorem is concerned with two intermediate numbers ξ_1, ξ_2, where $a\leq\xi_1\leq\xi_2\leq b$; but such that, however, $v(\xi_1)=v(\xi_2)$; plus the additional restriction that $v(a)=v(b)$.

Theorem 4. *Let the real-valued function v be continuously differentiable on the finite closed interval $a\leq x\leq b$, with $v(a)=v(b)$. Let ξ_1 and ξ_2 be real numbers such that $a\leq\xi_1\leq\xi_2\leq b$ and $v(\xi_1)=v(\xi_2)$. Then*

$$\int_a^b [v(x)-v(\xi_1)]^2\,dx$$

$$\leq \frac{1}{\pi^2}\max[(\xi_2-\xi_1)^2,(b-a-\xi_2+\xi_1)^2]\int_a^b [v'(x)]^2\,dx,\qquad (4.1)$$

where if $a=b$, equality always holds; while if $a<b$, equality holds

$$\text{when } 0<\xi_2-\xi_1<b-a \begin{cases} \text{and } \xi_2-\xi_1=\dfrac{b-a}{2}, \\[2mm] \quad\text{iff } v(x)=v(\xi_1)+B\sin\left(2\pi\cdot\dfrac{x-\xi_1}{b-a}\right), \\[2mm] \text{and } \xi_2-\xi_1\neq\dfrac{b-a}{2}, \\[2mm] \quad\text{iff } v(x)\equiv v(\xi_1); \end{cases}$$

when $0=\xi_2-\xi_1<b-a$, if and only if

$$v(x)=v(\xi_1)+B\sin\left(\pi\cdot\frac{x-a}{b-a}\right);$$

when $0<\xi_2-\xi_1=b-a$, if and only if

$$v(x)=v(a)+B\sin\left(\pi\cdot\frac{x-a}{b-a}\right);$$

for $a\leq x\leq b$.

Proof. Suppose that $a<b$, since if $a=b$, equality always holds in (4.1). It is convenient at the outset to extend the definition of the function v

"periodically" to the interval $a \leq x \leq \xi_1 + b - a$, by putting $v(x) = v(x - b + a)$ for $b \leq x \leq \xi_1 + b - a$.

(i) From Theorem 2, applied to the interval $\xi_1 \leq x \leq \xi_2$ (notice that, in the terminology of Theorem 2, in this application one is in the special case "$a = \xi_1 \leq \xi_2 = b$"), one obtains

$$\int_{\xi_1}^{\xi_2} [v(x) - v(\xi_1)]^2 \, dx \leq \left(\frac{\xi_2 - \xi_1}{\pi} \right)^2 \int_{\xi_1}^{\xi_2} [v'(x)]^2 \, dx, \qquad (4.2)$$

where if $\xi_1 = \xi_2$, equality always holds; while if $\xi_1 < \xi_2$, equality holds if and only if

$$v(x) = v(\xi_1) + B_1 \sin \left(\pi \frac{x - \xi_1}{\xi_2 - \xi_1} \right), \qquad (4.2')$$

for $\xi_1 \leq x \leq \xi_2$.

(ii) From Theorem 2, applied to the interval $\xi_2 \leq x \leq \xi_1 + b - a$ (notice that, in the terminology of Theorem 2, one is in the special case "$a = \xi_1 \leq \xi_2 = b$"), one obtains

$$\int_{\xi_2}^{\xi_1 + b - a} [v(x) - v(\xi_2)]^2 \, dx \leq \left(\frac{b - a - \xi_2 + \xi_1}{\pi} \right)^2 \int_{\xi_2}^{\xi_1 + b - a} [v'(x)]^2 \, dx, \qquad (4.3)$$

where if $\xi_2 - \xi_1 = b - a$, equality always holds; while if $\xi_2 - \xi_1 < b - a$, equality holds if and only if

$$v(x) = v(\xi_2) + B_2 \sin \left(\pi \frac{x - \xi_2}{b - a - \xi_2 + \xi_1} \right), \qquad (4.3')$$

for $\xi_2 \leq x \leq \xi_1 + b - a$.

Adding the inequalities (4.2) and (4.3) leads to

$$\int_{\xi_1}^{\xi_1 + b - a} [v(x) - v(\xi_1)]^2 \, dx$$

$$\leq \frac{1}{\pi^2} \left[(\xi_2 - \xi_1)^2 \int_{\xi_1}^{\xi_2} [v'(x)]^2 \, dx + (b - a - \xi_2 + \xi_1)^2 \int_{\xi_2}^{\xi_1 + b - a} [v'(x)]^2 \, dx \right],$$

which implies (4.1) upon recalling the extended definition of v.

Equality holds in (4.1) if and only if equality holds both in (4.2) and in (4.3), and one has

$$\left[(\xi_2 - \xi_1)^2 \int_{\xi_1}^{\xi_2} + (b - a - \xi_2 + \xi_1)^2 \int_{\xi_2}^{\xi_1 + b - a} \right] [v'(x)]^2 \, dx$$

$$= \max[(\xi_2 - \xi_1)^2, (b - a - \xi_2 + \xi_1)^2] \int_{\xi_2}^{\xi_1 + b - a} [v'(x)]^2 \, dx,$$

simultaneously. This last equation is equivalent to the following two:

$$\{\max[(\xi_2 - \xi_1)^2, (b - a - \xi_2 + \xi_1)^2] - (\xi_2 - \xi_1)^2\} \int_{\xi_1}^{\xi_2} [v'(x)]^2 \, dx = 0 \quad (4.4)$$

and

$$\{\max[(\xi_2 - \xi_1)^2, (b - a - \xi_2 + \xi_1)^2]$$
$$- (b - a - \xi_2 + \xi_1)^2\} \int_{\xi_2}^{\xi_1 + b - a} [v'(x)]^2 \, dx = 0. \quad (4.5)$$

There are four cases to consider, since $0 \leq \xi_2 - \xi_1 \leq b - a$:

(1) $0 < \xi_2 - \xi_1 < b - a$. That is, $\xi_1 < \xi_2$ and either $a < \xi_1$ or $\xi_2 < b$. Equality holds in (4.1) if and only if one has equality in (4.2), (4.3), and also has (4.4) and (4.5). That is to say, if and only if (4.2′) and (4.3′), plus

$$\{\max [(\xi_2 - \xi_1)^2, (b - a - \xi_2 + \xi_1)^2] - (\xi_2 - \xi_1)^2\} B_1^2 = 0 \quad (4.6)$$

and

$$\{\max[(\xi_2 - \xi_1)^2, (b - a - \xi_2 + \xi_1)^2] - (b - a - \xi_2 + \xi_1)^2\} B_2^2 = 0. \quad (4.7)$$

Now, if (4.2′) and (4.3′) hold, then since v' is continuous at ξ_2, it must be true that

$$-\frac{1}{\xi_2 - \xi_1} B_1 = \frac{1}{b - a - \xi_2 + \xi_1} B_2.$$

Hence, either $B_1 = B_2 = 0$, or both $B_1 \neq 0$ and $B_2 \neq 0$. Further, if $B_1 \neq 0$ and $B_2 \neq 0$ then, equating to zero the expressions within the braces in (4.6) and (4.7) gives

$$\xi_2 - \xi_1 = b - a - \xi_2 + \xi_1;$$

this means that $\xi_2 - \xi_1 (b = \frac{1}{2} - a)$.

(2) $0 = \xi_2 - \xi_1 < b - a$. Equality holds in (4.1) if and only if one has equality in (4.2), (4.3), and one also has (4.4) and (4.5). That is to say, if and only if (4.3′), since equality always holds in (4.2), and (4.4), (4.5) are both automatically satisfied. Translating the equality condition from the interval $\xi_1 = \xi_2 \leq x \leq \xi_2 + b - a$ to the interval $a \leq x \leq b$ yields the equality condition as stated in the theorem.

(3) $0 < \xi_2 - \xi_1 = b - a$. Equality holds if and only if one has equality in (4.2), (4.3), and one also has (4.4) and (4.5). That is to say, if and only if (4.2′), since equality always holds in (4.3), and (4.4), (4.5) are both automatically satisfied. This agrees with the equality condition in the case $a = \xi_1 < \xi_2 = b$ of Theorem 2.

(4) $0 = \xi_2 - \xi_1 = b - a$. Equality always holds in this case.

Remark 5. If $a < b$, and v' is not identically zero, the inequality (4.1) gives an upper bound for the ratio of the two definite integrals,

$$\int_a^b [v(x) - v(\xi_1)]^2 \, dx \Big/ \int_a^b [v'(x)]^2 \, dx.$$

This upper bound has the minimum value

$$\frac{1}{4}\left(\frac{b-a}{\pi}\right)^2 \qquad \text{when} \quad \xi_2 - \xi_1 = \tfrac{1}{2}(b-a).$$

The next theorem has the same hypotheses as Theorem 4 plus the additional restriction (5.1).

Theorem 5. *Let the real-valued function v be continuously differentiable on the finite closed interval $a \leq x \leq b$, with $v(a) = v(b)$. Let ξ_1 and ξ_2 be real numbers such that $a \leq \xi_1 \leq \xi_2 \leq b$, $v(\xi_1) = v(\xi_2)$, and*

$$0 \leq (b-a)v^2(\xi_1) - 2v(\xi_1) \int_a^b v(x) \, dx. \tag{5.1}$$

Then

$$\int_a^b v^2(x) \, dx \leq \frac{1}{\pi^2} \max[(\xi_2 - \xi_1)^2, (b-a-\xi_2+\xi_1)^2] \int_a^b [v'(x)]^2 \, dx, \tag{5.2}$$

where if $a = b$, equality always holds; while if $a < b$, equality holds

when $\xi_2 - \xi_1 = \tfrac{1}{2}(b-a)$, if and only if

$$v(x) = B \sin\left(2\pi \cdot \frac{x - \xi_1}{b - a}\right);$$

when $0 < \xi_2 - \xi_1 < b - a$ and $\xi_2 - \xi_1 \neq \tfrac{1}{2}(b-a)$, if and only if $v(x) \equiv 0$;

when $\xi_1 = \xi_2$, if and only if

$$v(x) = v(\xi_1) + B \sin\left(\pi \cdot \frac{x - a}{b - a}\right),$$

where $v(\xi_1)[B + (\pi/4)v(\xi_1)] = 0$;

when $a = \xi_1 < \xi_2 = b$, if and only if

$$v(x) = v(a) + B \sin\left(\pi \cdot \frac{x - a}{b - a}\right),$$

where $v(a)[B + (\pi/4)v(a)] = 0$;

for $a \leq x \leq b$.

Proof. Since

$$\int_a^b [v(x) - v(\xi_1)]^2\, dx = \int_a^b v^2(x)\, dx - 2v(\xi_1) \int_a^b v(x)\, dx + v^2(\xi_1)(b-a),$$

the inequality (5.2) follows directly from Theorem 4 and the hypothesis (5.1).

It only remains to discuss the equality condition. Equality always holds if $a = b$; while if $a < b$, equality holds if and only if equality holds both in Theorem 4 and in (5.1). Therefore, suppose that $a < b$.

If $\xi_2 - \xi_1 = \frac{1}{2}(b-a)$, equality holds if and only if

$$v(x) = v(\xi_1) + B \sin\left(2\pi \cdot \frac{x - \xi_1}{b-a}\right)$$

and

$$(b-a)v^2(\xi_1) = 2v(\xi_1) \int_a^b v(x)\, dx;$$

that is, if and only if

$$v(x) = v(\xi_1) + B \sin\left(2\pi \cdot \frac{x - \xi_1}{b-a}\right), \qquad \text{for} \quad a \le x \le b,$$

with $v(\xi_1) = 0$.

If $0 < \xi_2 - \xi_1 < b - a$, but $\xi_2 - \xi_1 \ne \frac{1}{2}(b-a)$, equality holds if and only if $v(x) \equiv v(\xi_1)$ and

$$(b-a)v^2(\xi_1) = 2v^2(\xi_1)(b-a);$$

that is, if and only if $v(x) \equiv 0$ for $a \le x \le b$.

If $0 = \xi_2 - \xi_1 < b - a$, equality holds if and only if

$$v(x) = v(\xi_1) + B \sin\left(\pi \cdot \frac{x - a}{b-a}\right)$$

and

$$(b-a)v^2(\xi_1) = 2v(\xi_1) \int_a^b v(x)\, dx = 2v(\xi_1)\left\{(b-a)v(\xi_1) + \frac{2}{\pi}(b-a)B\right\};$$

that is, if and only if

$$v(x) = v(\xi_1) + B \sin\left(\pi \cdot \frac{x - a}{b-a}\right), \qquad \text{for} \quad a \le x \le b,$$

where $v(\xi_1)[B + (\pi/4)v(\xi_1)] = 0$.

If $0 < \xi_2 - \xi_1 = b - a$, equality holds if and only if

$$v(x) = v(a) + B \sin\left(\pi \cdot \frac{x-a}{b-a}\right)$$

and

$$(b-a)v^2(a) = 2v(a)\int_a^b v(x)\,dx = 2v(a)\left\{(b-a)v(a) + \frac{2}{\pi}(b-a)B\right\};$$

that is, if and only if

$$v(x) = v(a) + B \sin\left(\pi \cdot \frac{x-a}{b-a}\right), \qquad \text{for} \quad a \leq x \leq b,$$

where $v(a)[B + (\pi/4)v(a)] = 0$.

Remark 6.   Obviously, a remark analogous to Remark 5 is applicable to the inequality (5.2).

Conclusion

For the purpose of comparison, this section contains in detail two proofs of Wirtinger's inequality: (1) the proof in Hardy *et al.* [1, pp. 185–186]; and (2) an alternative proof, which follows essentially as a special case of the proof of Theorem 5 in Sec. 2 of this paper.

Wirtinger's inequality [1, pp. 185–186, Theorem 258] is the following.

Theorem 6.   *Let the real-valued function v be continuously differentiable on the finite closed interval $0 \leq x \leq 2\pi$, with $v(0) = v(2\pi)$, and $\int_0^{2\pi} v(x)\,dx = 0$. Then*

$$\int_0^{2\pi} v^2(x)\,dx \leq \int_0^{2\pi} [v'(x)]^2\,dx, \tag{6.1}$$

where equality holds if and only if there are real numbers B and ξ such that

$$v(x) = B \sin (x - \xi), \qquad \text{for} \quad 0 \leq x \leq 2\pi.$$

(1)   The proof in [1, pp. 185–186], by Hans Lewy, is based on an integral identity involving the cotangent function. The main difficulty encountered in the proof is that the auxiliary function $\cot x$ has three infinities on the interval $0 \leq x \leq 2\pi$. The difficulty arising from these infinities may be circumvented thus. Consider the difference function $v(x + \pi) - v(x)$ on the interval $0 \leq x \leq \pi$. Since this function has the value $v(\pi) - v(0)$ at $x = 0$, and the value $v(0) - v(\pi) = -[v(\pi) - v(0)]$ at $x = \pi$, it follows that there is a ξ such that $0 \leq \xi < \pi$ and $v(\xi + \pi) - v(\xi) = 0$ (notice that $\xi = \pi$ is equivalent to $\xi = 0$).

Consider the function $[v(x) - v(\xi)]^2 \cot(x - \xi)$. If $0 < \xi < \pi$, then the first factor, $[v(x) - v(\xi)]^2$, has a zero of second order (at least) at ξ and at $\xi + \pi$, while the second factor, $\cot(x - \xi)$, has an infinity of first order at ξ and $\xi + \pi$. If $\xi = 0$, then the first factor has zeros of the second order at 0, π, and 2π, while the second factor has infinities of first order at 0, π, and 2π. Therefore, in every case, the product function has the limit zero as x tends to one of the infinities of the second factor.

The remainder of the proof is based on the relation

$$\frac{d}{dx}[(v(x) - v(\xi))^2 \cot(x - \xi)] = [v'(x)]^2 - [v(x) - v(\xi)]^2$$

$$- [v'(x) - [v(x) - v(\xi)] \cot(x - \xi)]^2$$

$$\leq [v'(x)]^2 - [v(x) - v(\xi)]^2,$$

where the last equality holds if and only if $v'(x) = [v(x) - v(\xi)] \cot(x - \xi)$. If $0 < \xi < \pi$, integration of this inequality over the *three* intervals

$$0 < \varepsilon \leq x \leq \xi - \varepsilon, \quad \xi + \varepsilon \leq x \leq \xi + \pi - \varepsilon, \quad \text{and} \quad \xi + \pi + \varepsilon \leq x \leq 2\pi,$$

addition of the three results and passage to the limit, letting ε tend to zero, yields the final result

$$0 = \{[v(x) - v(\xi)]^2 \cot(x - \xi)\}_0^{2\pi}$$

$$\leq \int_0^{2\pi} \{[v'(x)]^2 - v^2(x) + 2v(\xi)v(x) - v^2(\xi)\} \, dx$$

$$\leq \int_0^{2\pi} \{[v'(x)]^2 - v^2(x)\} \, dx + 2v(\xi) \int_0^{2\pi} v(x) \, dx \cdot$$

$$= \int_0^{2\pi} \{[v'(x)]^2 - v^2(x)\} \, dx.$$

Thus, (6.1) follows.

From the preceding argument, equality can be seen to hold in (6.1) if and only if

$$v'(x) = [v(x) - v(\xi)] \cot(x - \xi)$$

on $0 \leq x \leq 2\pi$ (with ξ and $\xi + \pi$ excepted), together with $v(\xi) = 0$, which means that if $0 < \xi < \pi$, one must have

$$v'(x) = v(x) \cot(x - \xi),$$

that is to say

$$\frac{d}{dx}\left[\frac{v(x)}{\sin(x - \xi)}\right] = 0$$

on each of the three open intervals $0 < x < \xi$, $\xi < x < \xi + \pi$, and $\xi + \pi < x < 2\pi$. This means that

$$v(x) = \begin{cases} B_1 \sin(x - \xi), & 0 < x < \xi \\ B_2 \sin(x - \xi), & \xi < x < \xi + \pi \\ B_3 \sin(x - \xi), & \xi + \pi < x < 2\pi. \end{cases}$$

But, in addition, one must have $v(0) = v(2\pi)$, which implies that $B_1 = B_3$. Further, one must still have $\int_0^{2\pi} v(x)\, dx = 0$, which implies that $B_1 = B_2$. This gives the equality condition, when $0 < \xi < \pi$, as stated in the theorem.

It still remains to consider the case $\xi = 0$. In this case one can argue similarly, starting instead with the *two* intervals $0 < \varepsilon \le x \le \pi - \varepsilon$ and $\pi + \varepsilon \le x \le 2\pi - \varepsilon$.

(2) Since v is continuous on $0 \le x \le 2\pi$, and $v(0) = v(2\pi)$, there exists a real number ξ such that $0 \le \xi < \pi$ and $v(\xi + \pi) - v(\xi) = 0$. (Hence, Theorem 5 actually contains Wirtinger's inequality, i.e., Theorem 6, upon choosing $a = 0$, $b = 2\pi$, $\xi_1 = \xi$, and $\xi_2 = \xi + \pi$.) The alternative direct proof to be given now will involve an application of Theorem I to *four* subintervals.

Extend the definition of the function v "periodically" to the interval $0 \le x \le \xi + 2\pi$ by putting $v(x) = v(x - 2\pi)$ for $2\pi \le x \le \xi + 2\pi$. Then:

(i)   From (1.1) of Theorem I, applied to the subinterval $\xi \le x \le \xi + \pi/2$, one obtains

$$\int_{\xi}^{\xi + \pi/2} [v(x) - v(\xi)]^2\, dx \le \int_{\xi}^{\xi + \pi/2} [v'(x)]^2\, dx, \tag{7.1}$$

with equality if and only if

$$v(x) = v(\xi) + B_1 \sin(x - \xi). \tag{7.1'}$$

(ii)   From (I.2) of Theorem I, applied to the subinterval $\xi + \pi/2 \le x \le \xi + \pi$, one obtains

$$\int_{\xi + \pi/2}^{\xi + \pi} [v(x) - v(\xi)]^2\, dx \le \int_{\xi + \pi/2}^{\xi + \pi} [v'(x)]^2\, dx, \tag{7.2}$$

with equality if and only if

$$v(x) = v(\xi) + B_2 \sin(x - \xi). \tag{7.2'}$$

(iii)   From (I.1) of Theorem I, applied to the subinterval $\xi + \pi \le x \le \xi + 3\pi/2$, one obtains

$$\int_{\xi + \pi}^{\xi + 3\pi/2} [v(x) - v(\xi)]^2\, dx \le \int_{\xi + \pi}^{\xi + 3\pi/2} [v'(x)]^2\, dx, \tag{7.3}$$

with equality if and only if

$$v(x) = v(\xi) + B_3 \sin(x - \xi). \tag{7.3'}$$

(iv)   From (I.2) of Theorem I, applied to the subinterval $\xi + 3\pi/2 \leq x \leq \xi + 2\pi$, one obtains

$$\int_{\xi + 3\pi/2}^{\xi + 2\pi} [v(x) - v(\xi)]^2 \, dx \leq \int_{\xi + 3\pi/2}^{\xi + 2\pi} [v'(x)]^2 \, dx \tag{7.4}$$

with equality if and only if

$$v(x) = v(\xi) + B_4 \sin(x - \xi). \tag{7.4'}$$

Adding these inequalities and remembering that the definition of v was extended periodically, one obtains

$$\int_0^{2\pi} [v(x) - v(\xi)]^2 \, dx \leq \int_0^{2\pi} [v'(x)]^2 \, dx \tag{7.5}$$

with equality if and only if equality holds in (7.1)–(7.4) simultaneously; that is, (7.1')–(7.4') hold, which, since v is continuous at $\xi + \pi/2$ and $\xi + 3\pi/2$, and v' is continuous at $\xi + \pi$, means that $B_1 = B_2 = B_3 = B_4$. Thus equality holds in (7.5) if and only if $v(x) = B \sin(x - \xi)$ on $0 \leq x \leq 2\pi$.

Now, since $\int_0^{2\pi} v(x) \, dx = 0$, (7.5) gives

$$\int_0^{2\pi} v^2(x) \, dx + v^2(\xi) 2\pi \leq \int_0^{2\pi} [v'(x)]^2 \, dx,$$

which implies (6.1). Equality clearly holds in (6.1) if and only if $v(\xi) = 0$ and equality holds in (7.5); that is, if and only if

$$v(x) = B \sin(x - \xi)$$

on $0 \leq x \leq 2\pi$.

REFERENCES

[1] Hardy, G. H., Littlewood, J. E., and Pólya, G., "Inequalities," 2nd ed. Cambridge Univ. Press, London and New York, 1959.

[2] Beesack, P. R., Integral inequalities of the Wirtinger type, *Duke Math. J.* **25**, 477–498 (1958).

[3] Bellman, R., A note on periodic functions and their derivatives, *J. London Math. Soc.* **18**, 140–142 (1943).

[4] Coles, W. J., A general Wirtinger-type inequality, *Duke Math. J.* **27**, 133–138 (1960).

[5] Coles, W. J., Wirtinger-type integral inequalities, *Pacific J. Math.* **11,** 871–877 (1960).

[6] Fan, K., Taussky, O., and Todd, J., Discrete analogs of inequalities of Wirtinger, *Monatsh. Math.* **59,** 73–90 (1955).

[7] Northcott, D. G., Some inequalities between periodic functions and their derivatives, *J. London Math. Soc.* **14,** 198–202 (1939).

[8] Reid, W. T., The isoperimetric inequality and associated boundary problems, *J. Math. Mech.* **8,** 897–905 (1959).

Inequalities for the Sum of Two M-Matrices[*]

KY FAN
Department of Mathematics
University of California
Santa Barbara, California

1. Introduction

M-matrices were first introduced by Ostrowski [12, 13], and have been studied by him and others [2–7, 10]. M-matrices arise naturally in the study of matrices with nonnegative elements; they also occur in convergence criteria of certain iterative methods for solving systems of linear equations [13–15], and in the numerical solution of elliptic partial differential equations [15].

Several inequalities for M-matrices were given in [4–6], but they do not involve the sum of M-matrices. The purpose of the present paper is to prove some inequalities for the sum of two M-matrices. However, the sum of two M-matrices is not always an M-matrix. Partly for this reason, our results are concerned only with M-matrices A, B satisfying $A \leq B$ or a milder condition that B proportionally dominates A.

2. Definitions and Notation

By an *M-matrix* we understand a square matrix A of the form $A = \rho I - P$, where P is a matrix with nonnegative elements, I denotes the identity matrix, and ρ is a positive number greater than the absolute value of every eigenvalue of P. Several alternative but equivalent definitions for M-matrices are known [3, Theorem 5; 7; 8, Chap. 13]. For our purpose, it suffices to recall the following: a square real matrix $A = (a_{ij})$ with $a_{ij} \leq 0$ for all $i \neq j$ is an M-matrix if and only if it satisfies one of the following two equivalent conditions:

$$A \text{ is nonsingular and all elements of } A^{-1} \text{ are nonnegative.} \tag{1}$$

$$\text{The determinant of every principal submatrix of } A \text{ is positive.} \tag{2}$$

[*] This work was supported in part by the National Science Foundation Grant GP-5578.

From criterion (2) it is clear that all principal submatrices of an M-matrix are M-matrices. Also, a simultaneous permutation of the rows and columns preserves the M-property.

For two real matrices $A = (a_{ij})$, $B = (b_{ij})$ of the same order, we write $A \leq B$ or $B \geq A$ to signify that $a_{ij} \leq b_{ij}$ for all i, j. Thus $B \geq 0$ means that all elements of B are nonnegative.

A complex matrix $B = (b_{ij})$ of order n is said to *dominate* an M-matrix $A = (a_{ij})$ of order n, if

$$a_{ii} \leq |b_{ii}| \quad \text{for all} \quad i; \quad |b_{ij}| \leq |a_{ij}| \quad \text{for} \quad i \neq j. \tag{3}$$

In case both A, B are M-matrices, "B dominates A" means of course $A \leq B$.

For two M-matrices $A = (a_{ij})$, $B = (b_{ij})$ of order n, we say that B *proportionally dominates* A, if

$$\frac{|b_{ij}|}{b_{ii}} \leq \frac{|a_{ij}|}{a_{ii}} \quad \text{and} \quad \frac{|b_{ij}|}{b_{jj}} \leq \frac{|a_{ij}|}{a_{jj}} \quad \text{for all} \quad i, j; \tag{4}$$

or, what is the same, if there exist positive numbers p_i $(1 \leq i \leq n)$ such that

$$p_i a_{ij} \leq b_{ij} \quad \text{and} \quad a_{ij} p_j \leq b_{ij} \quad \text{for all} \quad i, j. \tag{5}$$

For a matrix $A = (a_{ij})$ of order n, and for indices $1 \leq i_1 < i_2 < \cdots < i_k \leq n$, $1 \leq j_1 < j_2 < \cdots < j_k \leq n$, we denote by

$$A\begin{pmatrix} i_1, i_2, \ldots, i_k \\ j_1, j_2, \ldots, j_k \end{pmatrix}$$

the determinant of the submatrix of A formed by the rows with indices $i_1, i_2, \ldots, i_k$, and the columns with indices $j_1, j_2, \ldots, j_k$. However most minors considered will be principal minors, for which we use the notation $A(i_1, i_2, \ldots, i_k)$ instead of

$$A\begin{pmatrix} i_1, i_2, \ldots, i_k \\ i_1, i_2, \ldots, i_k \end{pmatrix}.$$

Thus $A\binom{i}{j} = a_{ij}$, $A(i) = a_{ii}$, and $A(1, 2, \ldots, n) = \det A$. If α denotes a subset of the set $\{1, 2, \ldots, n\}$, $A(\alpha)$ will denote the determinant of the principal submatrix of A formed by the rows and columns with indices contained in α. We denote by $\emptyset$ the empty set and define $A(\emptyset) = 1$.

For a matrix A of order n with $A(n) \neq 0$, we denote by $\tilde{A}$ the matrix of order $n - 1$ defined by

$$\tilde{A}\binom{i}{j} = \frac{A\begin{pmatrix} i, n \\ j, n \end{pmatrix}}{A(n)} \quad \text{for} \quad i, j = 1, 2, \ldots, n - 1. \tag{6}$$

The minors of $\tilde{A}$ and A are related by the classical Sylvester identity

$$\tilde{A}\begin{pmatrix} i_1, i_2, \ldots, i_k \\ j_1, j_2, \ldots, j_k \end{pmatrix} = \frac{A\begin{pmatrix} i_1, i_2, \ldots, i_k, n \\ j_1, j_2, \ldots, j_k, n \end{pmatrix}}{A(n)}, \tag{7}$$

where $1 \le i_1 < i_2 < \cdots < i_k \le n-1$, $1 \le j_1 < j_2 < \cdots < j_k \le n-1$.

3. Lemmas

We begin with some lemmas.

Lemma 1. *Let A, B, C be three real matrices of order n such that $A \le B \le C$. If A, C are M-matrices, then B is also an M-matrix.*

Proof. A is of the form $A = \rho I - P$, where $P \ge 0$ and ρ is greater than the absolute value of every eigenvalue of P. For any $\rho' > 0$, if we write $A = (\rho' + \rho)I - (\rho'I + P)$, then $\rho' + \rho$ will be greater than the absolute value of every eigenvalue of the matrix $\rho'I + P \ge 0$. For this reason, the two M-matrices A, C may be written $A = \rho I - P$, $C = \rho I - R$ with the same ρ, where $P \ge 0$, $R \ge 0$, and ρ is greater than the absolute value of every eigenvalue of P or R. Let $Q = \rho I - B$. Then since $P \ge Q \ge R$, we have $Q \ge 0$ and ρ is greater than the absolute value of every eigenvalue of Q [8, Chap. 13]. Hence $B = \rho I - Q$ is an M-matrix.

Lemma 2. *Let A, B be two M-matrices of order n. If B proportionally dominates A, then for any positive numbers t_1, t_2, $t_1 A + t_2 B$ is an M-matrix.*

Proof. For any positive numbers t_1, t_2, it is clear that $t_2 B$ proportionally dominates $t_1 A$. Therefore it suffices to consider the case $t_1 = t_2 = 1$; i.e., to prove that $A + B$ is an M-matrix.

Let $A = (a_{ij})$, $B = (b_{ij})$. By hypothesis, there exist positive numbers p_i $(1 \le i \le n)$ satisfying (5). Consider the matrices $A' = (a'_{ij})$, $B' = (b'_{ij})$ of order n defined by

$$a'_{ij} = (1 + p_i)a_{ij}, \qquad b'_{ij} = (1 + p_i^{-1})b_{ij}.$$

From criterion (2) for M-matrices, the M-property is preserved when each row of an M-matrix is multiplied by a positive number. Thus A', B' are M-matrices. We have $A' \le A + B \le B'$ by (5). Hence $A + B$ is an M-matrix by Lemma 1.

Lemma 3. *If A is an M-matrix of order n, then the matrix $\tilde{A}$ of order $n-1$ is an M-matrix. If a complex matrix C of order n dominates an M-matrix A of order n, then $\tilde{C}$ dominates $\tilde{A}$.*

Proof. See [5].

Lemma 4. *If two M-matrices A, B, and a complex matrix C, all of order n, are such that B proportionally dominates A, and C dominates A + B, then $\tilde{A}$, $\tilde{B}$ are M-matrices, $\tilde{B}$ proportionally dominates $\tilde{A}$, and $\tilde{C}$ dominates the M-matrix $\tilde{A} + \tilde{B}$.*

Proof. By Lemma 3, $\tilde{A}$, $\tilde{B}$ are M-matrices. Let $A = (a_{ij})$, $B = (b_{ij})$, $C = (c_{ij})$, $\tilde{A} = (\tilde{a}_{ij})$, $\tilde{B} = (\tilde{b}_{ij})$, and $\tilde{C} = (\tilde{c}_{ij})$. By hypothesis, there exist positive numbers p_i $(1 \leq i \leq n)$ satisfying (5). Then for $1 \leq i \leq n-1$ and $1 \leq j \leq n-1$, we have

$$p_i \tilde{a}_{ij} = p_i a_{ij} - \frac{p_i a_{in} p_n a_{nj}}{p_n a_{nn}} \leq b_{ij} - \frac{b_{in} b_{nj}}{b_{nn}} = \tilde{b}_{ij}$$

and similarly $\tilde{a}_{ij} p_j \leq \tilde{b}_{ij}$. Thus $\tilde{B}$ proportionally dominates $\tilde{A}$; and $\tilde{A} + \tilde{B}$ is an M-matrix by Lemma 2.

Since C dominates $A + B$, we have for $1 \leq i \leq n-1$:

$$|\tilde{c}_{ii}| \geq |c_{ii}| - \left| \frac{c_{in} c_{ni}}{c_{nn}} \right| \geq a_{ii} + b_{ii} - \frac{(a_{in} + b_{in})(a_{ni} + b_{ni})}{a_{nn} + b_{nn}}$$

and therefore

$$|\tilde{c}_{ii}| - (\tilde{a}_{ii} + \tilde{b}_{ii}) \geq \frac{a_{in} a_{ni}}{a_{nn}} + \frac{b_{in} b_{ni}}{b_{nn}} - \frac{(a_{in} + b_{in})(a_{ni} + b_{ni})}{a_{nn} + b_{nn}}. \qquad (8)$$

For any two distinct indices i, j between 1 and $n-1$, we have

$$|\tilde{c}_{ij}| \leq |c_{ij}| + \left| \frac{c_{in} c_{nj}}{c_{nn}} \right| \leq -(a_{ij} + b_{ij}) + \frac{(a_{in} + b_{in})(a_{nj} + b_{nj})}{a_{nn} + b_{nn}}$$

and therefore

$$|\tilde{a}_{ij} + \tilde{b}_{ij}| - |\tilde{c}_{ij}| = -(\tilde{a}_{ij} + \tilde{b}_{ij}) - |\tilde{c}_{ij}|$$

$$\geq \frac{a_{in} a_{nj}}{a_{nn}} + \frac{b_{in} b_{nj}}{b_{nn}} - \frac{(a_{in} + b_{in})(a_{nj} + b_{nj})}{a_{nn} + b_{nn}}. \qquad (9)$$

On the other hand, for $i, j = 1, 2, \ldots, n-1$, we have

$$\frac{a_{in} a_{nj}}{a_{nn}} + \frac{b_{in} b_{nj}}{b_{nn}} - \frac{(a_{in} + b_{in})(a_{nj} + b_{nj})}{a_{nn} + b_{nn}}$$

$$= \frac{(b_{in} a_{nn} - a_{in} b_{nn})(b_{nj} a_{nn} - a_{nj} b_{nn})}{a_{nn} b_{nn}(a_{nn} + b_{nn})}$$

and

$$b_{in} a_{nn} - a_{in} b_{nn} \geq 0, \qquad b_{nj} a_{nn} - a_{nj} b_{nn} \geq 0.$$

Thus

$$\frac{a_{in}a_{nj}}{a_{nn}} + \frac{b_{in}b_{nj}}{b_{nn}} - \frac{(a_{in}+b_{in})(a_{nj}+b_{nj})}{a_{nn}+b_{nn}} \geq 0 \tag{10}$$

for $i, j = 1, 2, \ldots, n-1$. Combining (8)–(10), we see that $\tilde{C}$ dominates the M-matrix $\tilde{A} + \tilde{B}$.

4. Inequalities for Two M-Matrices Such That One Proportionally Dominates the Other

The result given in this section is concerned with the sum of two M-matrices, of which one proportionally dominates the other. Inequalities (13), (14) below are known to be valid for any two positive-definite Hermitian matrices A, B of order n [1, p. 70–71].

Theorem 1. *Let A, B be M-matrices of order n such that B proportionally dominates A. If a complex matrix C of order n dominates $A + B$, then*

$$|\det C|^{1/n} \geq (\det A)^{1/n} + (\det B)^{1/n}, \tag{11}$$

$$\left|\frac{\det C}{C(k+1, \ldots, n)}\right|^{1/k} \geq \left(\frac{\det A}{A(k+1, \ldots, n)}\right)^{1/k} + \left(\frac{\det B}{B(k+1, \ldots, n)}\right)^{1/k}, \tag{12}$$

$$(1 \leq k \leq n-1).$$

In particular:

$$[\det(A+B)]^{1/n} \geq (\det A)^{1/n} + (\det B)^{1/n}, \tag{13}$$

$$\left(\frac{\det(A+B)}{(A+B)(k+1, \ldots, n)}\right)^{1/k} \geq \left(\frac{\det A}{A(k+1, \ldots, n)}\right)^{1/k} + \left(\frac{\det B}{B(k+1, \ldots, n)}\right)^{1/k}$$

$$(1 \leq k \leq n-1). \tag{14}$$

Proof. We first prove (11). The case $n = 1$ being trivial, we may assume $n \geq 2$. By Lemma 4, $\tilde{A}$, $\tilde{B}$, $\tilde{C}$ satisfy the hypotheses of the theorem, but for the order $n-1$. Therefore by an inductive assumption we have

$$|\det \tilde{C}|^{1/(n-1)} \geq (\det \tilde{A})^{1/(n-1)} + (\det \tilde{B})^{1/(n-1)},$$

which may be written [by Sylvester's identity (7)]

$$\left|\frac{\det C}{C(n)}\right|^{1/(n-1)} \geq \left(\frac{\det A}{A(n)}\right)^{1/(n-1)} + \left(\frac{\det B}{B(n)}\right)^{1/(n-1)},$$

or, what is the same,

$$|\det C|^{1/n} \geq |C(n)|^{1/n} \cdot \left[\left(\frac{\det A}{A(n)}\right)^{1/(n-1)} + \left(\frac{\det B}{B(n)}\right)^{1/(n-1)}\right]^{(n-1)/n}. \tag{15}$$

Let

$$x_1 = [A(n)]^{1/n}, \qquad x_2 = [B(n)]^{1/n},$$

$$y_1 = \left[\frac{\det A}{A(n)}\right]^{1/n}, \quad y_2 = \left[\frac{\det B}{B(n)}\right]^{1/n}.$$

Then from (15) and $|C(n)| \geq A(n) + B(n)$, we obtain

$$|\det C|^{1/n} \geq (x_1{}^n + x_2{}^n)^{1/n}(y_1^{n/(n-1)} + y_2^{n/(n-1)})^{(n-1)/n}$$

$$\geq x_1 y_1 + x_2 y_2 = (\det A)^{1/n} + (\det B)^{1/n}.$$

Before proving (12), note first that (11) implies $\det C \neq 0$. Furthermore, because the hypotheses of the theorem remain fulfilled by corresponding principal submatrices of A, B, C, every principal submatrix of C is non-singular.

When $n = 2$, (12) becomes

$$\left|\frac{\det C}{C(2)}\right| \geq \frac{\det A}{A(2)} + \frac{\det B}{B(2)}$$

or, what is the same, $|\tilde{C}(1)| \geq \tilde{A}(1) + \tilde{B}(1)$. This is true because $\tilde{C}$ dominates $\tilde{A} + \tilde{B}$ (Lemma 4). For $n \geq 3$, since $\tilde{A}$, $\tilde{B}$, $\tilde{C}$ fulfill the hypotheses of the theorem, but for the order $n - 1$, we have by an inductive assumption

$$\left|\frac{\det \tilde{C}}{\tilde{C}(k+1, \ldots, n-1)}\right|^{1/k}$$

$$\geq \left(\frac{\det \tilde{A}}{\tilde{A}(k+1, \ldots, n-1)}\right)^{1/k} + \left(\frac{\det \tilde{B}}{\tilde{B}(k+1, \ldots, n-1)}\right)^{1/k}$$

$$(1 \leq k \leq n-2) \qquad (16)$$

and by (11):

$$|\det \tilde{C}|^{1/(n-1)} \geq (\det \tilde{A})^{1/(n-1)} + (\det \tilde{B})^{1/(n-1)}. \qquad (17)$$

Then, using Sylvester's identity, the case $k \leq n-2$ of (12) follows from (16), and the case $k = n-1$ follows from (17).

In case $A = B$, Theorem 1 reduces to the following result of Ostrowski [12].

Corollary 1. *If a complex matrix C of order n dominates an M-matrix A of order n, then*

$$|\det C| \geq \det A, \qquad (18)$$

$$\left|\frac{\det C}{C(k+1, \ldots, n)}\right| \geq \frac{\det A}{A(k+1, \ldots, n)} \qquad (1 \leq k \leq n-1). \qquad (19)$$

Example 1.   For the M-matrices

$$A = \begin{pmatrix} 1 & -3 \\ 0 & 2 \end{pmatrix}, \qquad B = \begin{pmatrix} 2 & 0 \\ -1 & 1 \end{pmatrix},$$

inequalities (13) and (14) are reversed. Here neither of A, B proportionally dominates the other, although $A + B$ is an M-matrix.

5. Inequalities for M-Matrices A, B Such That $A \leq B$

In this section we derive several inequalities for a linear combination $tA + (1 - t)B$, $0 < t < 1$, of two M-matrices A, B satisfying $A \leq B$.

Theorem 2.   *Let A, B be M-matrices of order n such that $A \leq B$, and let $0 < t < 1$. If a complex matrix C of order n dominates $tA + (1 - t)B$, then C is nonsingular, and every element of $tA^{-1} + (1 - t)B^{-1}$ is at least equal to the absolute value of the corresponding element of C^{-1}, i.e.,*

$$\left| C^{-1}\binom{i}{j} \right| \leq tA^{-1}\binom{i}{j} + (1 - t)B^{-1}\binom{i}{j} \qquad \text{for all } i, j. \tag{20}$$

In particular,

$$[tA + (1 - t)B]^{-1} \leq tA^{-1} + (1 - t)B^{-1}. \tag{21}$$

Proof.   Applying inequality (11) of Theorem 1, we have

$$|\det C|^{1/n} \geq t(\det A)^{1/n} + (1 - t)(\det B)^{1/n} > 0,$$

which implies that C is nonsingular. By inequality (12), we can write

$$|C^{-1}(i)|^{-1} \geq \frac{t}{A^{-1}(i)} + \frac{1 - t}{B^{-1}(i)} \geq [tA^{-1}(i) + (1 - t)B^{-1}(i)]^{-1}$$

for $i = 1, 2, \ldots, n$, so the case $i = j$ of (20) is verified.

The case $i \neq j$ of (20) is proved by induction on n. Consider first the case $n = 2$. Let $A = (a_{ij})$, $B = (b_{ij})$, $C = (c_{ij})$, where $i, j = 1, 2$. Since $A \leq B$, we have $|a_{12}| \geq |b_{12}|$ and $\det A \leq \det B$ (Corollary 1). Then from the inequalities

$$\frac{|a_{12}|}{\det A} \geq \frac{|b_{12}|}{\det B}, \qquad (\det A)^{1/2} \leq (\det B)^{1/2}, \qquad \frac{|a_{12}|}{(\det A)^{1/2}} \geq \frac{|b_{12}|}{(\det B)^{1/2}},$$

we derive [9, p. 43]

$$\left[t \frac{|a_{12}|}{\det A} + (1 - t) \frac{|b_{12}|}{\det B} \right] \cdot \left[t(\det A)^{1/2} + (1 - t)(\det B)^{1/2} \right]^2$$

$$\geq \left[t \frac{|a_{12}|}{(\det A)^{1/2}} + (1 - t) \frac{|b_{12}|}{(\det B)^{1/2}} \right] \cdot [t(\det A)^{1/2} + (1 - t)(\det B)^{1/2}]$$

$$\geq t|a_{12}| + (1 - t)|b_{12}|.$$

Therefore, as C dominates $tA + (1 - t)B$, we have by Theorem 1

$$\left| \frac{c_{12}}{\det C} \right| \leq \frac{t|a_{12}| + (1 - t)|b_{12}|}{[t(\det A)^{1/2} + (1 - t)(\det B)^{1/2}]^2}$$

$$\leq t\frac{|a_{12}|}{\det A} + (1 - t)\frac{|b_{12}|}{\det B},$$

i.e.

$$\left| C^{-1}\binom{1}{2} \right| \leq tA^{-1}\binom{1}{2} + (1 - t)B^{-1}\binom{1}{2}.$$

Thus (20) is verified in the case $n = 2$.

Assume now $n \geq 3$. Since the hypotheses of the theorem remain fulfilled by the matrices $\tilde{A}$, $\tilde{B}$, $\tilde{C}$ of order $n - 1$ (Lemmas 3, 4), the inductive assumption gives us

$$\left| \tilde{C}^{-1}\binom{i}{j} \right| \leq t\tilde{A}^{-1}\binom{i}{j} + (1 - t)\tilde{B}^{-1}\binom{i}{j} \qquad (i, j = 1, 2, \ldots, n - 1).$$

On the other hand, it is a direct consequence of Sylvester's identity (7) that for $i, j = 1, 2, \ldots, n - 1$, we have $\tilde{C}^{-1}\binom{i}{j} = C^{-1}\binom{i}{j}$ and similar relations for A, B. Consequently inequality (20) is valid for indices i, j between 1 and $n - 1$. But any one of the indices $1, 2, \ldots, n$ could have been chosen to play the role of n in the construction of $\tilde{A}$, $\tilde{B}$, $\tilde{C}$, so (20) is valid for all i, j between 1 and n.

For inequality (21), it suffices to observe that because $tA + (1 - t)B$ is an M-matrix (Lemma 2), all elements of its inverse are nonnegative.

In case $A = B$, Theorem 2 reduces to the following result of Ostrowski [12].

Corollary 2. *If a complex matrix C of order n dominates an M-matrix A of order n, then C is nonsingular, and*

$$\left| C^{-1}\binom{i}{j} \right| \leq A^{-1}\binom{i}{j} \qquad (i, j = 1, 2, \ldots, n). \tag{22}$$

In case C is real, a topological proof for Corollaries 1 and 2 was given in [3].

Example 2. For the M-matrices

$$A = \begin{pmatrix} 5 & -3 \\ -3 & 2 \end{pmatrix}, \qquad B = \begin{pmatrix} 5/10 & -1/10 \\ -1/10 & 2/10 \end{pmatrix}$$

and $t = \frac{1}{2}$, inequality (21) is not satisfied. Here we have neither $A \leq B$ nor $B \leq A$, but B proportionally dominates A.

For the remaining part of this paper, we need the following lemma which is a special case of an earlier result [5, Theorem 2].

Lemma 5. *If a complex matrix C of order n dominates an M-matrix A of order n, then*

$$\frac{A(\alpha \cap \beta)A(\alpha \cup \beta)}{A(\alpha)A(\beta)} \leq \left| \frac{C(\alpha \cap \beta)C(\alpha \cup \beta)}{C(\alpha)C(\beta)} \right| \tag{23}$$

holds for any two subsets α, β of $\{1, 2, \ldots, n\}$.

Theorem 3. *Let A, B be M-matrices of order n such that $A \leq B$. If $0 < t < 1$ and $C = tA + (1 - t)B$, then*

$$\frac{C(k+1, \ldots, n)C(1, \ldots, n)}{C(1, \ldots, k-1, k+1, \ldots, n)C(k, \ldots, n)}$$

$$\geq t \frac{A(k+1, \ldots, n)A(1, \ldots, n)}{A(1, \ldots, k-1, k+1, \ldots, n)A(k, \ldots, n)}$$

$$+ (1-t) \frac{B(k+1, \ldots, n)B(1, \ldots, n)}{B(1, \ldots, k-1, k+1, \ldots, n)B(k, \ldots, n)} \tag{24}$$

holds for $2 \leq k \leq n$.

Proof. First we have

$$A(n) \leq B(n), \qquad \frac{A(1, \ldots, n)}{A(1, \ldots, n-1)A(n)} \leq \frac{B(1, \ldots, n)}{B(1, \ldots, n-1)B(n)}$$

(Lemma 5), which imply [9, p. 43]

$$t \frac{A(1, \ldots, n)}{A(1, \ldots, n-1)} + (1-t) \frac{B(1, \ldots, n)}{B(1, \ldots, n-1)}$$

$$\geq [tA(n) + (1-t)B(n)]$$

$$\cdot \left[t \frac{A(1, \ldots, n)}{A(1, \ldots, n-1)A(n)} + (1-t) \frac{B(1, \ldots, n)}{B(1, \ldots, n-1)B(n)} \right]. \tag{25}$$

On the other hand, since $(1 - t)B$ proportionally dominates tA, we have by (14):

$$\frac{C(1, \ldots, n)}{C(1, \ldots, n-1)} \geq t \frac{A(1, \ldots, n)}{A(1, \ldots, n-1)} + (1-t) \frac{B(1, \ldots, n)}{B(1, \ldots, n-1)}. \tag{26}$$

Combining (25), (26), we obtain

$$\frac{C(1, \ldots, n)}{C(1, \ldots, n-1)C(n)} \geq t\, \frac{A(1, \ldots, n)}{A(1, \ldots, n-1)A(n)} + (1-t)\, \frac{B(1, \ldots, n)}{B(1, \ldots, n-1)B(n)},$$

(27)

which is the case $k = n$ of (24).

Let $D = t\tilde{A} + (1-t)\tilde{B}$. Observe that $\tilde{A}, \tilde{B}, \tilde{C}, D$ are all M-matrices. By Lemmas 3 and 4, $\tilde{A} \leq \tilde{B}$, $\tilde{C} \geq D$. If we apply Lemma 5 to $\tilde{C} \geq D$ and apply (27) to the matrix $D = t\tilde{A} + (1-t)\tilde{B}$ of order $n-1$, we have

$$\frac{\tilde{C}(1, \ldots, n-1)}{\tilde{C}(1, \ldots, n-2)\tilde{C}(n-1)} \geq \frac{D(1, \ldots, n-1)}{D(1, \ldots, n-2)D(n-1)}$$

$$\geq t\, \frac{\tilde{A}(1, \ldots, n-1)}{\tilde{A}(1, \ldots, n-2)\tilde{A}(n-1)}$$

$$+ (1-t)\, \frac{\tilde{B}(1, \ldots, n-1)}{\tilde{B}(1, \ldots, n-2)\tilde{B}(n-1)},$$

which, in view of Sylvester's identity, is precisely the case $k = n-1$ of (24), i.e.

$$\frac{C(n)C(1, \ldots, n)}{C(1, \ldots, n-2, n)C(n-1, n)} \geq t\, \frac{A(n)A(1, \ldots, n)}{A(1, \ldots, n-2, n)A(n-1, n)}$$

$$+ (1-t)\, \frac{B(n)B(1, \ldots, n)}{B(1, \ldots, n-2, n)B(n-1, n)}.$$

(28)

Next, if we apply again Lemma 5 to $\tilde{C} \geq D$, and apply (28) to $D = t\,\tilde{A} + (1-t)\tilde{B}$, we obtain the case $k = n-2$ of (24). Repeating this argument, we prove successively the cases $k = n-3$, $k = n-4, \ldots$, and $k = 2$ of (24).

If we denote by A_k the principal submatrix formed by the first k rows and the first k columns of A, then by an obvious change of notation, inequality (24) may be written

$$\frac{C_k^{-1}(i)}{C^{-1}(i)} \geq t\, \frac{A_k^{-1}(i)}{A^{-1}(i)} + (1-t)\, \frac{B_k^{-1}(i)}{B^{-1}(i)} \qquad (1 \leq i \leq k \leq n-1). \quad (29)$$

Theorem 4. *Let A, B be M-matrices of order n such that $A \leq B$, and let α, β be subsets of $\{1, 2, \ldots, n\}$. If $0 < t < 1$ and $C = tA + (1-t)B$, then*

$$\frac{C(\alpha \cap \beta)C(\alpha \cup \beta)}{C(\alpha)C(\beta)} \geq \left[\frac{A(\alpha \cap \beta)A(\alpha \cup \beta)}{A(\alpha)A(\beta)}\right]^t \cdot \left[\frac{B(\alpha \cap \beta)B(\alpha \cup \beta)}{B(\alpha)B(\beta)}\right]^{1-t}. \quad (30)$$

Proof. We may assume that none of the sets α, β contains the other, for otherwise both sides of (30) are 1. Since the hypotheses remain fulfilled by corresponding principal submatrices of A, B, C, we may assume that $\alpha \cup \beta = \{1, 2, \ldots, n\}$. Then the case $n = 2$ is reduced to

$$\frac{C(1, 2)}{C(1)C(2)} \geq \left[\frac{A(1, 2)}{A(1)A(2)} \right]^t \cdot \left[\frac{B(1, 2)}{B(1)B(2)} \right]^{1-t},$$

which follows directly from Theorem 3. The general case $n > 2$ will be proved by induction on n.

Case 1. $\alpha \cap \beta \neq \varnothing$. We may assume that $n \in \alpha \cap \beta$. Let $\alpha' = \alpha - \{n\}$, $\beta' = \beta - \{n\}$, and $D = t\tilde{A} + (1 - t)\tilde{B}$. Then $\tilde{A}$, $\tilde{B}$, $\tilde{C}$, D are M-matrices, $\tilde{A} \leq \tilde{B}$ and $\tilde{C} \geq D$ (Lemmas 2–4). Lemma 5 and the inductive assumption give us

$$\frac{\tilde{C}(\alpha' \cap \beta')\tilde{C}(\alpha' \cup \beta')}{\tilde{C}(\alpha')\tilde{C}(\beta')} \geq \frac{D(\alpha' \cap \beta')D(\alpha' \cup \beta')}{D(\alpha')D(\beta')}$$

$$\geq \left[\frac{\tilde{A}(\alpha' \cap \beta')\tilde{A}(\alpha' \cup \beta')}{\tilde{A}(\alpha')\tilde{A}(\beta')} \right]^t \cdot \left[\frac{\tilde{B}(\alpha' \cap \beta')\tilde{B}(\alpha' \cup \beta')}{\tilde{B}(\alpha')\tilde{B}(\beta')} \right]^{1-t},$$

which is precisely (30), since we have by Sylvester's identity

$$\frac{\tilde{C}(\alpha' \cap \beta')\tilde{C}(\alpha' \cup \beta')}{\tilde{C}(\alpha')\tilde{C}(\beta')} = \frac{C(\alpha \cap \beta)C(\alpha \cup \beta)}{C(\alpha)C(\beta)}$$

and similar relations for A, B.

Case 2. $\alpha \cap \beta = \varnothing$. We may assume that $\alpha = \{1, 2, \ldots, k\}$, $\beta = \{k + 1, \ldots, n\}$, where $1 \leq k < n$. Applying Theorem 3 to the principal submatrices, we have

$$\frac{C(1, \ldots, k, n)}{C(1, \ldots, k)C(n)} \geq \left[\frac{A(1, \ldots, k, n)}{A(1, \ldots, k)A(n)} \right]^t \cdot \left[\frac{B(1, \ldots, k, n)}{B(1, \ldots, k)B(n)} \right]^{1-t}. \quad (31)$$

On the other hand, the result of Case 1 gives us

$$\frac{C(n)C(1, \ldots, n)}{C(1, \ldots, k, n)C(k + 1, \ldots, n)}$$

$$\geq \left[\frac{A(n)A(1, \ldots, n)}{A(1, \ldots, k, n)A(k + 1, \ldots, n)} \right]^t$$

$$\cdot \left[\frac{B(n)B(1, \ldots, n)}{B(1, \ldots, k, n)B(k + 1, \ldots, n)} \right]^{1-t}. \quad (32)$$

From (31) and (32) we get the desired inequality

$$\frac{C(1, \ldots, n)}{C(1, \ldots, k)C(k+1, \ldots, n)}$$
$$\geq \left[\frac{A(1, \ldots, n)}{A(1, \ldots, k)A(k+1, \ldots, n)}\right]^t \cdot \left[\frac{B(1, \ldots, n)}{B(1, \ldots, k)B(k+1, \ldots, n)}\right]^{1-t}.$$

Theorem 5. *Let A, B be M-matrices of order n such that $A \leq B$. Let $\alpha_1, \alpha_2, \ldots, \alpha_m$ be m subsets of $\{1, 2, \ldots, n\}$ such that each of $1, 2, \ldots, n$ is contained in exactly k of the α_i's. If $0 < t < 1$ and if a complex matrix C of order n dominates $tA + (1-t)B$, then*

$$\left|\frac{\det C^k}{\prod_{i=1}^m C(\alpha_i)}\right| \geq \left(\frac{\det A^k}{\prod_{i=1}^m A(\alpha_i)}\right)^t \left(\frac{\det B^k}{\prod_{i=1}^m B(\alpha_i)}\right)^{1-t}. \tag{33}$$

Proof. The case $n = 1$ being trivial, we may assume $n > 1$ and proceed by induction on n. We may assume that $n \in \bigcap_{i=1}^k \alpha_i$ and $n \notin \bigcup_{i=k+1}^m \alpha_i$. Let $\alpha_i' = \alpha_i - \{n\}$ for $i \leq k$, and $\alpha_i' = \alpha_i$ for $i > k$. Then each of the indices $1, 2, \ldots, n-1$ is contained in exactly k of the sets $\alpha_1', \alpha_2', \ldots, \alpha_m'$.
$\tilde{A}, \tilde{B}$ are M-matrices, and $\tilde{A} \leq \tilde{B}$ (Lemma 3). $\tilde{C}$ dominates $t\tilde{A} + (1-t)\tilde{B}$ (Lemma 4). Therefore by our inductive assumption,

$$\left|\frac{\det \tilde{C}^k}{\prod_{i=1}^m \tilde{C}(\alpha_i')}\right| \geq \left(\frac{\det \tilde{A}^k}{\prod_{i=1}^m \tilde{A}(\alpha_i')}\right)^t \left(\frac{\det \tilde{B}^k}{\prod_{i=1}^m \tilde{B}(\alpha_i')}\right)^{1-t}. \tag{34}$$

Let $D = tA + (1-t)B$. Since C dominates the M-matrix D and $n \notin \alpha_j$ for $j > k$, we have by Lemma 5 and Theorem 4:

$$\left|\frac{C(\alpha_j \cup \{n\})}{C(\alpha_j)C(n)}\right| \geq \frac{D(\alpha_j \cup \{n\})}{D(\alpha_j)D(n)}$$
$$\geq \left(\frac{A(\alpha_j \cup \{n\})}{A(\alpha_j)A(n)}\right)^t \left(\frac{B(\alpha_j \cup \{n\})}{B(\alpha_j)B(n)}\right)^{1-t} \qquad (k+1 \leq j \leq m). \tag{35}$$

On the other hand, by Sylvester's identity, we have

$$\frac{\det \tilde{C}^k}{\prod_{i=1}^m \tilde{C}(\alpha_i')} \cdot \prod_{j=k+1}^m \frac{C(\alpha_j \cup \{n\})}{C(\alpha_j)C(n)} = \frac{\det C^k}{\prod_{i=1}^m C(\alpha_i)}$$

and similar relations for A, B. Hence (33) follows from (34) and (35).

When $A = B$, Theorem 5 reduces to the following result which was obtained in [6].

Corollary 3. *Let α_1, α_2, $\ldots$, α_m be m subsets of $\{1, 2, \ldots, n\}$ such that each of $1, 2, \ldots, n$ is contained in exactly k of the α_i's. If a complex matrix C of order n dominates an M-matrix A of order n, then*

$$\left| \frac{\det C^k}{\prod\limits_{i=1}^{m} C(\alpha_i)} \right| \geq \frac{\det A^k}{\prod\limits_{i=1}^{m} A(\alpha_i)}, \tag{36}$$

$$\prod_{i=1}^{m} A(\alpha_i) \geq \det A^k. \tag{37}$$

Inequality (37) is obtained from (36) by taking C with $C(i) = A(i)$ for all i, and $C\binom{i}{j} = 0$ for $i \neq j$. The same inequality (37) was proved by Marcus [11] for positive-definite Hermitian matrices.

REFERENCES

[1] Beckenbach, E. F., and Bellman, R., "Inequalities." Springer, Berlin, 1961.

[2] Crabtree, D. E., Applications of M-matrices to non-negative matrices, *Duke Math. J.* **33**, 197–208 (1966).

[3] Fan, K., Topological proofs for certain theorems on matrices with non-negative elements, *Monatsh. Math.* **62**, 219–237 (1958).

[4] Fan, K., Note on M-matrices, *Quart. J. Math. Oxford Ser.* **11**, 43–49 (1960).

[5] Fan, K., Inequalities for M-matrices, *Proc. Koninkl. Ned. Akad. Wetenschap., Ser. A.* **67**, 602–610 (1964).

[6] Fan, K., Some matrix inequalities, *Abh. Math. Sem. Univ. Hamburg.* **29**, 185–196 (1966).

[7] Fiedler, M., and Pták, V., On matrices with non-positive off-diagonal elements and positive principal minors, *Czechoslovak Math. J.* **12**, 382–400 (1962).

[8] Gantmacher, F. R., "The Theory of Matrices," Vol. 2. Chelsea, New York, 1959.

[9] Hardy, G. H., Littlewood, J. E., and Pólya, G., "Inequalities." Cambridge Univ. Press, London and New York, 1934.

[10] Kotelyanskii, D. M., On some properties of matrices with positive elements, *Mat. Sb.* **31**, 497–506 (1952).

[11] Marcus, M., Matrix applications of a quadratic identity for decomposable symmetrized tensors, *Bull. Amer. Math. Soc.* **71**, 360–364 (1965).

[12] Ostrowski, A. M., Über die Determinanten mit überwiegender Hauptdiagonale, *Comment. Math. Helv.* **10**, 69–96 (1937).

[13] Ostrowski, A. M., Determinanten mit überwiegender Hauptdiagonale und die absolute Konvergenz von linearen Iterationsprozessen, *Comment. Math. Helv.* **30**, 175–210 (1956).

[14] Ostrowski, A. M., Iterative solution of linear systems of functional equations, *J. Math. Anal. Appl.* **2**, 351–369 (1961).

[15] Varga, R. S., "Matrix Iterative Analysis." Prentice-Hall, Englewood Cliffs, New Jersey, 1962.

On Some Inequalities and Their Application to the Cauchy Problem*

AVNER FRIEDMAN
Department of Mathematics
Northwestern University
Evanston, Illinois

1. Two Inequalities

Let A be a bounded operator in a complex Banach space X, and denote by $\sigma(A)$ the spectrum of A, and by $R(\lambda; A)$ its resolvent $(\lambda I - A)^{-1}$. If f is analytic on $\sigma(A)$, i.e., in some neighborhood W of $\sigma(A)$, then $f(A)$ is defined by [1, p. 568]

$$f(A) = \frac{1}{2\pi i} \int_{\Gamma} f(\lambda) R(\lambda; A) \, d\lambda \tag{1.1}$$

where Γ is a contour lying in $W \backslash \sigma(A)$. If $f(z)$ has a Taylor series expansion $\sum a_m z^m$ which converges in W, then $f(A) = \sum a_m A^m$. We denote by $\|A\|$ the norm of A. If A is an $N \times N$ matrix then we consider it as an operator in the complex N-dimensional Euclidean space.

First Inequality. Let A be an $N \times N$ matrix and let f be an analytic function on $\sigma(A)$ having a Taylor series expansion about $z = 0$, which converges in a neighborhood W of $\sigma(A)$. Then

$$\|f(A)\| \leq \sum_{j=0}^{N-1} 2^j \|A\|^j \underset{\lambda \in H(A)}{\text{l.u.b.}} |f^{(j)}(\lambda)|, \tag{1.2}$$

where $H(A)$ is the convex hull of the eigenvalues of A.

This result is due to Gelfand and Shilov [3].

We now derive, by a different method, an inequality of the same nature as (1.2); namely, there is a constant C depending only on N, such that, for any δ sufficiently small,

$$\|f(A)\| \leq \frac{C}{\delta^{N-1}} (1 + \|A\|)^{N-1} \underset{\lambda \in \sigma_\delta(A)}{\text{l.u.b.}} |f(\lambda)| \tag{1.3}$$

where $\sigma_\delta(A) = \{\lambda; \text{dist}[\lambda, \sigma(A)] < \delta\}$; δ is restricted only by the requirements that $\sigma_\delta(A) \subset W$ and that $\delta \leq 1$.

* This work was partially supported by the Alfred P. Sloan Foundation and by NASA Grant NGR 14-007-021.

Proof of (1.3). We employ (1.1) and shrink Γ to a contour B which, after canceling out integrals on the same arcs but in reverse orientations, has length $\leq C'\delta$ (C' depending only on N) and is such that $|\lambda - \lambda_j| \geq \delta$ for any eigenvalue λ_j of A, with equality for at least one j, and for all λ in the uncanceled part B' of B. Then $|\det(\lambda I - A)| = |(\lambda - \lambda_1)^{\alpha_1} \cdots (\lambda - \lambda_k)^{\alpha_k}| \geq \delta^{-N}$ on B'. Noting that $|\lambda| \leq \|A\| + \delta \leq \|A\| + 1$ on B', we get $\|R(\lambda; A)\| \leq C''(1 + \|A\|)^{N-1}\delta^{-N}$ on B' (C'' depending only on N), and (1.3) follows.

Second Inequality.   Consider a polynomial equation

$$\lambda^N + P_1(s)\lambda^{N-1} + \cdots + P_N(s) = 0 \tag{1.4}$$

where $P_j(s)$ are polynomials of degree p_j in the n-dimensional complex variable $s = (s_1, \ldots, s_n)$, and set

$$p_0 = \max_{1 \leq j \leq N} p_j/j.$$

Let $\lambda_j(s)$ be the roots of (1.4), and denote

$$\Lambda(s) = \max_{1 \leq j \leq N} \mathrm{Re}[\lambda_j(s)], \qquad \Lambda(r) = \max_{|s| \leq r} \Lambda(s),$$

$$M(s) = \max_{1 \leq j \leq N} |\lambda_j(s)|, \qquad M(r) = \max_{|s| \leq r} M(s).$$

Then,

$$\begin{aligned}
\Lambda(r) &= \alpha r^{p_0} + O(r^q) \qquad (\alpha > 0, \quad q < p_0), \\
M(r) &= \beta r^{p_0} + O(r^q) \qquad (\beta > 0).
\end{aligned} \tag{1.5}$$

A slightly weaker result, namely, $\Gamma(r) = O(r^{p_0})$, $\Gamma(r_m) \geq \gamma r_m^{p_0}$ for some $\gamma > 0$, $r_m \to \infty$ and $\Gamma = \Lambda$, M was proved by Gelfand and Shilov [3], but there is some gap in their proof; this is fixed up in [2], where also the more general version (1.5) is given.

2. The Cauchy Problem

Consider the problem of finding a function u satisfying

$$\frac{\partial u}{\partial t} = P\left(\sqrt{-1}\,\frac{\partial}{\partial x}\right)u \qquad (0 < t \leq T, \quad x \in R^n), \tag{2.1}$$

$$u(x, 0) = u_0(x) \qquad (x \in R^n) \tag{2.2}$$

(u is to be continuous for $0 \leq t \leq T$, $x \in R^n$) where R^n is the real n-dimensional Euclidean space; $u = (u_1, \ldots, u_N)$, $u_0 = (u_{01}, \ldots, u_{0N})$, $P(s)$ is an $N \times N$ matrix whose elements are polynomials of degree $\leq p$ in

$s = (s_1, \ldots, s_n)$; and $\partial/\partial x = (\partial/\partial x_1, \ldots, \partial/\partial x_n)$. For simplicity we take P to be independent of t, but all the results of this work extend to the case where $P = P(t, \sqrt{-1}\, \partial/\partial x)$. The system (2.1), (2.2) is called a Cauchy system. To solve it we first take, formally, the Fourier transform, and get

$$\partial v/\partial t = P(\sigma)v, \tag{2.3}$$

$$v(\sigma, 0) = v_0(\sigma), \tag{2.4}$$

whose formal solution is given by $e^{tP(\sigma)}v_0(\sigma)$ $(\sigma \in R^n)$, and then we have to analyze the inverse transform, which should yield a solution of (2.1), (2.2). Actually, this procedure is too crude and a more sophisticated procedure is needed which employs certain topological spaces and their conjugate spaces; for details the reader is referred to [2, 3].

One concludes that uniqueness holds under the assumption that

$$|u(x, t)| \leq B \exp(\beta |x|^q) \qquad \text{for} \quad 0 \leq t \leq T, \tag{2.5}$$

where B, β are positive constants, $1/q + 1/p_0 = 1$, and p_0 is defined as in Sec. 1, where (1.4) is the characteristic equation for $P(s)$.

In proving this result one has to show that $e^{tP^*(\sigma)}v_0(\sigma)$ is a solution of (2.3), (2.4) with P replaced by P^* ($P^* = $ transpose of P) in some "W space" of entire functions. This proof is based upon the relation

$$\|e^{tP(s)}\| \leq C(1 + |s|)^{(N-1)p} \exp(ct |s|^{p_0}) \tag{2.6}$$

where C, c are positive constants. Thus the uniqueness proof employs, in a substantial manner, the inequality (2.6), which in turn follows from the two inequalities of Sec. 1.

To prove existence one first reduces the problem (up to some routine estimates of integrals) to the problem of studying the inverse Fourier transform of $e^{tP(\sigma)}$ (i.e., Green's function), see [2]. Next, a better inequality than (2.6) is needed, but only for $s = \sigma$ real. One assumes that

$$\Lambda(\sigma) \leq \gamma |\sigma|^h + \delta \tag{2.7}$$

and, depending on γ, h one obtains different bounds on $e^{tP(\sigma)}$ and on its derivatives, and thus different structures for Green's function. If $\gamma < 0$, $0 < h \leq p_0$, then one can prove that there exists a classical solution of (2.1), (2.2), and that it satisfies (2.5), provided u_0 and some of its derivatives have at most an exponential growth; if $h = p_0$, it suffices to assume that $u_0(x)$ is continuous and is $O[\exp(\beta |x|^q)]$ where $0 < \beta < \beta_0 T^{-1/(p_0-1)}$, β_0 depending only on P. If $\gamma \geq 0$, then more restrictive assumptions are made on u_0 (see [2, 3]).

The Goursat problem:

$$\frac{\partial^\nu u}{\partial t_1 \cdots \partial t_2} = P\left(i \frac{\partial}{\partial x}\right) u,$$ (2.8)

$$u(x, t)\Big|_{t_i = 0} = u_{0i}(x, t_1, \ldots, t_{i-1}, t_{i+1}, \ldots, t_\nu) \qquad (i = 1, \ldots, \nu)$$

can be handled along the same lines (see [2]). Instead of $e^{tP(s)}$ we now have to deal with $\sum_{m=0}^{\infty} [P(s)]^m/(m!)^\nu$. Uniqueness holds under the assumption (2.5) where $1/q + \nu/p_0 = 1$. Existence theorems can also be derived, but there is a remarkable difference between the case $\nu = 2$ where solutions exist under "reasonable" conditions on u_0 (i.e., a finite number of derivatives of u_0 are assumed to exist and to be bounded by $O(|x|^\gamma)$ for some γ) and on the eigenvalues of $P(\sigma)$, and the case $\nu > 2$ where very restrictive assumptions on u_0 are required.

3. Additional Inequalities

We consider some generalizations of the first inequality of Sec. 1 to general bounded operators A. The last result of this section will be used in a substantial manner in Sec. 4.

Proposition 1.   *If $\|A\| < r$ and f is analytic in $|\lambda| \leq r$, then*

$$\|f(A)\| \leq \frac{r}{r - \|A\|} \operatorname*{l.u.b.}_{|\lambda| \leq r} |f(\lambda)|.$$ (3.1)

This follows from (1.1) upon using Neumann's series for $R(\lambda; A)$. A better result holds in Hilbert spaces (but is false in Banach spaces!).

Proposition 2.   *Let A be a bounded operator in a Hilbert space X, and let f be an analytic function in $|\lambda| \leq \|A\|$. Then*

$$\|f(A)\| \leq \operatorname*{l.u.b.}_{|\lambda| \leq \|A\|} |f(\lambda)|.$$ (3.2)

This result is due to von Neumann [5]; a simpler proof was given by Heinz [4] (see also [6]). It is also proved in [5] (and in [4]) that if

$$\operatorname{Re}(A\varphi, \varphi) \geq 0 \qquad \text{for all} \quad \varphi \in X,$$ (3.3)

then $(A - I)(A + I)^{-1}$ exists and has a norm ≤ 1. Employing Proposition 2, one gets:

Proposition 3.   *Let A be a bounded operator in a Hilbert space X and assume that it satisfies (3.3). If f is an entire function then*

$$\|f(A)\| \leq \operatorname*{l.u.b.}_{\operatorname{Re} \lambda \geq 0} |f(\lambda)|.$$ (3.4)

4. The Cauchy Problem for Infinite Systems

We extend the results of Sec. 2 to an infinite system of equations, i.e.,

$$\frac{\partial u_i}{\partial t} = \sum_{j=1}^{\infty} p_{ij}\left(\sqrt{-1}\,\frac{\partial}{\partial x}\right)u_j \qquad (i = 1, 2, \ldots), \qquad (4.1)$$

$$u_i(x, 0) = u_{0i}(x) \qquad\qquad (i = 1, 2, \ldots). \qquad (4.2)$$

At this point we have to introduce the space $W_{p,a}^{p,b}$ which occurs in the case of finite systems. $W_{p,a}^{p,b}$ is a Fréchet space whose elements are those entire functions $f(z)$ $[z = (z_1, \ldots, z_n)]$ satisfying

$$|f(z)| \leq C' \exp\left[-\frac{a'}{p}\,|x|^p + \frac{b'}{p}\,|y|^p\right] \qquad (z = x + iy)$$

for all $a' < a$, $b' > b$ where C' is a constant depending on a', b', f. The metric is given by a sequence of norms $\|f\|_j = \sup\, M_j(z)\,|\varphi(z)|$ $(j = 1, 2, \ldots)$ where

$$M_j(z) = \exp\left[a\left(1 - \frac{1}{j}\right)\frac{|x|^p}{p} - b\left(1 + \frac{1}{j}\right)\frac{|y|^p}{p}\right];$$

i.e.,

$$d(f, g) = \sum_{j=1}^{\infty} \frac{1}{2^j}\,\frac{\|f - g\|_j}{1 + \|f - g\|_j}.$$

In the case of Sec. 2, the component u_j is considered as a functional over W_j, where $W_j = W_{p,a}^{p,b}$ for all j. In the present case we introduce the direct product $\prod_{j=1}^{\infty} W_j$, and the metric

$$\hat{d}(\varphi, \psi) = \sum_{j=1}^{\infty} \frac{1}{2^j}\,\frac{\|\varphi - \psi\|_j}{1 + \|\varphi - \psi\|_j} \qquad \text{where} \quad \|\varphi\|_j = \sum_{i=1}^{\infty} \|\varphi_i\|_j\,; \qquad (4.3)$$

here $\varphi = (\varphi_1, \varphi_2, \ldots)$, $\psi = (\psi_1, \psi_2, \ldots)$. The elements φ with $\|\varphi\|_j < \infty$ for $j = 1, 2, \ldots$ form a Fréchet space $\hat{W}_{p,a}^{p,b}$.

Assume now that

$$|p_{ij}(s)| \leq \pi_{ij}(1 + |s|^p), \qquad \pi_{ij} \text{ constants}, \qquad \sup_i \sum_{j=1}^{\infty} \pi_{ij} \leq \gamma < \infty. \qquad (4.4)$$

In order to prove uniqueness for (4.1), (4.2), we proceed as in the case of finite systems and thus reduce the problem to showing that

$$\psi(\sigma, t) = e^{tP^*(\sigma)}\psi_0(\sigma) \qquad (\psi_0 \in \hat{W}_{p,b}^{p,a}, \quad P^* = \text{transpose of } P)$$

is a solution in $\hat{W}_{p,\,a-c}^{p,\,b+c}$ (for some $c < a$) of

$$\frac{\partial \psi}{\partial t} = P^*(\sigma)\psi, \qquad \psi(\sigma, 0) = \psi_0. \tag{4.5}$$

(It is actually enough to consider ψ_0 with all but one component equal to zero.)

Since

$$\sum_{i=1}^{\infty} |(P^*(s)\psi(s, t))_i| \le (1 + |s|^p) \sum_{i=1}^{\infty} \sum_{j=1}^{\infty} \pi_{ji} |\psi_j(s)| \le \gamma(1 + |s|^p) \sum_{j=1}^{\infty} |\psi_j(s)|,$$

it follows that P^* is a bounded operator in $\hat{W}_{p,\,a}^{p,\,b}$. Next,

$$\sum_{i=1}^{\infty} |(e^{tP^*(s)}\psi(s, t))_i| \le \sum_{i=1}^{\infty} \sum_{m=0}^{\infty} \left| \left[\frac{t^m (P^*(s))^m}{m!} \psi(s, t) \right]_i \right|$$

$$\le \sum_{m=0}^{\infty} \frac{\gamma^m t^m (1 + |s|)^{pm}}{m!} \sum_{i=1}^{\infty} |\psi_i(s)|$$

$$= \exp[\gamma t (1 + |s|)^p] \sum_{i=1}^{\infty} |\psi_i(s)|,$$

and we thus find that $\psi(s, t)$ is in $\hat{W}_{p,\,a-c}^{p,\,b+c}$ for some $c < a$ (depending on γ, T). The proof that $\psi(\sigma, t)$ satisfies (4.5) follows without difficulty (cf. [2]). We thus obtain the following uniqueness theorem:

Theorem 1. *If* (4.4) *holds, then there exists at most one classical solution of* (4.1), (4.2) *satisfying*

$$|u_i(x, t)| \le C e^{\beta |x|^q} \qquad \left(\frac{1}{q} + \frac{1}{p} = 1 \right) \tag{4.6}$$

for some $C > 0$, $\beta > 0$ and $x \in R^n$, $0 \le t \le T$, $i = 1, 2, \ldots$.

As in [2], [3] the condition (4.6) can be replaced by

$$\int_{R^n} |u_i(x, t)| \exp[-\beta |x|^q]\, dx \le C. \tag{4.7}$$

Consider now the question of existence. As in the case of a finite system, a "generalized solution" always exists, and we wish to prove that it is also a solution in the classical sense. For this we need to make some differentiability and boundedness assumptions on $u_0(x)$, and also put some conditions on $P(\sigma)$. In the finite case we impose conditions on the eigenvalues $\lambda_i(\sigma)$ of $P(\sigma)$. In the present infinite case we give a different kind of condition on $P(\sigma)$ which will turn out to have the same effect as in the finite case.

We wish to consider $e^{tP(\sigma)}$ as a bounded operator in l^2. We thus need to know that $P(\sigma)$ is a bounded operator in l^2. For this it suffices to assume that

$$\sum_{i=1}^{\infty} \sum_{j=1}^{\infty} |p_{ij}(\sigma)|^2 < \infty. \tag{4.8}$$

We now impose the following condition: For any $\sigma \in R^n$,

$$\mathrm{Re}[P(\sigma)v, \ v] \leq (-C|\sigma|^h + C_1)(v, v) \qquad (C > 0, \quad 0 < h \leq p) \tag{4.9}$$

where $(v, w) = \sum v_i \bar{w}_i$. If $h = p$, $C_1 = 0$, and P is equal to its principal part, then this condition is known as the *strong ellipticity condition* for P.

Using (4.9) and applying Proposition 3, we deduce

$$\|e^{tP(\sigma)}\| \leq C_0 \exp[-tC|\sigma|^h] \qquad (C_0 = e^{T|C_1|}) \tag{4.10}$$

where $e^{tP(\sigma)}$ is considered as an operator in l^2. Thus, in particular,

$$\sum_{j=1}^{\infty} |(e^{tP(\sigma)})_{ij}|^2 \leq C_0 \exp[-tC|\sigma|^h]. \tag{4.11}$$

Using this bound one can now analyze Green's function $G(x, t)$ (i.e., the inverse Fourier transform of $e^{tP(\sigma)}$) and then the abstract convolution $G(x, t) * u_0(x)$. This is done along the same lines as for finite systems, and we obtain analogous existence theorems. The cases where $C = 0$, $C < 0$ can be treated in a similar manner. We list below just two results which are thus obtained (one could easily write down all the other existence theorems by following the arguments for finite systems):

Theorem 2. *If $h = p$ in (4.9), then for any continuous function $u_0(x)$ whose components satisfy*

$$|u_{0j}(x)| \leq C_j \exp[\gamma |x|^q], \quad \sum_{j=1}^{\infty} C_j^2 < \infty, \qquad 0 < \gamma \leq \gamma_0 T^{-1/(p-1)} \tag{4.12}$$

(γ_0 depending only on P), there exists a classical solution of (4.1), (4.2) satisfying (4.6) for some constants C, β.

Theorem 3. *If $C = 0$ in (4.9) and if for some $\nu \geq 0$, $\gamma > 0$ the first $p + \nu + n$ derivatives of $u_0(x)$ are continuous functions satisfying*

$$\left| \frac{\partial^i}{\partial x^i} u_{0j}(x) \right| \leq C_j(1 + |x|)^\nu, \quad \sum_{j=1}^{\infty} C_j^2 < \infty \qquad (0 \leq i \leq p + n + \nu) \tag{4.13}$$

where $\gamma + n + 1 \leq \nu/\mu$ ($\mu > 0$ depending only on P), then there exists a classical solution of (4.1), (4.2) satisfying

$$\left| \frac{\partial^i}{\partial x^i} u_j(x, t) \right| \leq C(1 + |x|)^\nu \qquad (0 \leq i \leq p). \tag{4.14}$$

If $p = 1$ and $C = 0$ in (4.9), then we have the same situation as in the finite hyperbolic case where Green's function has a compact support.

The norms and metric in (4.3) were chosen quite arbitrarily; other definitions can be made and we then obtain variants of the previous results. Thus if we modify the definition (4.3) by setting $\|\varphi\|_j = \sup_i \|\varphi_i\|_j$ and then modify (4.4) by replacing the last condition by

$$\sup_j \sum_{i=1}^{\infty} \pi_{ij} \leq \gamma,$$

then Theorem 1 remains true if in (4.6) C is replaced by C_i and $\sum C_i < \infty$.

We finally wish to observe that our results do not yield anything new in the case of finite systems. In fact, the condition (4.9) implies the condition (2.7) with $\gamma = -C$. This follows from the obvious inequality

$$e^{t\Lambda(\sigma)} \leq \|e^{tP(\sigma)}\| \tag{4.15}$$

(as $e^{t\lambda_i(\sigma)}$ are the eigenvalues of $e^{tP(\sigma)}$) and (4.10). From (4.10), (4.15) we also get:

Corollary. *If P is strongly elliptic, then $\partial u / \partial t = Pu$ is parabolic in the sense of Petrowski (i.e., $h = p_0 = p$).*

REFERENCES

[1] Dunford, N., and Schwartz, J. T., "Linear Operators," Part I: General Theory. Wiley (Interscience), New York, 1958.
[2] Friedman, A., "Generalized Functions and Partial Differential Equations." Prentice-Hall, Englewood Cliffs, New Jersey, 1963.
[3] Gelfand, I. M., and Shilov, G. E., "Generalized Functions," Vol. 3: "Some Questions in the Theory of Differential Equations." Gosudarstvennoe, Moscow, 1958. [English transl.: Academic Press, New York, 1967.]
[4] Heinz, E., Ein v. Neumannscher Satz über beschränkte Operatoren im Hilbertschen Raum, *Göttinger Nachr.* pp. 5–6 (1952).
[5] von Neumann, J., Eine Spektraltheorie für allgemeine Operatoren eine unitären Raumes, *Math. Nachr.* **4,** 258–281 (1950–51).
[6] Riesz, F., and Sz.-Nagy, B., "Leçons D'Analyse Fonctionelle." Acad. Sci. Hongrie, 1953.

General Subaddittive Functions*

R. P. GOSSELIN
University of Connecticut
Storrs, Connecticut

Introduction

The purpose of this paper is to give a unified presentation of some aspects
of a class of functions which include subadditive functions as a very special
case. Previously, special methods have been used to treat special cases (cf.
[1–3]). The results center around integral norms of the form

$$\left\{ \int_{R_k} \frac{|\phi^p(u)|}{|u|^{k+p\alpha}} \, du \right\}^{1/p}, \qquad 0 < p \leq \infty, \quad \alpha \text{ real}$$

where R_k denotes k-dimensional Euclidean space. The functions to be considered are those which satisfy point inequalities: i.e. those involving the
evaluation of the function at individual points. For example, if ϕ is an
ordinary subadditive function, it satisfies

$$\phi(u + v) \leq \phi(u) + \phi(v)$$

To avoid pathological situations, we insist that all functions considered be
measurable. Since we are dealing with integral norms, the functions will all
be nonnegative and normally finite everywhere.

There are two kinds of point inequalities to be considered:

(I) $$\phi(u + v) \leq C \sum_{i=1}^{N} \phi(a_i u + b_i v), \qquad C > 0, \quad a_i \neq b_i$$

(II) $$\phi(u) \leq C \sum_{i=1}^{N} \phi(a_i u + b_i v), \qquad C > 0, \quad b_i \neq 0$$

The parameters N, C, a_i, b_i may change with the function, but the integral
inequalities obtained from (I) and (II) will depend upon these parameters.
Inequalities (I) and (II) automatically make sense if the domain is R_k.
Occasionally, we shall consider other domains such as the interval $(0, \infty)$,
and then appropriate modifications must be made so that they are satisfied
for some u and v. We note that (II) is a kind of evenness requirement. Thus,

* This research was supported by the National Science Foundation Grant
GP-4580.

if ϕ is subadditive and also an even function, then $\phi(u) \leq \phi(u+v) + \phi(v)$, which is of type (II). We note that, because of the positivity requirement, any positive multiple or positive power of a function satisfying (I) or (II) will satisfy an inequality of the same form. The same applies to the sum of two such functions.

1. Generalized Subadditivity

Given two nonnegative functions μ defined on R_j, and ϕ defined on R_k, where j is not necessarily equal to k, it may happen that there exist constants A, B, and C such that $C > 0$, $0 < A < B < \infty$, and such that for $u \neq 0$

$$\mu(u) \leq \frac{C}{|u|^k} \int_{A|u| \leq |v| \leq B|u|} \phi(v) \, dv \tag{1}$$

The integration then takes place over an annular region in R_k. This is susceptible to modification (cf. [3] where spherical regions were used), but it is convenient for our purposes. If $j = k$, and if $\mu = \phi$, we say that ϕ is *generalized subadditive*. We note that nonnegative subharmonic functions in R_k are generalized subadditive. The importance of (1) lies in the following result.

Theorem A. *Let μ and ϕ satisfy (1). Let $1 \leq p < q \leq \infty$, and let α be real. Then*

$$\left(\int_{R_j} \frac{\mu^q(u)}{|u|^{j+q\alpha}} \, du \right)^{1/q} \leq C \left(\int_{R_k} \frac{\phi^p(u)}{|u|^{k+p\alpha}} \, du \right)^{1/p}$$

The constant C appearing in the right-hand side depends upon α, p, q, j, k, and the constants appearing in (1). It should be pointed out that, since the measure used is $du/|u|^k$, the $q = \infty$ norm refers to ess sup $\mu(u)/|u|^\alpha$. The proof of Theorem A is very close to the proof of the corresponding result in [3] and need not be repeated.

If ϕ is generalized subadditive, Theorem A gives a comparison for different integral norms of ϕ. This is the significance of our first theorem.

Theorem 1. *If ϕ satisfies (I) on R_k, then it is generalized subadditive.*

For $u \neq 0$, we write

$$\phi(u) = \phi[(u-v)+v] \leq C \sum_{i=1}^{N} \phi[a_i(u-v)+b_i v]$$

Both sides are to be integrated (with respect to v) over $S(u)$ which is a ball of radius $\rho|u|$ about σu. σ is to be chosen first so that $a_i + (b_i - a_i)\sigma \neq 0$ for each i, and then ρ so that

$$0 < \rho < |a_i + (b_i - a_i)\sigma|/|b_i - a_i|$$

Hence

$$|u|^k \phi(u) \le C \sum_{i=1}^{N} \int_{S(u)} \phi[a_i u + (b_i - a_i)v] \, dv$$

For the ith term, we write

$$w = u[a_i + \sigma(b_i - a_i)] + (b_i - a_i)(v - \sigma u)$$

From this it follows that

$$|u| \{|a_i + \sigma(b_i - a_i)| - \rho |b_i - a_i|\}$$
$$\le |w_i| \le |u| \{|a_i + \sigma(b_i - a_i)| + |b_i - a_i| \rho\}$$

Thus, because of the conditions on σ and ρ, each w_i is restricted to an annular region; and the constants A and B of (1) can be chosen in an obvious way. We remark that we may always take $B > 1$ and $A < 1$ by enlarging the region of integration so that (1) becomes a mean-value condition.

The restriction that $a_i \ne b_i$ for each i in condition (I) is, of course, not necessary for ϕ to be generalized subadditive; for, given ϕ satisfying (I), we may always add a term $\phi(u + v)$ to the right-hand side. However, this restriction does rule out certain nontrivial situations for which there is no generalized subadditivity. For definiteness, we consider $N = 1$ and $a_1 = b_1 = 2$: i.e., $\phi(u) \le \phi(2u)$ if $C = 1$. We construct a function satisfying this inequality on R_1 which is not generalized subadditive. Let $\phi(u) = 0$ for $u \le 0$. Let $\phi(2^{-n}) = 1$ for $n = 1, 2, \ldots$. Let $\phi(2^{-n} \pm 8^{-n}) = 0$, and let ϕ be linear in the intervals $(2^{-n} - 8^{-n}, 2^{-n})$ and $(2^{-n}, 2^{-n} + 8^{-n})$. Thus, in $(0, 5/8)$, ϕ is a sum of "roof" functions. Finally, let $\phi(u) = 1$ if $3/4 \le u$. It is not hard to verify that $\phi(u) \le \phi(2u)$. In fact, if u lies under a roof with peak at 2^{-n}, then either $\phi(2u) = 1$, or $2u$ lies under a roof with peak at 2^{-n+1}. Since the slopes of the roofs decrease in absolute value to the right, then $\phi(u) \le \phi(2u)$. ϕ cannot be generalized subadditive, for if $u = 2^{-n}$, $\phi(u) = 1$. But the integral

$$2^n \int_{A2^{-n}}^{B2^{-n}} \phi(v) \, dv$$

must be small with fixed A and B and large n.

2. A Maximal Theorem

The maximal function corresponding to the nonnegative function ϕ on R_k is defined to be

$$\mu(t) = \sup_{0 < |u| \le t} \phi(u), \qquad t > 0$$

The definition of μ may be extended to all of R_1 by evenness and by taking $\mu(0) = 0$. If μ and ϕ satisfy (1), then according to Theorem A certain integrals involving μ and ϕ are comparable. It is not hard to see that, in this case, the inequalities can be reversed. The next theorem indicates when (1) will be satisfied and is a generalization of a result of [3].

Theorem 2. *Let ϕ satisfy* (I) *and* (II) *on R_k. Then μ, the maximal function of ϕ, and ϕ satisfy* (1).

We first prove the theorem in one dimension. According to Theorem 1, ϕ is generalized subadditive on R_1. Hence, there exist constants A, B, and C such that

$$\phi(u) \leq \frac{C}{|u|} \int_{A|u| \leq |v| \leq B|u|} \phi(v) \, dv$$

Let us fix $t > 0$. If $Dt \leq |u| \leq t$, $D > 0$, then

$$\phi(u) \leq \frac{C}{Dt} \int_{ADt \leq |v| \leq Bt} \phi(v) \, dv \tag{2}$$

At a later stage we impose some conditions on D. Now let u satisfy $0 < |u| \leq Dt$. According to the inequality (II),

$$\phi(u) \leq \frac{C}{|u|} \int_{A|u| \leq |v| \leq B|u|} \phi(v) \, dv$$

$$\leq C' \sum_{i=1}^{N} \frac{1}{|u|} \int_{A|u| \leq |v| \leq B|u|} \phi(a_i v + b_i w) \, dv$$

where w may be chosen at our convenience. It is convenient to isolate those terms for which $a_i = 0$. Thus

$$\phi(u) \leq C' \sum_{a_i = 0} \phi(b_i w) + \frac{C'}{|u|} \sum_{a_i \neq 0} \int_{A|u| \leq |v| \leq B|u|} \phi(a_i v + b_i w) \, dv \tag{3}$$

It is required to prove the existence of constants $C' > 0$, $0 < A' < B'$ such that if $0 < |u| = t$,

$$\phi(u) \leq \frac{C'}{t} \int_{A't \leq |v| = B't} \phi(v) \, dv$$

This has already been done in (2) if $Dt \leq |u| \leq t$, and we have now assumed that $0 < |u| \leq Dt$. We consider the terms $\phi(b_i w)$ in the first sum on the right-hand side of (3). We choose a w such that $(1 - D)t \leq w \leq 2t$. Then, by the generalized subadditivity of ϕ,

$$\phi(b_i w) \le \frac{C_1}{t} \int_{A_1 t \le |v| \le B_1 t} \phi(v) \, dv; \qquad A_1 = A(1-D) \min_i |b_i|$$

$$B_1 = 2B \max_i |b_i|$$

$$C_1 = \frac{C}{(1-D) \min_i |b_i|}$$

To motivate our choice of w we introduce the function

$$\chi(s) = \sum_{a_i \neq 0} \frac{1}{a_i} \int_{-a_i B|u| + b_i s}^{-a_i A|u| + b_i s} \phi(v) \, dv + \sum_{a_i \neq 0} \frac{1}{a_i} \int_{a_i A|u| + b_i s}^{a_i B|u| + b_i s} \phi(v) \, dv,$$

$$t - |u| \le s \le 2(t - |u|)$$

Note that with $s = w$, $\chi(s)$ is, apart from a factor $C'/|u|$, the second term on the right of (3). Being continuous in the given interval, χ has a minimum at s_0, say. For the completion of the proof of the theorem for the case $k = 1$, it is enough to show that by taking $w = s_0$ in (3), there exist constants A', B', and C' such that $C' > 0$, $0 < A' < B'$, and

$$\frac{\chi(s_0)}{|u|} \le \frac{C'}{t} \int_{A't \le |v| \le B't} \phi(v) \, dv \tag{4}$$

Since $0 < |u| < Dt$,

$$(1-D)t\chi(s_0) \le (t - |u|)\chi(s_0) \le \int_{t-|u|}^{2(t-|u|)} \chi(s) \, ds$$

Substituting the defining expression for χ, interchanging the order of integration, and enlarging the region of integration somewhat shows that

$$\int_{t-|u|}^{2(t-|u|)} \chi(s) \, ds \le (B-A)|u| \sum_{a_i \neq 0} \frac{1}{b_i} \left\{ \int_{b_i(t-|u|) - a_i B|u|}^{2b_i(t-|u|) - a_i A|u|} \phi(v) \, dv \right.$$

$$\left. + \int_{b_i(t-|u|) + a_i A|u|}^{2b_i(t-|u|) + a_i B|u|} \phi(v) \, dv \right\}.$$

The condition to be imposed on D is as follows: D is to be so small that

$$\frac{1}{D} - 1 > B \frac{\max_i |a_i|}{\min_i |b_i|}$$

Now it is possible to estimate the limits in the above integrals. Thus

$$|b_i(t - |u|) - a_i B|u|| \ge \min_i |b_i|(1 - D)t - \max_i |a_i| BDt \ge A't.$$

Similar estimates hold for the other limits. It is to be noted that the first term in each limit dominates and the sign of the integral is determined by the sign of b_i. If this is negative, it is counteracted by the factor $1/b_i$. These estimates prove (4) and the theorem for the case $k = 1$.

We now proceed to the proof of Theorem 2 for ϕ satisfying (I) and (II) on R_k, $k > 1$. First, let us note that if ω is a fixed unit vector in R_k, then ϕ satisfies (I) and (II) when u and v are restricted to the one-dimensional subspace $\{r\omega\}$ where r is real. Hence, according to the result already proved,

$$\sup_{0 < |r| \le t} \phi(r\omega) \le \frac{C}{t} \int_{At \le |r| \le Bt} \phi(r\omega) \, dr \le 2C(B - A) \sup_{At \le |r| \le Bt} \phi(r\omega)$$

Since the constants A, B, and C depended only on the constants occurring in (I) and (II), they may be fixed for all unit vectors ω. Thus,

$$\mu(t) = \sup_{0 < |u| \le t} \phi(u) \le 2C(B - A) \sup_{At \le |u| \le Bt} \phi(u)$$

But ϕ is generalized subadditive on R_k. Hence, there exist constants A', B', and C' such that

$$\phi(u) \le \frac{C'}{|u|^k} \int_{A'|u| \le |v| \le B'|u|} \phi(v) \, dv$$

and so

$$\mu(t) \le \frac{2CC'(B - A)}{A^k t^k} \int_{AA't \le |v| \le BB't} \phi(v) \, dv$$

This is condition (1), and the theorem is proved.

To justify the hypotheses of Theorem 2, we first note that if μ, the maximal function of ϕ, satisfies (1), then ϕ is certainly generalized subadditive. The inequality (I) is more or less a natural condition for generalized subadditivity. It is not hard to prove a variant of Theorem 2 for ϕ generalized subadditive on the interval $(0, \infty)$ and satisfying there the inequality (II) if the condition $b_i \ne 0$ is replaced by the stronger condition $b_i > 0$. Nonnegative and decreasing fuctions are generalized subadditive on $(0, \infty)$; but, since their maximal functions are constants, no general maximal theorem is possible for them. The extra condition required for a maximal theorem is, for our result, inequality (II).

3. A Restriction Theorem

The point of our last theorem is that for ϕ satisfying (I) on R_k, its norm is not appreciably increased when it is restricted to certain one-dimensional subspaces. This result represents a generalization of one in [2] which applied only to subadditive functions and for which the proof was more difficult than the present one.

Theorem 3. *Let ϕ satisfy* (I) *on* R_k, $k > 1$. *Given* α *real and* $0 < p \leq \infty$, *there exists a constant* C *depending only on* α, p, k *and the constants occurring in* (I) *such that*

$$\int_0^\infty \frac{\phi^p(r\omega)}{r^{1+p\alpha}} \, dr \leq C \int_{R_k} \frac{\phi^p(u)}{|u|^{k+p\alpha}} \, du$$

for every unit vector ω.

Let M denote the integral on the right above, and $M(\omega)$ the integral on the left. Then

$$\int_\Omega M(\omega) \, d\omega = M$$

where Ω denotes the unit sphere in R_k and $d\omega$ denotes spherical measure. By the homogeneity of the inequality, M may be taken to equal 1. It is required to find a C such that $M(\omega) \leq CM$ for all ω. Given $\varepsilon > 0$, there exists a constant D and a measurable subset Γ of Ω such that $M(\omega) \leq DM$ for all ω in Γ, and $|\Gamma|_s \geq |\Omega|_s - \varepsilon$ where $|\Gamma|_s$ denotes the spherical measure of Γ. The choice of ε is specified below.

Given $0 < A < B$, let K denote the set $\{r\omega \,|\, \omega$ in $\Gamma,\ A \leq r \leq B\}$. Let us assume temporarily that the constants A, B, and ε may be chosen so that for each ω_0 of Ω, the set

$$\bigcap_{i=1}^N \frac{K - b_i\omega_0}{a_i - b_i} \tag{5}$$

is nonempty. The constants a_i, b_i refer to those occurring in (I), and $(K - b_i\omega_0)/(a_i - b_i)$ denotes the set K translated by $-b_i\omega_0$ and then multiplied by the scalar $1/(a_i - b_i)$. If this is so, then we may proceed as follows.

Let $\rho\omega$ denote a point of the set (5). Then $(a_i - b_i)\rho\omega + b_i\omega_0$ belongs to K for each i. Hence there exist unit vectors ω_i in Γ and scalars r_i, $A \leq r_i \leq B$, such that

$$(a_i - b_i)\rho\omega + b_i\omega_0 = r_i\omega_i, \qquad i = 1, 2, \ldots, N$$

By (I),

$$\phi(r\omega_0) = \phi[r\rho\omega + (r\omega_0 - r\rho\omega)] \leq C \sum_{i=1}^N \phi[a_i r\rho\omega + b_i r(\omega_0 - \rho\omega)]$$

$$= C \sum_{i=1}^N \phi(rr_i\omega_i)$$

Dividing by $r^{1+p\alpha}$ and integrating gives

$$M(\omega_0) \leq C(A^{p\alpha} + B^{p\alpha}) \sum_{i=1}^N M(\omega_i) \leq CN(A^{p\alpha} + B^{p\alpha})DM$$

The last inequality follows from the fact that each ω_i belongs to Γ.

In view of this argument, it is enough to establish that the set (5) is non-empty for each ω_0 of Ω. To accomplish this we first choose B so large that

$$\max_i \{|b_i| + |a_i - b_i|\} < B$$

Let S_a denote the ball of radius a with center at the origin, and let $|S_a|$ denote its k-dimensional measure. We now choose ε and A so small that

$$\delta = \frac{A^k}{k} |\Omega|_s + \frac{B^k - A^k}{k} \varepsilon < |S_1| \min_i \frac{|a_i - b_i|^k}{N}$$

It is clear that $K \subset S_B$, and a simple computation shows that

$$|K| \geq |S_B| - \delta$$

Now let us define the sets

$$K_i = \left(\frac{K - b_i\omega_0}{a_i - b_i}\right) \cap S_1, \qquad i = 1, 2, \ldots, N$$

To show that the set (5) is nonempty, it is enough to show that the intersection of the sets K_i is nonempty. Let

$$J_i = K \cap (S_{c_i} + b_i\omega_0), \qquad c_i = |a_i - b_i|$$

and so

$$K_i = \frac{J_i - b_i\omega_0}{a_i - b_i}$$

Since $K \subset S_B$, and since $c_i + |b_i| < B$, then $J_i \subset S_B$. Furthermore

$$|S_{c_i}| - \delta \leq |J_i|$$

since otherwise the part of S_B which does not intersect K would have measure exceeding δ. Thus

$$|K_i| = \left|\frac{J_i - b_i\omega_0}{a_i - b_i}\right| = \left|\frac{J_i}{a_i - b_i}\right| = \frac{|J_i|}{c_i^k} \geq \frac{|S_{c_i}|}{c_i^k} - \frac{\delta}{c_i^k} > |S_1|\left(1 - \frac{1}{N}\right)$$

Let $\tilde{K}_i$ denote the complement of K_i with respect to S_1. Then

$$\left|\bigcup_{i=1}^{N} \tilde{K}_i\right| \leq \sum_{i=1}^{N} |\tilde{K}_i| < |S_1|$$

This implies that the K_i's have a nonempty intersection so that the set (5) is nonempty. The proof of the theorem is complete.

It is worth noting that in the special case that ϕ is subadditive there is a converse to Theorem 3 (cf. [2].)

REFERENCES

[1] Gosselin, R. P., Some integral inequalities, *Proc. Amer. Math. Soc.* **13,** 378–384 (1962).

[2] Gosselin, R. P., Integral norms of subadditive functions, *Bull. Amer. Math. Soc.* **69,** 255–259 (1963).

[3] Gosselin, R. P., A maximal theorem for subadditive functions, *Acta Math.* **112,** 163–180 (1964).

Chebyshevian Spline Functions*

SAMUEL KARLIN
Department of Mathematics
Stanford University, Stanford, California
and
ZVI ZIEGLER
Department of Mathematics
Technion—Israel Institute of Technology
Haifa, Israel

Introduction

In recent years there has been a flurry of interest in the theory of approximation of functions and best quadrature formulas involving spline functions. Polynomial spline functions, i.e., functions which are piecewise polynomials, were first introduced by Schoenberg in 1946 while investigating various problems pertaining to smoothing of data [12]. Some minimality properties for certain cubic splines were discovered by Holladay [5] in 1957. Later Schoenberg [13] uncovered a relation between spline functions and mechanical quadrature, and subsequently Schoenberg [14] unraveled the relation between spline functions and Sard's [11] "best formula" for approximation to certain linear operators. In 1963 de Boor [2] developed smoothing and best-mean-square approximation properties for spline functions utilizing an elegant method relying on a basic interpolation theorem of Schoenberg and Whitney [17]. de Bruijn informed us in a private communication that he obtained de Boor's results independently. His approach is similar to that of Walsh *et al.* [18].

All the above considerations were restricted to ordinary spline polynomials. In 1964 Schoenberg [15] initiated an important departure from the restricted class of polynomial splines through the concept of trigonometric splines, and derived for them several of their extremal properties. We further call attention to Walsh *et al.* [18] and [19] who dealt with some versions of approximation of periodic functions by polynomial splines suitably extended periodically.

* Work supported in part by Contract Nonr. 225(28) and NSF Grant GP 2487 at Stanford University.

Greville [4] and Ahlberg *et al.* [1] introduced splines corresponding to a general linear differential equation and developed the analogues of de Boor's results concerning best-mean-square approximation of functions by these generalized spline functions. Recently, de Boor and Lynch [3] examined the theory of spline approximation in the framework of finite-dimensional Hilbert spaces possessing a reproducing kernel. Their approach is natural and offers an intrinsic abstract formulation of the theory. However, in their set-up, the results are limited in that it is necessary in each concrete case to compute the reproducing kernel of the relevant Hilbert space which is usually a formidable task.

In this paper we investigate smoothness and approximation properties of a wide class of spline functions associated with a general linear differential operator of the type possessing "property W" in the sense of Pólya [9]. We call them Chebyshevian spline functions for reasons that will be apparent in our discussions of Sec. 1. We should point out that Ahlberg *et al.* and Greville in their work were also in essence restricted to differential operators possessing "property W."

The most significant contribution of this paper rests in that we can handle completely the interpolation problem for the case of spline functions admitting *multiple* knots where the interpolation points need not coincide with the knots.

The importance of the case of multiple knots was underscored by Schoenberg who pointed out that many of the classical quadrature formulas involve spline polynomials with actual multiple knots. These include, specifically, Hermite's quadrature formula, the Euler–Maclaurin summation formula, some examples of Sard [11] and others (see Schoenberg [16]). The analysis for the case of multiple knots seems to be considerably more difficult. We direct special attention to Theorem 3 of Sec. 2 which embodies the demonstration that a function and its derivatives at prescribed knots can be interpolated uniquely by a natural Chebyshevian spline (see Definition 3). The analysis rests on Theorem 2 which gives precise conditions when the fundamental solution of the underlying differential equation possesses nonvanishing Fredholm determinants. This last result is also of relevance for the discussion of oscillation properties of eigenfunctions of certain boundary value problems of differential operators associated with vibrating mechanical systems (see Karlin [6] for further details).

With the interpolation theorem in hand we adapt the method of de Boor [2] to establish the best-mean-square approximation properties of natural Chebyshevian spline functions. This is the content of Sec. 3. In the case of distinct knots this was done originally by Greville [4]. An alternative approach can be found in Ahlberg *et al.* [1] who also announced some convergence properties of splines under successive refinements of the system of knots.

Section 4 is devoted to a generalization of Schoenberg's theory concerning the best quadrature formulas approximating certain linear operators [14]. This theory was carried out, as far as we know, only for the case of ordinary spline polynomials. de Boor and Lynch [3] describe an alternative approach employing the theory of projections of operators in Hilbert spaces. Our methods are different and appear to be more explicit.

We omit most of the detailed proofs. These can be found by the interested reader in [8a]. We put the emphasis here on the motivation of the investigation and on the results.

1. Definitions and Preliminaries

Let $\{w_i(t)\}_0^{n-1}$ be positive functions of class $C^{n-i}[a, b]$ and associate with them the first-order differential operators

$$D_i\varphi = \frac{d}{dt}\frac{1}{w_i(t)}\varphi \qquad i = 0, 1, \ldots, n-1, \tag{1}$$

and the nth-order differential operator

$$L_n\varphi = D_{n-1}\cdots D_1 D_0\varphi. \tag{2}$$

It can be easily established that the functions $\{u_k(t)\}_{k=0}^{n-1}$ defined by

$$u_0(t) = w_0(t)$$

$$u_1(t) = w_0(t)\int_a^t w_1(\xi_1)\,d\xi_1 \tag{3}$$

$$\vdots$$

$$u_{n-1}(t) = w_0(t)\int_a^t w_1(\xi_1)\int_a^{\xi_1}\cdots\int_a^{\xi_{n-2}} w_{n-1}(\xi_{n-1})\,d\xi_{n-1}\cdots d\xi_1$$

constitute a fundamental system of solutions for $L_n\varphi = 0$.

Thus, each solution of $L_n\varphi = 0$ can be expressed as a linear combination of $\{u_k\}_0^{n-1}$; such a linear combination is called a *u-polynomial*.

It has been shown [8] that $\{u_k\}_0^{n-1}$ form an extended complete Chebyshevian (ECC) system (see [8] for the definition and properties of such systems). This shows in particular that L_n possesses "property W" in the sense of Pólya [9].

Conversely, it is known that every differential operator L_n with "property W" admits a factorization of the form (2) where w_i are strictly positive and of continuity class $C^{n-i}[a, b]$ (see [8] for details).

The fundamental solution of $L_n\varphi = 0$, which can be characterized as the solutions of

$$d\left\{\frac{1}{w_{n-1}(t)}\left[\frac{1}{w_{n-2}(t)}\,D_{n-3}\cdots D_1D_0\varphi(t)\right]_R\right\} = \delta_x(t), \qquad a < x < b, \quad (*)$$

where $\delta_x(t)$ denotes the delta measure concentrating at x (the subscript R denotes the right derivative of the indicated function), play an essential role in all the subsequent analysis.

Definition 1. The fundamental solution satisfying (*) and the initial conditions

$$\varphi(a) = 0, \qquad D_{i-1}\cdots D_1D_0\varphi(a) = 0, \qquad i = 1, 2, \ldots, n-1,$$

will be denoted by $\varphi_{n-1}(t; x)$.

Analogously we define $\varphi_{r-1}(t; x)$, $1 \le r \le n$, as the fundamental solution corresponding to $L_r\varphi \equiv D_{r-1}\cdots D_1D_0\varphi = 0$.

After these preliminaries, we introduce now the spline functions.

Definition 2. A function $p(t)$ defined on $[a, b]$ is called a *Chebyshevian spline function* (CSF) of order n possessing the knots

$$x_1, x_2, \ldots, x_k \qquad (a < x_1 < x_2 < \cdots < x_k < b) \tag{4}$$

with associated multiplicities

$$\mu_1, \mu_2, \ldots, \mu_k \qquad (1 \le \mu_i \le n, \quad i = 1, 2, \ldots, k), \tag{5}$$

provided

  (i) in each of the intervals $[a, x_1), [x_1, x_2), \ldots, [x_k, b]$, $p(t)$ coincides with a *u*-polynomial;
  (ii) $p(t)$ is of continuity class $C^{n-\mu_i-1}$ at x_i $(i = 1, \ldots, k)$.

The following lemma exhibits a canonical representation of a TSF with prescribed knots and multiplicities.

Lemma 1. *A Chebyshevian spline function $p(t)$ possessing the knots $\{x_i\}_1^k$ with associated multiplicities $\{\mu_i\}_1^k$ admits the representation*

$$p(t) = \sum_{i=1}^{k}\sum_{j=1}^{\mu_i} a_{ij}\varphi_{n-j}(t; x_i) + \sum_{i=0}^{n-1} b_i u_i(t). \tag{6}$$

Proof. A function of the form (6) clearly satisfies properties (i) and (ii) above.

Conversely, let $p(t)$ be a CSF fulfilling the stipulations of Definition 2. Then, $p(t)$ coincides with a u-polynomial on each of the intervals $[a, x_1)$, $[x_1, x_2), \ldots, [x_k, b]$. The functions

$$g_{i, \mu_i}(t) = \frac{1}{w_{n-\mu_i}(t)} D^R_{n-\mu_i-1} D_{n-\mu_i-2} \cdots D_0 p(t), \qquad i = 1, \ldots, k$$

exist in each of the respective intervals. Let a_{i, μ_i}, $i = 1, \ldots, k$ be the jump of $g_{i, \mu_i}(t)$ at the point x_i, $i = 1, \ldots, k$. Then, $p(t) - \sum_{i=1}^{k} a_{i, \mu_i} \varphi_{n-\mu_i}(t; x_i)$ will display the same knots as $p(t)$ with each of the multiplicities lowered by one. Continuing in this fashion, the resulting expression

$$p(t) - \sum_{i=1}^{k} \sum_{j=1}^{\mu_i} a_{ij} \varphi_{n-j}(t; x_i)$$

reduces to a u-polynomial. This proves the lemma.

We shall now define a special type of CSF of importance in the solution to certain minimization problems.

With the operator L_n we associate the adjoint operator $L_n{}^*$

$$L_n{}^* \varphi = D_0{}^* D_1{}^* \cdots D^*_{n-1} \varphi \tag{7}$$

where

$$D_i{}^* \varphi = \frac{1}{w_i(t)} \frac{d\varphi}{dt}, \qquad i = 0, 1, \ldots, n-1. \tag{8}$$

Clearly, the $2n$-order differential operator $L_n{}^* L_n$ whose generating functions are

$$w_0, \ldots, w_{n-1}, \quad 1, \quad w_{n-1}, \ldots, w_1, \tag{9}$$

possesses "property W," and we may construct the ECC system $\{u_i\}_0^{2n-1}$ from these functions as in (3). An important subclass of the CSF's with respect to $L_n{}^* L_n$ is the class of *natural CSF's* defined as follows.

Definition 3. A function $p(t)$ defined on $[a, b]$ is called a *natural Chebyshevian spline functions* (NCSF) of order $2n$ possessing the knots (4) with associated multiplicities (5) provided

(a) $p(t)$ is a CSF for $L_n{}^* L_n$ with these knots and multiplicities; and p obeys the further restriction that

(b) $L_n p(t) = 0$ for $t > x_k$ and $t < x_1$.

Recall that any CSF for the operator $L_n{}^* L_n$ has the form (6) with n replaced by $2n$. Since each term in the double sum trivially vanishes for $t < x_1$, condition (b) requires

$$L_n \left[\sum_{i=0}^{2n-1} b_i u_i(t) \right] = 0 \qquad \text{for} \quad t < x_1,$$

which, in view of the fact that $u_0, u_1, \ldots, u_{n-1}$ are solutions of $L_n\varphi = 0$, reduces to

$$\sum_{i=n}^{2n-1} b_i L_n u_i(t) = 0 \qquad \text{for} \quad t < x_1. \tag{10}$$

Observe now that $\{L_n u_i(t)\}_{i=n}^{2n-1}$ is exactly the ECC system associated with $1, w_{n-1}, \ldots, w_1$. Hence, (10) implies $b_i = 0, i = n, n+1, \ldots, 2n-1$. Thus, every NCSF with respect to $L_n{}^*L_n$ possessing the knots (4) with the associated multiplicities (5) admits the representation

$$p(t) = \sum_{i=1}^{k} \sum_{j=1}^{\mu_i} a_{ij}\varphi_{2n-j}(t; x_i) + \sum_{i=0}^{n-1} b_i u_i(t) \tag{11}$$

where the a_{ij} are subject to the further restriction

$$\sum_{i=1}^{k} \sum_{j=1}^{\mu_i} a_{ij} L_n \varphi_{2n-j}(t; x_i) = 0, \qquad t > x_k. \tag{12}$$

From these representations it is evident that questions of existence and uniqueness of interpolating CSF's can be settled by considering properties of determinants whose entries are the fundamental solutions. This is the content of the next section.

2. The Basic Total Positivity Property and Applications

Our primary objective in this section is to state the basic interpolation theorem for natural CSF's (see Definition 3). Theorems 1 and 2 serve as auxiliary theorems to accomplish this purpose, and are of fundamental value in the study of eigenvalue problems determined by a differential operator of the form L_n coupled with classical boundary conditions.

The following theorem states the total positivity property of the fundamental solution of $L_n\varphi = 0$.

Theorem 1. *Let $\{u_i\}_0^{n-1}$, $n \geq 1$, be an ECC system of the form (3) on $[a, b]$, and let $\varphi_l(t; x)$, $l = 0, 1, \ldots, n-1$ be defined as in Sec. 1. Suppose $t_i, x_j, i, j = 1, 2, \ldots, k$ obey the restrictions*

(i) $a \leq t_1 \leq t_2 \leq \cdots \leq t_k \leq b, \qquad a \leq x_1 \leq \cdots \leq x_k \leq b;$ (13)

(ii) $r + s \leq n + 1$ (14)

whenever r of the x_i's $(1 \leq r)$ coincide, say equal to c $(a \leq c \leq b)$, and s of the t_i's $(1 \leq s)$ agree with the same point c;

(iii) *no more than n consecutive t's (or x's) coincide.* (15)

Then

$$\det \|\varphi_{n-1}(t_i \, ; \, x_j)\|_{i,j=1}^{k} \geq 0. \tag{16}$$

Remark. We need to clarify the meaning of the determinant (16) in the event that coincidences occur. Specifically, suppose that $x_{j_0-1} < x_{j_0} = x_{j_0+1} = \cdots = x_{j_0+l-1} < x_{j_0+l}$, then in forming the determinant of (16) we replace the $(j_0 + i)$th column vector $(1 \leq i \leq l - 1)$, by

$$\left\{ \frac{d^i}{dx^i} \, \varphi_{n-1}(t_\nu \, ; \, x_{j_0}) \right\}_{\nu=1}^{k} .$$

Similar adjustments are made when several t-values coincide. Notice that conditions (14) and (15) guarantee that all necessary derivations can be performed and thus the elements of the matrix of the determinant (16) are well defined.

The proof of this theorem relies on the fact that the function $\varphi_{n-1}(t; x)$ admits the representation

$$\varphi_{n-1}(t; x) = \int_a^b \varphi_i(t; \alpha) \tilde{\varphi}_{n-i-2}(\alpha; x) \, d\alpha, \qquad i = 0, 1, \ldots, n - 2$$

where $\tilde{\varphi}_{n-i-2}(t; x)$ is the fundamental solution corresponding to the differential operator $D_{n-1} D_{n-2} \cdots D_{i+2} D_{i+1} \varphi = 0$. Using these representations, and employing an induction argument with the aid of the basic "composition formula" for kernels of integral equations (see Pólya and Szegö [10, p. 48]), the result follows.

However, in order to ascertain the existence and uniqueness of the interpolating CSF's at general points, we need the precise criteria that assure that the determinant (16) is strictly positive.

Theorem 2. *Let $\{u_i\}_0^{n-1}$ and $\varphi_l(t; x)$, $l = 0, 1, \ldots, n - 1$ be defined as in Theorem 1. Let t_i, x_j, i, $j = 1, 2, \ldots, k$ satisfy conditions* (13)–(15). *Then*

$$\det \|\varphi_{n-1}(t_i \, ; \, x_j)\|_{i,j=1}^{k} > 0 \tag{17}$$

if and only if

$$t_{i-n} < x_i < t_i, \qquad i = 1, 2, \ldots, k \tag{18}$$

where for $i < n$ only the right-hand inequality is relevant. In the case $n = 1$, equality is permitted in the right-hand side of (18).

We omit the proof of this theorem, which involves a delicate analysis of determinantal inequalities. The details can be found in [8a] and especially in [6, Chap. 10].

We can now state one kind of *interpolation theorem* for NCSF's.

Theorem 3. *Let* $\{x_i\}_1^k$ *be prescribed satisfying* $a < x_1 < \cdots < x_k < b$. *Then for every set of real numbers* $\{y_i^j\}$, $i = 1, \ldots, k$; $j = 0, 1, \ldots, \mu_i - 1$, *where* $1 \le \mu_i \le n$, $i = 1, 2, \ldots, k$ *and* $\mu = \sum_{i=1}^k \mu_i \ge n$, *there exists a unique NCSF* $p(t)$ *possessing the knots* (4) *with associated multiplicities* (5) *such that*

$$p^{(j)}(x_i) = y_i^j, \qquad i = 1, 2, \ldots, k; \quad j = 0, 1, \ldots, \mu_i - 1. \tag{19}$$

Remark. Theorem 3, in the special case of ordinary spline polynomials with distinct knots where only the values of the function (not its derivatives) are prescribed, is due to de Boor [2]. A few particular cases of the theorem involving multiple knots (only at the ends of the interval) leading to some classical quadrature formulas were discussed by Schoenberg [16]. The extension to the case of CSF's with distinct knots was elaborated by Greville [4]. An alternative discussion of the same case is contained in Ahlberg *et al.* [1].

The proof proceeds by considering the corresponding homogeneous system of linear equations and appealing several times to Rolle's theorem. This yields a homogeneous system of equations whose determinant is nonzero by virtue of Theorem 2. Hence the homogeneous system admits only the trivial solution, and this is equivalent to the statement of Theorem 3. For details see [8a].

The same method also proves the following theorem.

Theorem 3'. *Let* $\{x_i\}_0^{k+1}$ *be prescribed satisfying* $x_0 = a < x_1 < \cdots < x_k < b = x_{k+1}$. *Then for every set of real numbers* $\{y_i^j\}$, $i = 0, 1, \ldots, k, k+1$; $j = 0, 1, \ldots, \mu_i - 1$, *where* $1 \le \mu_i \le n$, $i = 1, 2, \ldots, k$, $\mu_0 = \mu_{k+1} = n$, *and* $\mu = \sum_{i=1}^k \mu_i \ge n$, *there exists a unique CSF of order* $2n$, $s(t)$, *possessing the knots* (4) *with associated multiplicities* (5) *such that*

$$s^{(j)}(x_i) = y_i^j, \qquad i = 0, 1, \ldots, k+1; \quad j = 0, 1, \ldots, \mu_i - 1. \tag{20}$$

3. Best-Mean-Square Approximation and Smoothing Properties of Chebyshevian Spline Functions

In possession of the interpolation theorems of Sec. 2, we can now proceed to develop the minimality properties of the interpolating NCSF's with respect to approximation in mean square of a given function. Actually, the main work is already done in Theorems 3 and 3' which demonstrate existence and uniqueness of CS interpolating functions. From here on we need merely adapt the method of de Boor [2].

For each pair of functions g and h possessing a square-integrable nth derivative, we define the quasi inner product

$$(g, h)_n = \int_a^b L_n g \cdot L_n h \ dt \tag{21}$$

and the quasinorm

$$\|g\|_n = [(g, g)_n]^{1/2}.$$

An extremal characterization of the NCSF's is the substance of the next theorem.

Theorem 4. *Let x_1, x_2, ..., x_k be prescribed satisfying $a < x_1 < \cdots < x_k < b$, and let $\{y_i{}^j\}$, $i = 1, 2, ..., k$; $j = 0, 1, ..., \mu_i - 1$ $(1 \le \mu_i \le n)$, be arbitrary real numbers. Let $p(t)$ denote the unique NCSF possessing the knots $\{x_i\}_1{}^k$ with corresponding multiplicities $\{\mu_i\}_1{}^k$ which interpolates $\{y_i{}^j\}$ in the sense of Theorem 3. Then among all functions g which interpolate $\{y_i{}^j\}$ in the sense of Theorem 3 and whose nth derivative is square integrable, the function $p(t)$ minimizes $\|g\|_n$ uniquely.*

The proof of Theorem 4 relies on the following lemma.

Lemma 2. *If g and p satisfy the hypotheses of Theorem 4 then*

$$\|g\|_n^2 - \|p\|_n^2 = \|g - p\|_n^2. \tag{22}$$

Lemma 2 is proved by establishing the identity $(g - p, g)_n = 0$, which follows on performing repeated integrations by parts and using the continuity properties of CSF's and the special end conditions imposed by the requirement that $p(t)$ be a NCSF.

The same analysis also proves the following.

Theorem 4'. *Let x_0, x_1, x_2, ..., x_k, x_{k+1} be prescribed satisfying $x_0 = a < x_1 < \cdots < x_k < b = x_{k+1}$ and let $\{y_i{}^j\}$, $i = 0, 1, ..., k + 1$; $j = 0, 1, ..., \mu_i - 1$ $(1 \le \mu_i \le n, i = 1, ..., k, \mu_0 = \mu_{k+1} = n)$, be arbitrary real numbers. Let $s(t)$ denote the unique CSF possessing the knots $\{x_i\}_1{}^k$ with associated multiplicities $\{\mu_i\}_1{}^k$ which interpolates $\{y_i{}^j\}$ in the sense of Theorem 3', i.e., which satisfies*

$$s^{(j)}(x_i) = y_i{}^j, \qquad i = 0, 1, ..., k + 1; \qquad j = 0, 1, ..., \mu_i - 1. \tag{23}$$

Then among all functions g possessing a square-integrable nth derivative, which interpolate $\{y_i{}^j\}$ in the sense of Theorem 3', $s(t)$ minimizes $\|g\|_n$ uniquely.

These two theorems show that the respective CSF's are the smoothest functions fitting the data, in the sense of deviating the least from being a solution of the differential equation $L_n \varphi = 0$. The next theorems demonstrate best mean-square approximation properties.

Theorem 5. *Let $\mathscr{S}$ be the class of all NCSF's possessing the knots* (4) *with corresponding multiplicities as specified in* (5). *Let $p^*(t)$ be the function of $\mathscr{S}$ interpolating at $\{x_i\}_1^k$ with multiplicities $\{\mu_i\}_1^k$ (i.e., in the sense of Theorem 3), to a given function $f(x)$ possessing a square-integrable nth derivative. If $p \in \mathscr{S}$ and p^* and p do not differ by a u-polynomial, then*

$$\|f - p^*\|_n < \|f - p\|_n . \tag{24}$$

Theorem 5'. *Let f be a given function possessing a square integrable nth derivative. Consider the class $\mathscr{T}$ of all CSF's possessing the knots* (4) *with associated multiplicities* (5). *Let s^* be the function of $\mathscr{T}$ which interpolates f in the sense of Theorem 3'. If $s \in S$, and s^* and s do not differ by a u-polynomial, then*

$$\|f - s^*\|_n < \|f - s\|_n . \tag{25}$$

4. Approximation of Linear Functionals

In this section we present another extremal characterization of the NCSF's. These results generalize some work of Schoenberg [13, 14] on the best approximation of linear functionals. Our discussion embraces the case of multiple knots and for this case the results appear to be new, even for ordinary spline polynomials.

Consider the class $\mathscr{K}$ of functions $f(x) \in C^{n-1}[a, b]$ for which $f^{(n-1)}(x)$ is absolutely continuous. Let $\mathscr{L}$ be a linear functional defined for this class of the form

$$\mathscr{L}f = \sum_{\mu=0}^{n-1} \alpha_\mu \int_a^b D_{\mu-1} D_{\mu-2} \cdots D_0 f(x) \, d\sigma_\mu(x)$$

where $\sigma_\mu(x)$ denotes signed measures of bounded variation.

Let the points $\{x_i\}_1^k$, $a < x_1 < \cdots < x_k < b$, and the associated multiplicities $\{\mu_i\}_1^k$, $1 \le \mu_i \le n$, be prescribed with $\sum_{i=1}^k \mu_i \ge n$. Consider the class of quadrature formulas

$$\mathscr{L}f = \sum_{\nu=1}^k \sum_{j=0}^{\mu_\nu-1} B_{\nu j} f^{(j)}(x_\nu) + \mathscr{R}f \tag{26}$$

The first term on the right is the approximant and the second is the remainder. The B_{vj} are chosen so that

$$\mathscr{R}u_i = 0, \qquad i = 0, 1, \ldots, n-1, \tag{27}$$

i.e., the quadrature formula is exact for every solution of $L_n\varphi = 0$. In the case $\sum_{i=1}^{k} \mu_i = n$, the conditions (27) uniquely determine the constants $\{B_{vj}\}$. However, for $\sum_{i=1}^{k} \mu_i > n$ there are still $\sum_{i=1}^{k} \mu_i - n$ free parameters.

For each f in $\mathscr{K}$, repeated integration by parts and the "exactness" conditions (27) yield

$$\mathscr{R}f = \int_a^b \mathscr{R}_t\varphi_{n-1}(t; x)L_nf(x)\, dx \tag{28}$$

where the subscript t indicates that the operation is performed with respect to the variable t while x is held fixed.

The formula (28) yields

$$|\mathscr{R}f|^2 \leq \int_a^b [\mathscr{R}_t\varphi_{n-1}(t; x)]^2\, dx \cdot \int_a^b [L_nf(x)]^2\, dx. \tag{29}$$

Thus, a natural minimization problem is to determine $\{B_{vj}\}$ satisfying (27) which render the integral

$$\int_a^b [\mathscr{R}_t\varphi_{n-1}(t; x)]^2\, dx = \text{a minimum} \tag{30}$$

This is Sard's [11] criterion for "best formula" of approximation of linear functionals. Notice that the minimization problem is formulated to involve only the ECC system $u_0, u_1, \ldots, u_{n-1}$. However, it is a remarkable fact that the solution requires introducing the NCSF's for an associated ECC system of $2n$ functions. In this sense Theorem 6 provides an intrinsic significance to the concept of NCSF's.

Let $L_{vj}(t)$ be the unique NCSF possessing the knots $\{x_i\}_1^k$ with associated multiplicities $\{\mu_i\}_1^k$ such that

$$L_{vj}^{(i)}(x_\mu) = \delta_{ij}\,\delta_{v\mu} \qquad \text{for all} \quad i, j, v, \mu, \text{ [cf. Theorem 3].}$$

The explicit solution to the minimization problem is then given by:

Theorem 6. *The linear approximation of the operator $\mathscr{L}$ of the form* (26) *which minimizes* (30) *under the conditions* (27) *is uniquely defined by*

$$B_{vj}^* = \mathscr{L}L_{vj}, \qquad v = 1, 2, \ldots, k; \quad j = 0, 1, \ldots, \mu_v - 1. \tag{31}$$

For the proof see [8a].

This explicit solution has the advantage that once the setup (including the points with their multiplicities and the differential equation) is given, the fundamental NCSF's $\{L_{\nu j}(t)\}$ can be computed, and they are independent of the linear functional. For each linear functional the optimal $\{B_{\nu j}\}$ can then easily be determined by (31).

ACKNOWLEDGMENTS

We express special thanks to I. J. Schoenberg who stimulated our interest in several of these problems during his visit to Stanford University in May 1964. The bulk of the results of this paper were obtained during that late spring.

REFERENCES

[1] Ahlberg, J. H., Nilson, E. N., and Walsh, L. J., Fundamental properties of generalized splines, *Proc. Nat. Acad. Sci. USA* **52**, 1412–1419 (1964).

[2] de Boor, C., Best approximation properties of spline functions of odd degree, *J. Math. Mech.* **12**, 747–750 (1963).

[3] de Boor, C., and Lynch, R. E., On splines and their minimum properties, *J. Math. Mech.* **15**. 953–969 (1966).

[4] Greville, T. N. E., Interpolation by generalized spline functions, *MRC Tech. Rept. 476.* Univ. of Wisconsin, May, 1964.

[5] Holladay, J. C., Smoothest curve approximation, *Math. Tables Aids to Comp.* **11**, 233–243 (1957).

[6] Karlin, S., "Total Positivity and Applications to Analysis." Stanford Univ. Press, Stanford, California, 1967.

[7] Karlin, S., Total positivity and convexity preserving transformations, *Proc. Symp. in Pure Math.* **7**, Convexity, 329–347 (1963).

[8] Karlin, S., and Studden, W., "Tchebycheff Systems and Applications." Wiley (Interscience), New York, 1966.

[8a] Karlin, S., and Ziegler, Z., Chebyshevian spline functions, *J. SIAM. Numer. Anal.* **3**, 514–543 (1966).

[9] Pólya, G., On the mean value theorem corresponding to a given linear homogeneous differential equation, *Trans. Amer. Math. Soc.* **24**, 312–324 (1922).

[10] Pólya, G., and Szegö, G., "Aufgaben und Lehrsätze aus der Analysis," Vol. 1. Springer, Berlin, 1925.

[11] Sard, A., "Linear Approximation" (Math. Surveys No. 9), Amer. Math. Soc., Providence, Rhode Island, 1963.

[12] Schoenberg, I. J., Contributions to problems of approximation of equidistant data by analytic functions. *Quart. Appl. Math.* **4A**, 45–99 (1946); **4B**, 112–141 (1946).

[13] Schoenberg, I. J., Spline functions, convex curves and mechanical quadratures, *Bull. Amer. Math. Soc.* **64**, 352–357 (1958).

[14] Schoenberg, I. J., On best approximations of linear operators, *Nederl. Akad. Wetensch. Indig. Math.* **26**, 155–163 (1964).

[15] Schoenberg, I. J., On trigonometric spline interpolation, *J. Math. Mech.* **13,** 795–825 (1964).

[16] Schoenberg, I. J., On monosplines of least deviation and best quadrature formulae, *J. SIAM, Num. Anal. Series B*, **2,** 144–170 (1965).

[17] Schoenberg, I. J., and Whitney, A. On Pólya frequency functions, III. The positivity of translation determinants with an application to the interpolation by spline curves, *Trans. Amer. Math. Soc.* **74,** 246–259 (1953).

[18] Walsh, J. L., Ahlberg, J. H., and Nilson, E. N., Best approximation properties of the spline fit, *J. Math. Mech.* **11,** 225–234 (1962).

[19] Walsh, J. L., Ahlberg, J. H., and Nilson, E. N., Best approximation and convergence properties of higher order spline fits, Abstract 63t-103, *Notices Amer. Math. Soc.* **10,** 202 (1963).

[20] Ziegler, Z., Generalized convexity cones, *Pacific J. Math.*, **17,** 561–580 (1966).

Some New Inequalities and Unsolved Problems

J. E. LITTLEWOOD
Trinity College
Cambridge, England

1

The first inequality is as follows. Let a_n, b_n be nonnegative, let u_n be positive and monotonic increasing, let

$$\alpha_n{}^2 = \sum_n^\infty a_m{}^2, \qquad \beta_n{}^2 = \sum_n^\infty b_m{}^2, \qquad A_n = \sum_1^n a_m, \qquad B_n = \sum_1^n b_m;$$

$$L = \sum u_n \alpha_n \beta_n (a_n B_n + b_n A_n), \qquad R = \sum u_n (a_n{}^2 B_n{}^2 + b_n{}^2 A_n{}^2);$$

and let L_1, R_1 be L, R for $u_n = 1$. Then we have the group of possibilities:

(A?) $L \leq AR$.
(A$_1$?) $L_1 \leq AR_1$.
(A$_2$) $L \leq AR$
(A$_3$) $L_1 \leq AR_1$ $\Big\}$ if a_n, b_n are monotonic decreasing.
(A$_4$) $\sum u_n \alpha_n{}^2 \beta_n{}^2 \leq AR$ if a_n, b_n are monotonic decreasing.

In each case A is to be a positive absolute constant.

The group occurs in a work of Dr. J. Bray, unpublished except as a Ph.D. thesis in the University Library, Cambridge, England.

A new "elementary inequality"—one in terms of nonnegative discrete a_n, b_n—is something of an event; still more is one which is difficult to decide. Of the group, (A$_2$) to (A$_4$) are true, (A) and (A$_1$) are undecided, and a decision seems very far from simple.

(A$_1$) is true in the special case $a_n \equiv b_n$, and then there is also an opposite inequality $R_1 \leq AL_1$.

No extension to more than two letters can be always true even when a_n, etc., are decreasing.

The form would be (for three letters) either

$$L_1 = \sum \alpha_n \beta_n \gamma_n (a_n B_n C_n + \cdots), \qquad R_1 = \sum (a_n{}^2 B_n{}^2 C_n{}^2 + \cdots),$$

or

$$L_1 = \sum \alpha_n \beta_n \gamma_n (a_n b_n C_n + \cdots), \qquad R_1 = \sum (a_n{}^2 b_n{}^2 C_n{}^2 + \cdots).$$

To fit in with $a_n = n^{-p}$, $b_n = n^{-q}$, $c_n = n^{-r}$, we should, in the first case, have to define

$$\alpha_n = \left(\sum_n^\infty a_m^{3/2} \right)^{2/3}, \qquad \text{etc.}$$

and in the second,

$$\alpha_n = \left(\sum_n^\infty a_m^{3} \right)^{1/3}, \qquad \text{etc.}$$

In the first case $p = 2/3$, $q = r = 23/24$ makes $L_1 = \infty$, $R_1 < \infty$; in the second case $p = 1/3$, $q = r = 2/3$ has the same result.

We may note, however, that the problems come alive again for the special case $a_n \equiv b_n \equiv c_n$. Thus, for example, the second form gives $R_1 = \sum a_n^4 A_n^2$, $L_1 = \sum_{n=1}^\infty (\sum_n^\infty a_m^3) a_n^2 A_n$.

By changing order of summation (and interchanging n and m),

$$L_1 = \sum_{n=1}^\infty a_n^3 \left(\sum_{m=1}^n a_m^2 A_m \right).$$

Whether $L_1 \leq AR_1$ seems not easy to decide even when a_n is decreasing. (It is true when all a's are 0 or 1.)

This restriction to two letters makes the (A) group more, not less, interesting.

In what follows, I give an account of Bray's work in which there are very interesting applications of (A_2), (A_3), (A_4).

Since

$$u_n \alpha_n \beta_n a_n B_n \leq u_n (\alpha_n^2 \beta_n^2 + a_n^2 B_n^2),$$

and similarly for $u_n \alpha_n \beta_n b_n A_n$, we see at once that (A_4) implies (A_2) and (A_3). But (A_4), at least, is not true for unrestricted a_n, b_n; take $a_N = b_N = 1$ and all other a_n, $b_n = 0$.

2

Bray's proof of (A_4) is as follows. We have

$$\sum u_n \alpha_n^2 \beta_n^2 + \sum u_n a_n^2 b_n^2 = \sum_{n=1}^\infty u_n \left(\sum_{r \geq s \geq n} \sum a_r^2 b_s^2 + \sum_{s \geq r \geq n} \sum a_r^2 b_s^2 \right)$$

so that it is enough, by symmetry, to prove

$$L' = \sum_{n=1}^\infty \sum_{r \geq s \geq n} \sum u_n a_r^2 b_s^2 \leq A \sum u_n a_n^2 B_n^2.$$

Now

$$L' = \sum_{r=1}^\infty a_r^2 \left(\sum_{s \leq r} b_s^2 \sum_{n=1}^s u_n \right) = \sum a_r^2 V_r, \qquad \text{say.}$$

Since $\sum_{n=1}^{s} u_n \leq su_r$, we have

$$V_r \leq u_r \sum_{s \leq r} sb_s{}^2 = u_r \sum_{s \leq r} b_s(sb_s) \leq u_r \sum_{s \leq r} b_s B_r = u_r B_r{}^2.$$

Thus $L' \leq A \sum u_n a_n{}^2 B_n{}^2$, as desired.

3

Bray's ultimate aim is to prove the following theorem.

Theorem (B). *Let* $[\varphi_n^{(1)}(t)], [\varphi_n^{(2)}(t)], \ldots, [\varphi_n^{(k)}(t)]$ *be* k *sets of real bounded normal orthogonal functions in* $(0, 1)$, *with bounds* $M_1, M_2, \ldots, M_k$. *Let*

$$f_1(t) \sim \sum a_n \varphi_n^{(1)}(t), \ldots, f_k(t) \sim \sum j_n \varphi_n^{(k)}(t),$$

where for simplicity the $a_n, \ldots, j_n$ *are real. Let* $a_n{}^*$ *be the nth* $|a_m|$ *in descending order, and* $A_n{}^* = \sum_1^n a_m{}^*$, *etc. Let* $q_r \geq 2$ $(1 \leq r \leq k)$. *Then*

$$\int_0^1 \prod_1^k |f_r|^{q_r} \, dt \leq KM'S^*,$$

where

$$S^* = \sum a_n^{*2} A_n^{*q_1-2} B_n^{*q_2} \cdots J_n^{*q_k} + \sum A_n^{*q_1} b_n^{*2} B_n^{*q_2-2} \cdots J_n^{*q_k} + \cdots,$$

K *depends only on the* q*'s, and* $M' = (\sum_1^k M_r^{-2}) \prod_1^k M_r$.

This is a natural generalization of the case, $k = 1$, which is known [2].

We shall be concerned (apart from Sec. 4) only with (B_1), *the special case when all the* q*'s are integers* $[\geq 2]$.

4

I should nonetheless mention Bray's work on nonintegral q. He uses a fairly straightforward adaptation of a method of Paley [6], who proves the following important result.

Let (φ_n) *be a set of bounded normal orthogonal functions with bound* M, *and let* $f \sim \sum_1^\infty a_n \varphi_n(t)$. *Then for* $q > 2$

$$\int_0^1 S^q(t) \, dt \leq A_q M^q \sum a_n^{*q} n^{q-2},$$

where

$$S(t) = \sup_{(n)} \left| \sum_1^n a_m \varphi_m(t) \right|.$$

If this result were true for $q = 2$ it would prove that the series $\sum a_n \varphi_n(t)$ for an $f \in L^2$ is bounded $p.p.$ This is well known to be false (for suitable φ_n), and with nearly a logarithm to spare [4]. Thus Paley's method, and accordingly Bray's adaptation, must fail for $q = 2$. There thus arises the odd situation that Theorem (B) is proved when all q (≥ 2) are integral, and when all q are > 2; the case when some q's are 2 and the others are nonintegral being undecided. (And since the methods for the two cases have no point of contact the difficulty goes quite deep.)

5

Before going on to Bray's proof of (B₁), I will digress, with a purpose, to describe some background. Suppose a_n, b_n, ..., j_n are nonnegative, that a_0 is the greatest a_n etc., and that $a_n = a_{-n}$, etc.

Then [3, p. 265] we have, for $k \geq 2$ letters,

$$\sum_{r+s+\cdots=0} a_r b_s \cdots \leq \sum_{r+s+\cdots=0} a_r^* b_s^* \cdots,$$

where a_n^*, a_{-n}^* are the nth pair a_m, a_{-m} in order of magnitude. (If we drop the conditions $a_n = a_{-n}$, ..., there is a corresponding result with a constant A on the right.) The case $k = 2$ is trivial; $k = 3$ extends easily to any $k \geq 3$, so that $k = 3$ is the key result. There is an attractive proof of this by Gabriel [1], with lessons for work in the field. It is not in [3], and I give it here.

Consider

$$\rho = \sum_{r+s+t=0} a_r b_s c_t \Big/ \sum_{r+s+t=0} a_r^* b_s^* c_t^*.$$

We may suppose $a_0 = b_0 = c_0 = 1$, so that $0 \leq a_n \leq 1$, etc. Suppose a set of a_n, and so also the a_{-n}, all have the same value α, where $0 < \alpha < 1$, and take the greatest group G of such pairs $a_{\pm n}$. Let $\alpha + \beta$, $\alpha - \gamma$ be the nearest values of an a on either side. Now change each a of G to $\alpha + x$, with x in the range R, or $(-\gamma \leq x \leq \beta)$. The a^* corresponding to a of G also become $\alpha + x$, and all others are unchanged. The new ρ is of the form

$$\rho(x) = \frac{A + Bx}{C + Dx} = A' + \frac{B'}{C + Dx}$$

and for x of R the last denominator > 0 (it contains $a_0 b_0 c_0 = 1$ and all other terms are nonnegative). *This being so, $\rho(x)$ is monotonic in R, and attains its maximum at one end or other of R.* We thus get a new configuration in which G is enlarged by at least one pair and for which ρ is not decreased. It follows that, for fixed b, c, ρ is greatest when all the a's are 0 or 1. We now fix these a's and vary the b's, and so on. ρ is then greatest when all a, b, c, ... are either 0 or 1: there is a "reduction to 0, 1." The reduced case has then to be proved: here I have nothing to add to what is in [3].

The first use of the a, b, c, ... theorem, for an even number $2k$ of letters all the same, was to prove the inequality

$$\int_{-\pi}^{\pi} |f|^{2k}\, d\theta \le \int_{-\pi}^{\pi} |f^*|^{2k}\, d\theta,$$

$$f \sim \sum a_n \cos n\theta, \qquad f^* = \sum a_n{}^* \cos n\theta.$$

The moral is that even if we are concerned with a case where all letters or functions are the same, it may be easier to deal with the case when they are not, or, again, when they are equal only in pairs. This principle is involved in Bray's proof of (B_1).

Another point to note is the possible importance of the case when "everything is 0 or 1."

6

Bray's proof of (B_1). This uses (A_2), etc., and also the following rather remarkable algebraic identity:

(C) *Given k sets of numbers* (a_n), (b_n), ..., (j_n) $(1 \le n \le N)$, *let* A_n, *or* $_n\sum a_m$, *denote one or other of* $\sum_1^n a_m$, $\sum_1^{n-1} a_m$, *and let* $\bar{A}_n$, *or* $_n\sum a_m$, *denote one or other of* $\sum_n^N a_m$, $\sum_{n+1}^N a_m$, *and similarly for b, c, ..., j. Then*

$$\left(\sum_1^N a_n\right)\left(\sum_1^N b_n\right) \cdots \left(\sum_1^N j_n\right)$$

$$= \sum_1^N A_n \bar{B}_n c_n D_n E_n \cdots J_n + \sum_1^N \bar{A}_n B_n C_n d_n E_n \cdots J_n$$

$$+ \sum_1^N A_n b_n \bar{C}_n D_n E_n \cdots J_n + \cdots,$$

where the summands on the right-hand side are all the possible $k\binom{k-1}{2} = \frac{1}{2}k(k-1)(k-2)$ *different letter sequences, a to j, with one small letter, two barred capitals, and the rest unbarred capitals. Which of the two interpretations a particular capital, barred or unbarred, has in a given summand, we do not need to specify, but it has one and the same throughout the corresponding sum* $\sum$.

Bray's proof of this is given in the Appendix.

Consider now (B_1). In the first place, given any set (φ_n) of the k sets, we may change the sign of any φ, and we may permute the suffixes in any way so as to get a bounded normal orthogonal set with the same bound. Hence, *provided we suppose the $(\varphi_n^{(r)})$ to be all different to begin with,* we may permute each set separately, and in such a manner that

$$f_1(t) \sim \sum a_n{}^*\varphi_n^{(1)}, \quad \text{etc.}$$

We may suppose this done, and suppress the *'s in what follows.

Next, any $\prod |f_r|^{q_r}$ with integral $q_r \geq 2$ may be written as a product of $|f|^q$ with all q either 2 or 3. Since, in general, some $|f|$ will be repeated, we must again suppose them to be different and with different (φ_n) to begin with. Finally, the product $|f|^2|g|^2|h|^3$ is entirely typical, as will be apparent from the proof.

We proceed, then, to prove that if (a_n), (b_n), (c_n) are in descending order, and

$$f = \sum_1^N a_n\varphi_n, \qquad g = \sum_1^N b_n\psi_n, \qquad h = \sum_1^N c_n\chi_n,$$

then

$$\int_0^1 |f|^2|g|^2|h|^3 \, dt \leq AM'S_N{}^*,$$

$$S_N{}^* = \sum_1^N a_n{}^2 B_n{}^2 C_n{}^3 + \sum_1^N A_n{}^2 b_n{}^2 C_n{}^3 + \sum_1^N A_n{}^2 B_n{}^2 c_n{}^2 C_n.$$

The transition to $N = \infty$ is a matter of routine ($S^* < \infty$ implies $\sum a_n{}^2 < \infty$, $\sum b_n{}^2 < \infty$, $\sum c_n{}^2 < \infty$).

The identity (C) expresses $f^2g^2h^3$, which is a product (with repetitions) of seven factors, as the sum of $\frac{1}{2}7(7-1)(7-2) = 105$ sums $\sum_1^N$. These fall into groups, of which

$$\sum_1^N X_n, \quad \sum_1^N Y_n, \quad \sum_1^N Z_n, \quad \sum_1^N W_n$$

are sufficiently typical: $(_n\sum a_m)$ now means $(_n\sum a_m\varphi_m(x))$ and

$$X_n = \{(_n\sum a_m)(_n\sum b_m)\} \cdot a_n\varphi_n \cdot \{(^n\sum b_m)(^n\sum c_m)(^n\sum c_m)(^n\sum c_m)\},$$

$$Y_n = \{(_n\sum a_m)(_n\sum b_m)\} \cdot c_n\chi_n \cdot \{(^n\sum a_m)(^n\sum b_m)(^n\sum c_m)(^n\sum c_m)\},$$

$$Z_n = \{(_n\sum a_m)(_n\sum c_m)\} \cdot b_n\psi_n \cdot \{(^n\sum a_m)(^n\sum b_m)(^n\sum c_m)(^n\sum c_m)\},$$

$$W_n = \{(_n\sum a_m)(_n\sum a_m)\} \cdot c_n\chi_n \cdot \{(^n\sum b_m)(^n\sum b_m)(^n\sum c_m)(^n\sum c_m)\}.$$

In each of the 105 expressions of this kind there are two factors $_n\sum$, one single term, and four factors $^n\sum$. In each expression, of course, there are two factors involving a's, two involving b's, and three involving c's.

$\int_0^1 |f|^2 |g|^2 |h|^3 \, dt$ is now less than or equal to

$$\sum_1^N \int_0^1 |X_n| \, dt + \cdots + \sum_1^N \int_0^1 |W_n| \, dt + 101 \text{ sufficiently similar terms,}$$

and it is enough to show that

$$\sum_1^N \int_0^1 |X_n| \, dt \le AM'S^*, \ldots, \sum_1^N \int_0^1 |W_n| \, dt \le AM'S^*.$$

In each case we replace the single factor and the four $_n\sum$ by their crude upper bounds. Thus

$$\int_0^1 |X_n| \, dt \le M_1 a_n \cdot M_2 B_n \cdot M_3{}^3 C_n{}^3 \cdot \int_0^1 |(_n\sum a_m \varphi_m)(_n\sum b_m \psi_m)| \, dt.$$

In this

$$M_1 M_2 M_3{}^3 = M_1{}^2 M_2{}^2 M_3{}^3 / M_1 M_2 \le M_1{}^2 M_2{}^2 M_3{}^2 (M_1^{-2} + M_2^{-2}) \le M',$$

and

$$\int_0^1 \le \left\{ \int_0^1 |_n\sum a_m \varphi_m|^2 \, dt \right\}^{1/2} \cdot \left\{ \int_0^1 |(_n\sum b_m \psi_m)|^2 \, dt \right\}^{1/2} \le \alpha_n \beta_n,$$

(whichever interpretation is given to the two $_n\sum$). So

$$\sum_1^N \int_0^1 |X_n| \, dt \le M' \sum C_n{}^3 \alpha_n \beta_n a_n B_n. \tag{1}$$

The sum on the right-hand side is one of the terms of L in (A_2), with $u_n = C_n{}^3$, and we can infer by (A_2) that

$$\sum_1^N \int_0^1 |X_n| \, dt \le AM' \sum (a_n{}^2 B_n{}^2 + b_n{}^2 A_n{}^2) C_n{}^3 \le AM'S^*. \tag{2}$$

[In the special case of $h \equiv 1$, or of $\int_0^1 |f^2 g^2| \, dt$, with which it is natural to begin, the expansion by (C) involves *only* terms of the type of $\sum X_n$, and (A_3) deals with this at once. This was the genesis of (A_3) and the (A) group.] $\sum Y_n$, etc., are, however, not amenable to this way of reaching (2). For uniformity, therefore, we reconsider the deduction of (2) from (1). We have from (1)

$$\int_0^1 |X_n| \, dt \le M' \sum \alpha_n \beta_n C_n^{3/2} \cdot a_n B_n C_n^{3/2} \le M' \sum C_n{}^3 \alpha_n{}^2 \beta_n{}^2$$

$$+ M' \sum a_n{}^2 B_n{}^2 C_n{}^3.$$

The second term $\le M'S^*$, and the first $\le AM'S^*$ by (A_4).

Next we have, similarly,

$$\sum \int_0^1 |Y_n|\, dt \le M' \sum \alpha_n \beta_n \cdot c_n \cdot A_n B_n C_n{}^2 = M' \sum \alpha_n \beta_n C_n^{3/2} \cdot A_n B_n c_n C_n^{1/2}$$
$$\le M' \sum C_n{}^3 \alpha_n{}^2 \beta_n{}^2 + M' \sum c_n{}^2 C_n A_n{}^2 B_n{}^2 \le A M' S^*;$$

$$\sum \int_0^1 |Z_n|\, dt \le M' \sum \alpha_n \gamma_n \cdot b_n A_n B_n C_n{}^2 = M' \sum \alpha_n \gamma_n B_n C_n^{1/2} \cdot b_n A_n C_n^{3/2}$$
$$\le M' \sum \alpha_n{}^2 \gamma_n{}^2 B_n{}^2 C_n + M' \sum b_n{}^2 A_n{}^2 C_n{}^3$$
$$\le M' \sum (a_n{}^2 C_n{}^2 + c_n{}^2 A_n{}^2) B_n{}^2 C_n + A M' S^* \le A M' S^*;$$

$$\sum \int_0^1 |W_n|\, dt \le M' \sum \alpha_n{}^2 \cdot c_n B_n{}^2 C_n{}^2 = M' \sum (a_n{}^2 + a_{n+1}^2 + \cdots) \cdot c_n B_n{}^2 C_n{}^2$$
$$= M' \sum a_n{}^2 \left(\sum_{m \le n} c_m B_m{}^2 C_m{}^2 \right)$$
$$\le M' \sum a_n{}^2 B_n{}^2 C_n{}^2 \sum_{m \le n} c_m = M' \sum a_n{}^2 B_n{}^2 C_n{}^3 \le M' S^*.$$

A little consideration now shows that we have effectively covered all possible types of the 105 sums, and have completed the proof of Theorem (B₁).

7

Let S be the "unstarred" form of S^*, namely where the a_n, etc., are the original unstarred a, etc., and $A_n = \sum_1^n |a_m|$, etc. When $k = 1$ we have

$$S_q{}^* = \sum a_n^{*2} A_n^{*q-2} \le S_q \qquad \text{(and } S_p \le S_p{}^* \text{ for } p \le 2\text{)}.$$

The proof [5] is an application (not altogether trivial) of differential calculus to show that if $|a_{n+1}| > |a_n|$, S_q is decreased by interchanging a_n and a_{n+1}. Since for $k = 1$

$$\int_0^1 |f|^q\, dt \le A_q M^{q-2} S_q{}^*,$$

we have also $\int_0^1 |f|^q\, dt \le A_q M^{q-2} S_q$. All this fails for $k > 1$. Thus, for $k = 2$ and any $q_{1,2} \ge 2$, we may take a_1 and b_2 to be 1, and all other a_n, $b_n = 0$, when $S = 1$, $S^* = 2$.

It remains possible that $S^* \le KS$, where K depends only on the q's. The simplest case:

$$\sum (a_n^{*2} B_n^{*2} + b_n^{*2} A_n^{*2}) \le A \sum (a_n{}^2 B_n{}^2 + b_n{}^2 A_n{}^2) \tag{?}$$

is yet another "elementary inequality" that seems very difficult to decide. It is of interest that it is true when all a's and b's are either 0 or 1 (the latter in finite number). (There is however, no "reduction to 0, 1" of the general case.)

Let $a_n = 0$ except for $n = p_r$, $r = 1, 2, \ldots, M$; $b_n = 0$ except for $n = q_s$, $s = 1, 2, \ldots, N$. We may suppose $M \geq N$, and also $N \geq 3$, the cases $N = 1, 2$, being easily disposed of.

Let $\rho(s)$ be the number of p_r satisfying $q_s \leq p_r < q_{s+1}$, interpreting q_0 to be 0 and q_{N+1} to be ∞ (to deal with the end ranges of p_r). We have

$$S = \sum_1^\infty B_{p_r}^2 + \sum_1^\infty A_{q_s}^2$$

[both series, of course, terminate]. Now

$$\sum_r B_{p_r}^2 \geq \sum_{s=1}^\infty \sum_{q_s \leq p_r < q_{s+1}} B_{p_r}^2 \geq \sum_1^\infty \rho(s) B_{q_s}^2 = \sum \rho(s) s^2.$$

Next,

$$A_{q_s} \geq \sum_{t=0}^{s-1} \rho(t),$$

$$\sum_1^\infty A_{q_s}^2 \geq \sum_{s=1}^\infty \left[\sum_{t=0}^{s-1} \rho(t)\right]^2,$$

so that

$$S \geq \sum_{s=1}^{N+1} \left\{ \rho(s) s^2 + \left[\sum_{t=0}^{s-1} \rho(t)\right]^2 \right\}. \tag{3}$$

Also

$$\sum_{s=0}^{N+1} \rho(s) = M. \tag{4}$$

There are now two cases;

$$\text{(a)} \quad \sum_0^{N'} \rho(s) \leq \tfrac{1}{2} M, \qquad \sum_{N'+1}^{N+1} \rho(s) \geq \tfrac{1}{2} M,$$

$$\text{(b)} \quad \sum_0^{N'} \rho(s) \geq \tfrac{1}{2} M, \qquad \sum_{N'+1}^{N+1} \rho(s) \leq \tfrac{1}{2} M,$$

where

$$N' = [\tfrac{1}{2}(N+1)] \geq \tfrac{1}{2} N.$$

In (a) we have from (3),

$$S \geq \sum_1^{N+1} \rho(s) s^2 \geq \sum_{N'+1}^{N+1} \rho(s) s^2 \geq N'^2 \cdot \tfrac{1}{2} M > A M N^2. \tag{5}$$

In (b)

$$\sum_{t=0}^{s-1} \rho(t) \geq \tfrac{1}{2}M \qquad \text{for} \quad s \geq N'+1,$$

and so, from (3),

$$S \geq \sum_{N'+1}^{N+1} (\tfrac{1}{2}M)^2 > AM^2N \geq AMN^2,$$

and (5) is true in either case.

Next,

$$a_n{}^* = 1, \quad A_n{}^* = n \quad (n \leq M); \qquad b_n{}^* = 1, \quad B_n{}^* = n \quad (n \leq N).$$

So

$$S^* = \sum_{n=1}^{N} A_n^{*2} + \sum_{1}^{M} B_n^{*2} = \sum_{1}^{N} n^2 + \sum_{1}^{N} n^2 + \sum_{N+1}^{M} N^2$$
$$\leq 2N^3 + (M-N)N^2 \leq 2MN^2,$$

since $M \geq N$. From this and (5) we have $S^* \leq AS$, as desired.

Appendix.   Proof of (C)

The proof is constructive.

Consider a term $a_l b_m \cdots j_t$ in the left-hand side

$$L = \left(\sum_{n=1}^{N} a_n \right) \left(\sum_{n=1}^{N} b_n \right) \cdots \left(\sum_{1}^{N} j_n \right)$$

of (C).   Suppose the third greatest of $l, m, \ldots, t$ is n; then we shall say that the term $a_l b_m \cdots j_t$ belongs to L_n. (The second, or again the first and second greatest of $l, m, \ldots$ may also be n, and so may the fourth, etc.) The L_n are uniquely defined, and $L = \sum_{n=1}^{N} L_n$.

Consider the letter sequences

$$(S_n) \begin{cases} \bar{A}_n \bar{B}_n c_n D_n E_n \cdots J_n, & \bar{A}_n \bar{B}_n C_n d_n E_n \cdots J_n, \ldots, \\ A_n b_n \bar{C}_n D_n E_n \cdots J_n, & \bar{A}_n B_n \bar{C}_n d_n E_n \cdots J_n, \ldots, \\ \text{etc.}; \end{cases}$$

these are the summands in the right-hand side of (C). We begin with all alternatives left open of the interpretations of capitals (barred or unbarred) as sums (but one and the same set of interpretations is to hold for the various n of a sum $\sum_{n=1}^{N}$). We then determine by stages which interpretations are to be given to the capitals in a particular S_n. Let the sum of the S_n be R_n, and call the S_n the components of R_n. Let $R = \sum_{n=1}^{N} R_n$ (the R_n and R start by being ambiguous).

Now whatever the interpretations in R_n, each term $(a_l \cdots j_t)$ of R_n will appear in L_n, and once at most (since the terms of L_n and L are all different). *We have now to choose interpretations such that, conversely, each term* $(s_l \cdots j_t)$ *of* L_n *appears once and only once in* R_n. Then $L_n = R_n$, $L = R$ and the identity is established.

We deal once and for all with the unbarred capitals. In each component of R_n let every unbarred capital alphabetically preceding the small letter have n excluded from its summation [interpretation $^n\sum = \sum_1^{n-1}$], and let every unbarred capital following the small letter have n included in its summation [interpretation $^n\sum = \sum_1^n$].

Now the terms $(a_l \cdots j_t)$ of L_n fall into three classes: (i) those with two suffixes greater than n; (ii) those with one suffix greater than n; (iii) those with no suffix greater than n.

Class (i). Any term of L_n belonging to this will appear just once in R_n; for the component of R_n in which it occurs is uniquely determined by the two factors with suffixes greater than n, which determine the barred capitals, together with the alphabetically first factor of those with suffix n, which determines the small letter. Thus the term of L_n occurs once in R_n, in a particular component only, and so once only in R_n, since no term can appear twice in any one component of R_n. This disposes of class (i).

We now arrange the $k(k-1)(k-2)$ barred letters of the components of R_n in order as follows. Arrange the *components* so that the (three-letter) "words" formed from each component by the two barred capitals in alphabetical order, followed by the single letter, are words in lexicographical order; and *within* each component take the barred letters in alphabetical order. Starting with n excluded from all the summations defining the barred letters (interpretation $_n\sum = \sum_{n+1}^N$), and taking the barred letters in their order, we successively add in the term n in $_n\sum$ (previously absent) if and only if this does not introduce into the R_n just reached a term already in it. This secures that no term in L_n can occur twice in R_n.

We can now deal with classes (ii) and (iii).

Class (ii). The terms of L_n of class (ii), with one suffix greater than n, lie in the component of R_n of which this one suffix determines one barred capital, and the alphabetically first letter with suffix n the other barred capital; the second letter with suffix n determining the small letter. This other barred capital will necessarily include n in its summation, for this component of R_n is lexicographically the first which could contain the term in question. This disposes of class (ii).

Class (iii). Those [class (iii)] terms in L_n with no suffix greater than n lie in the component of R_n with the first two letters with suffix n barred, the third term with suffix n being the small letter.

Thus each term in L_n occurs at least once in R_n. Since we have seen that it occurs at most once, every term in L_n occurs just once in R_n. The converse being also true we have completed the proof of (C).

REFERENCES

[1] Gabriel, R. M., An additional proof of a theorem upon rearrangements, *J. London Math. Soc.* **3,** 134–136 (1928).

[2] Hardy, G. H., and Littlewood, J. E., Notes on the theory of series (VI): two inequalities, *J. London Math. Soc.* **2,** 196–201 (1927).

[3] Hardy, G. H., Littlewood, J. E., and Pólya, G., "Inequalities," 2nd ed. Cambridge Univ. Press, London and New York, 1952.

[4] Kaczmarz, S., and Steinhaus, H., "Theorie der Orthogonalreihen," p. 170. Lwow, Warsaw, 1935.

[5] Littlewood, J. E., On a theorem of Paley, *J. London Math. Soc.* **29,** 387–395 (1954).

[6] Paley, R. E. A. C., Some theorems on orthogonal functions, *Studia Math.* **3,** 226–238 (1931).

Lengths of Tensors*

MARVIN MARCUS
Department of Mathematics
University of California
Santa Barbara, California

1. Introduction

Let X be an n-square matrix with entries in some field R. Almost all the matrix functions that one studies are linear in the rows (and columns) of X and have certain symmetry properties. Thus if the rows of X are $x_1, \ldots, x_n$ and $d(x_1, \ldots, x_n)$ is the determinant, $\det(X)$, then

$$d(x_{\sigma(1)}, \ldots, x_{\sigma(n)}) = \varepsilon(\sigma) \, d(x_1, \ldots, x_n) \tag{1}$$

for all $\sigma \in S_n$. If d is the permanent function [6], per (X), then instead of (1) we have

$$d(x_{\sigma(1)}, \ldots, x_{\sigma(n)}) = d(x_1, \ldots, x_n) \tag{2}$$

for all σ. As another example, let $d(X)$ be the product of the determinants of the principal submatrices X_p and X_{n-p} lying in rows $1, \ldots, p$ and $p + 1, \ldots, n$, respectively. Then

$$d(x_{\sigma(1)}, \ldots, x_{\sigma(n)}) = \varepsilon(\sigma) \, d(x_1, \ldots, x_n) \tag{3}$$

where σ is now restricted to being a permutation in the direct product of the symmetric group on $1, \ldots, p$ with the symmetric group on $p + 1, \ldots, n$.

These examples can be constructed in profusion but they are all of the same kind. A coherent general theory for all such matrix functions was first introduced by Schur [10]. Schur was interested in comparing the values of various generalized matrix functions on positive-definite Hermitian matrices. The classical Hadamard and Fischer inequalities are examples of such comparisons; in fact Schur [10] obtained a very general class of inequalities extending these two results. An excellent account of many inequalities like these is found in Wedderburn [11].

The purpose of this article is twofold. First, the theory of such matrix functions will be placed in its proper setting as a corollary to the general

* This research was supported by the U.S. Air Force under Grant AFOSR-698-65.

163

theory of symmetry classes of tensors. In this way it is well known, at least for the determinant function, that one obtains the classical identities as applications of familiar facts about inner products, e.g., the Cauchy–Binet theorem is Parseval's identity in an appropriate Grassmann space [11]. We will then indicate how most of the inequalities for positive-definite Hermitian matrices can be formulated as inequalities for lengths of tensors.

2. Symmetry Classes

Let V be an n-dimensional vector space over a field R. Let H be a subgroup of S_m, $m \leq n$, and let χ be a character of degree 1 on H, that is, a nonzero homomorphism mapping H into R. A function f on $V \times \cdots \times V$ (m occurrences of V in the cartesian product) with values in some vector space P over R is said to be symmetric with respect to H and χ if $f(v_1, \ldots, v_m)$ is linear separately in each v_i and for any $v_1, \ldots, v_m$ and any $\sigma \in H$

$$f(v_{\sigma(1)}, \ldots, v_{\sigma(m)}) = \chi(\sigma)f(v_1, \ldots, v_m).$$

If the pair P, f satisfies

(a) $\langle \text{rng } f \rangle = P$, i.e., the linear closure of the range of f is all of P;

(b) if φ is any multilinear function symmetric with respect to H and χ with values in a vector space U, then there exists a linear function $h: P \to U$ for which

$$\varphi = hf,$$

then P, f is called a *symmetry class of tensors over* V associated with H and χ. Condition (b) is called the *universal factorization property* for P, f. This situation is customarily summarized in the diagram

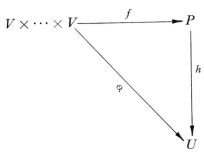

As an example, take both P and V to be the space of 3-tuples over R, $V_3(R)$. Let $m = 2$, $H = \{e, (12)\}$ and $\chi = \text{sgn}$. Let $f(v_1, v_2) = v_1 \times v_2$ be the usual vector product. Then $f(v_1, v_2) = -f(v_2, v_1) = \chi[(12)]f(v_2, v_1)$. Let U be any vector space over R and suppose φ is an alternating bilinear function on $V \times V$ to U. Let $e_1 = (1, 0, 0)$, $e_2 = (0, 1, 0)$, $e_3 = (0, 0, 1)$. Then it is clear that any value of φ can be written in terms of the vectors $\varphi(e_1, e_2)$, $\varphi(e_1, e_3)$, and $\varphi(e_2, e_3)$. (Recall that φ is alternating.) Now define $h: V_3(R) \to U$ by

$$h(e_i \times e_j) = \varphi(e_i, e_j), \qquad 1 \leq i < j \leq 3,$$

and then linear extension to all of $V_3(R)$. We show that $\varphi = hf$.

Let $v_1 = \sum_{i=1}^3 \xi_i e_i$, $v_2 = \sum_{i=1}^3 \eta_i e_i$ and

$$\varphi(v_1, v_2) = \varphi\left(\sum_{i=1}^3 \xi_i e_i, \sum_{j=1}^3 \eta_j e_j \right)$$
$$= \sum_{i,j=1}^3 \xi_i \eta_j \varphi(e_i, e_j).$$

Since $\varphi(e_i, e_i) = 0$ and $\varphi(e_i, e_j) = -\varphi(e_j, e_i)$, this last sum becomes

$$\varphi(v_1, v_2) = \sum_{1 \leq i < j \leq 3} (\xi_i \eta_j - \xi_j \eta_i) \varphi(e_i, e_j)$$
$$= \sum_{1 \leq i < j \leq 3} (\xi_i \eta_j - \xi_j \eta_i) h(e_i \times e_j)$$
$$= h\left[\sum_{1 \leq i < j \leq 3} (\xi_i \eta_j - \xi_j \eta_i) e_i \times e_j \right].$$

Now $e_i \times e_i = 0$ and $e_i \times e_j = -e_j \times e_i$ so that

$$\sum_{1 \leq i < j \leq 3} (\xi_i \eta_j - \xi_j \eta_i) e_i \times e_j = v_1 \times v_2.$$

Hence

$$\varphi(v_1, v_2) = h(v_1 \times v_2).$$

In other words, $V_3(R)$ together with the vector product $f(v_1, v_2) = v_1 \times v_2$ constitute a symmetry class of tensors associated with $H = \{e, (12)\}$ and $\chi = \mathrm{sgn}$.

In general we will let the single symbol $V_\chi^m(H)$ denote a symmetry class of tensors over V associated with H and χ. The most familiar and useful examples are

(i) (*Tensor product*) $H = \{e\}$ in which case $V_\chi^m(H)$ is ordinarily written $\otimes_{i=1}^m V$ and

$$f(v_1, \ldots, v_m) = v_m \otimes \cdots \otimes v_m;$$

(ii) (*Grassmann space*) $H = S_m$, $\chi = \mathrm{sgn}$ in which case the usual notation for $V_\chi^m(H)$ is $\bigwedge^m V$ and $f(v_1, \ldots, v_m)$ is written $x_1 \wedge \cdots \wedge x_m$ [8];

(iii) (*Symmetric space*) $H = S_m$, $\chi \equiv 1$; $V_\chi^m(H)$ is written $V^{(m)}$ and $f(v_1, \ldots, v_m)$ is denoted by $v_1 \cdots v_m$.

It is quite easy to show that if P, f and P_1, f_1 are two symmetry classes over V associated with H and χ, then there exists an onto isomorphism $\theta \colon P \to P_1$ for which $\theta f = f_1$. Thus the conditions (a) and (b) above determine P, f. We can thereby construct a concrete model of symmetry classes to facilitate their study. First, let V have a basis $e_1, \ldots, e_n$ and let P be a vector space of dimension n^m. Index the basis vectors in P by the set of sequences $\Gamma_{m,n}$ consisting of all $\alpha = (\alpha_1, \ldots, \alpha_m)$, $1 \leq \alpha_i \leq n$, and call a typical basis vector e_α. Define $f \colon V \times \cdots \times V \to P$ by

$$f(v_1, \ldots, v_m) = \sum_{\alpha \in \Gamma_{m,n}} \prod_{t=1}^{m} \xi_{t\alpha_t} e_\alpha$$

where $v_t = \sum_{j=1}^{n} \xi_{tj} e_j$, $t = 1, \ldots, m$. Then it is easy to see that P, f is in fact the symmetry class over V associated with the identity group, i.e., it is the tensor product $\otimes_{i=1}^{m} V$ and $f(v_1, \ldots, v_m)$ is written $v_1 \otimes \cdots \otimes v_m$ as before. If V is a unitary space with inner product (u, v), then $\otimes_{i=1}^{m} V$ can be directly made into a unitary space in which the inner product satisfies

$$(u_1 \otimes \cdots \otimes u_m, v_1 \otimes \cdots \otimes v_m) = \prod_{i=1}^{m} (u_i, v_i). \tag{4}$$

Now any $V_\chi^m(H)$ can be regarded as a subspace of $\otimes_{i=1}^{m} V$ and in fact as the range of an idempotent Hermitian operator on $\otimes_{i=1}^{m} V$. More specifically, for any $\sigma \in S_m$ define a *permutation operator* $P(\sigma) \colon \otimes_{i=1}^{m} V \to \otimes_{i=1}^{m} V$ by the universal factorization property:

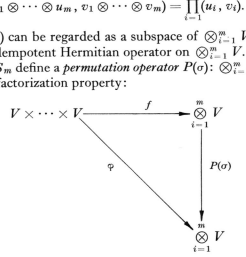

where $\varphi(v_1, \ldots, v_m) = f(v_{\theta(1)}, \ldots, v_{\theta(m)}) = v_{\theta(1)} \otimes \cdots \otimes v_{\theta(m)}$, $(\theta = \sigma^{-1})$, and $P(\sigma)f = \varphi$. In other words

$$P(\sigma) v_1 \otimes \cdots \otimes v_m = v_{\theta(1)} \otimes \cdots \otimes v_{\theta(m)}. \tag{5}$$

Then define a *symmetry operator* $T_\chi \colon \otimes_{i=1}^{m} V \to \otimes_{i=1}^{m} V$ by

$$T_\chi = \frac{1}{h} \sum_{\sigma \in H} \chi(\sigma) P(\sigma) \tag{6}$$

where h is the order of H. Then the range of T_χ can be easily proved to be a symmetry class of tensors over V associated with H and χ by simply defining $P = \text{rng } T_\chi$ and $f(v_1, \ldots, v_m) = T_\chi v_1 \otimes \cdots \otimes v_m$. We shall in general write $f(v_1, \ldots, v_m) = v_1 * \cdots * v_m$ and call this generic tensor the *star product* of $v_1, \ldots, v_m$. Observe next that

$$(P(\sigma)u_1 \otimes \cdots \otimes u_m, v_1 \otimes \cdots \otimes v_m) = \prod_{i=1}^{m} (u_{\sigma^{-1}(i)}, v_i)$$

$$= \prod_{i=1}^{m} (u_i, v_{\sigma(i)})$$

$$= (u_1 \otimes \cdots \otimes u_m, P(\sigma^{-1})v_1 \\ \otimes \cdots \otimes v_m)$$

so that $P(\sigma)^* = P(\sigma^{-1})$. Moreover $P(\sigma_1)P(\sigma_2) = P(\sigma_1\sigma_2)$ and hence if $\theta \in H$

$$P(\theta)T_\chi = \frac{1}{h} \sum_{\sigma \in H} \chi(\sigma)P(\theta\sigma) = \chi(\theta^{-1})T_\chi \tag{7}$$

and hence $T_\chi^2 = T_\chi$, and $T_\chi^* = T_\chi$.

We now tie this up with the original matrix problems introduced in Sec. 1. Thus, for any $m \times m$ matrix $X = (x_{ij})$, define *the generalized matrix function* d_χ associated with χ and H by

$$d_\chi(X) = \sum_{\sigma \in H} \chi(\sigma) \prod_{i=1}^{m} x_{i\sigma(i)}. \tag{8}$$

If $x_1, \ldots, x_m$ and $y_1, \ldots, y_m$ are arbitrary vectors in V then

$$(x_1 * \cdots * x_m, y_1 * \cdots * y_m)$$

$$= (T_\chi x_1 \otimes \cdots \otimes x_m, T_\chi y_1 \otimes \cdots \otimes y_m)$$

$$= (T_\chi^* T_\chi x_1 \otimes \cdots \otimes x_m, y_1 \otimes \cdots \otimes y_m)$$

$$= (T_\chi^2 x_1 \otimes \cdots \otimes x_m, y_1 \otimes \cdots \otimes y_m)$$

$$= (T_\chi x_1 \otimes \cdots \otimes x_m, y_1 \otimes \cdots \otimes y_m)$$

$$= \left(\frac{1}{h} \sum_{\sigma \in H} \chi(\sigma)P(\sigma)x_1 \otimes \cdots \otimes x_m, y_1 \otimes \cdots \otimes y_m \right)$$

$$= \frac{1}{h} \sum_{\sigma \in H} \chi(\sigma)(x_1 \otimes \cdots \otimes x_m, P(\sigma^{-1})y_1 \otimes \cdots \otimes y_m)$$

$$= \frac{1}{h} \sum_{\sigma \in H} \chi(\sigma) \prod_{i=1}^{m} (x_i, y_{\sigma(i)}).$$

We thus have the fundamental identity

$$(x_1 * \cdots * x_m, y_i * \cdots * y_m) = \frac{1}{h} d_\chi[(x_i, y_j)]. \tag{9}$$

It is interesting that by using (9) alone, without further refinements, several classical inequalities can be obtained. Thus, if the Cauchy–Schwarz inequality is applied to the inner product $(x_1 * \cdots * x_m, y_1 * \cdots * y_m)$, we have

$$\frac{1}{h} |d_\chi((x_i, y_j))| = |(x_1 * \cdots * x_m, y_1 * \cdots * y_m)|$$

$$\leq \|x_1 * \cdots * x_m\| \, \|y_1 * \cdots * y_m\|$$

$$= \left[\frac{1}{h} d_\chi((x_i, x_j))\right]^{1/2} \left[\frac{1}{h} d_\chi((y_i, y_j))\right]^{1/2}$$

or

$$|d_\chi((x_i, y_j))| \leq [d_\chi((x_i, x_j))]^{1/2} [d_\chi((y_i, y_j))]^{1/2}. \tag{10}$$

Now let $x_i = \sum_{k=1}^n a_{ik} e_k$, $y_j = \sum_{k=1}^n b_{kj} e_k$ where $e_1, \ldots, e_n$ is an orthonormal basis of V. Then $(x_i, y_j) = \sum_{k=1}^n a_{ik} b_{kj} = (AB)_{ij}$ where $A = (a_{ik})$ is $m \times n$, and $B = (b_{kj})$ is $n \times m$. Also $(x_i, x_j) = \sum_{k=1}^n a_{ik} \bar{a}_{jk} = (AA^*)_{ij}$ and $(y_i, y_j) = \sum_{k=1}^n \bar{b}_{ki} b_{kj} = (B^*B)_{ij}$. Thus (10) becomes

$$|d_\chi(AB)| \leq d_\chi(AA^*)^{1/2} \, d_\chi(B^*B)^{1/2} \tag{11}$$

for any two matrices A and B. In particular, let $m = n$ and $B = I_m$ so that (11) specializes to

$$|d_\chi(A)| \leq d_\chi(AA^*)^{1/2}. \tag{12}$$

Now suppose K is an $n \times n$ positive-semidefinite Hermitian matrix. Then K can be written as $K = AA^*$ where A is triangular so that

$$d_\chi(A) = \prod_{i=1}^n a_{ii} = \det(A).$$

Thus (12) yields

$$\det(K) = |\det(A)|^2 \leq d_\chi(AA^*) = d_\chi(K). \tag{13}$$

The remarkable inequality (13) was originally proved by Schur [10] using a different, rather intricate approach. If we specialize the group H to be the direct product of the two symmetric groups on the integers $1, \ldots, p$ and $p + 1, \ldots, n$, and if $\chi \equiv \mathrm{sgn}$, then $d_\chi(K) = \det(K_p) \det(K_{n-p})$ where K_p is the principal submatrix lying in rows $1, \ldots, p$ of K, and K_{n-p} is the complementary submatrix. Then (13) becomes the classical *Fischer inequality*:

$$\det(K) \le \det(K_p)\det(K_{n-p}). \tag{14}$$

In order to obtain somewhat deeper results it is necessary to introduce two additional ideas: the structure of an orthonormal basis of $V_\chi{}^m(H)$, and the notion of an associated transformation on $V_\chi{}^m(H)$. We need a bit of combinatorial machinery to discuss the elements of a basis in $V_\chi{}^m(H)$. Given the group H and the character χ, introduce an equivalence relation in the set of sequences $\Gamma_{m,n}$ by $\alpha \sim \beta$ if and only if there exists a $\sigma \in H$ such that $\alpha^\sigma = (\alpha_{\sigma(1)}, \ldots, \alpha_{\sigma(m)}) = \beta$. Let $\Delta(H)$ be a system of distinct representatives for $\sim$ for which each $\gamma \in \Delta(H)$ is lowest in the lexicographic ordering among the sequences in the equivalence class to which γ belongs. Define H_γ to be the subgroup of H consisting of those σ for which $\gamma^\sigma = \gamma$. Define $\bar\Delta(H)$ to be the subset of $\Delta(H)$ consisting of those γ for which

$$\sum_{\sigma \in H_\gamma} \chi(\sigma) = \nu(\gamma) \ne 0.$$

One has the following result: *if $e_1, \ldots, e_n$ is a basis of V, then the tensors $e_\gamma{}^* = e_{\gamma_1} * \cdots * e_{\gamma_m}$, $\gamma \in \bar\Delta(H)$, constitute a basis of $V_\chi{}^m(H)$; if $e_1, \ldots, e_n$ is an orthonormal basis of V then the tensors*

$$[h/\nu(\gamma)]^{1/2} e_\gamma{}^*, \qquad \gamma \in \bar\Delta(H), \tag{15}$$

constitute an orthonormal basis of $V_\chi{}^m(H)$.

Examples:

(i) $H = \{e\}$. Then $\bar\Delta(H) = \Delta(H) = \Gamma_{m,n}$. Thus $\otimes_{i=1}^m V$ has as an orthonormal basis the tensors $e_\gamma{}^* = e_{\gamma_1} \otimes \cdots \otimes e_{\gamma_m}$, $\gamma \in \Gamma_{m,n}$.

(ii) $H = S_m$, $\chi = \mathrm{sgn}$, $(m \le n)$. Then $\bar\Delta(H)$ is the totality $Q_{m,n}$ of strictly increasing sequences γ, $1 \le \gamma_1 < \cdots < \gamma_m \le n$. Thus the Grassman space $\bigwedge^m$ has the orthonormal basis $(m!)^{1/2} e_\gamma{}^* = (m!)^{1/2} e_{\gamma_1} \wedge \cdots \wedge e_{\gamma_m}$, $\gamma \in Q_{m,n}$.

(iii) $H = S_m$, $x \equiv 1$. Then $\bar\Delta(H) = \Delta(H)$ is the totality $G_{m,n}$ of non-decreasing sequences γ, $1 \le \gamma_1 \le \cdots \le \gamma_m \le n$. Thus the symmetric space $V^{(m)}$ has the orthonormal basis

$$\left(\frac{m!}{\prod_{t=1}^n m_t(\gamma)!} \right)^{1/2} e_{\gamma_1} \cdots e_{\gamma_m}, \qquad \gamma \in G_{m,n}$$

where $m_t(\gamma)$ is the multiplicity of occurrence of the integer t in γ; e.g., $m_4(1, 2, 4, 4, 6, 8, 8) = 2$.

The proofs of the general result (15) and these special cases are omitted here, but they are purely combinatorial in nature and rely only on the fact that $V_\chi{}^m(H) = \mathrm{rng}\ T_\chi$.

Next, let $A: V \to V$ be a linear transformation and consider the diagram

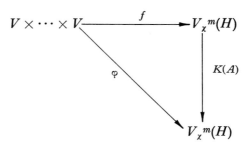

where $\varphi(v_1, \ldots, v_m) = f(Av_1, \ldots, Av_m) = Av_1 * \cdots * Av_m$. Then by the universal factorization property there exists a linear transformation $K(A): V_\chi{}^m(H) \to V_\chi{}^m(H)$ satisfying

$$K(A)v_1 * \cdots * v_m = Av_1 * \cdots * Av_m \tag{16}$$

for all $v_1, \ldots, v_m$ in V. The transformation $K(A)$ is called the *associated* transformation. The formula (16) tells us that if A has eigenvalues $\lambda_1, \ldots, \lambda_n$, then $K(A)$ has eigenvalues $\lambda_{\gamma_1} \cdots \lambda_{\gamma_m}$, $\gamma \in \bar{\Delta}(H)$. Moreover $K(A)$ is easily seen to inherit the following properties from A: being normal, Hermitian, unitary, and nonsingular. Also, if A and B are two linear transformations on V then $K(AB) = K(A)K(B)$ and $K(A)^* = K(A^*)$.

3. Further Inequalities

An interesting set of inequalities due to Weyl [*12*] relate the eigenvalues and singular values of an arbitrary linear transformation A. Recall that the singular values of A are the nonnegative square roots of the eigenvalues of A^*A. It is well known that if λ_1 is an eigenvalue of A of largest modulus and α_1 is the largest singular value then

$$|\lambda_1| \leq \alpha_1. \tag{17}$$

(Let $Av = \lambda_1 v$, $\|v\| = 1$; then $|\lambda_1| = |(Av, v)| \leq \|Av\| = (A^*Av, v)^{1/2} \leq \alpha_1$.) Now $K(A)^*K(A) = K(A^*)K(A) = K(A^*A)$ so that the singular values of $K(A)$ are the numbers $\alpha_{\gamma_1} \cdots \alpha_{\gamma_m} = \prod_{t=1}^{n} \alpha_t^{m_t(\gamma)}$, $\gamma \in \bar{\Delta}(H)$, where $\alpha_1 \geq \cdots \geq \alpha_n$ are the singular values of A. If $\lambda_1, \ldots, \lambda_n$, $|\lambda_i| \geq |\lambda_{i+1}|$, are all the eigenvalues of A it follows from (17) applied to $K(A)$ that

$$\max_{\gamma \in \bar{\Delta}(H)} \prod_{t=1}^{n} |\lambda_t|^{m_t(\gamma)} \leq \max_{\gamma \in \bar{\Delta}(H)} \prod_{t=1}^{n} \alpha_t^{m_t(\gamma)}. \tag{18}$$

Weyl actually used this proof but applied it in the case $H = S_m$, $\chi = \mathrm{sgn}$. As we indicated before, in this case $\bar{\Delta}(H)$ becomes $Q_{m,n}$, the strictly increasing sequences, and thus (18) specializes to

$$\prod_{t=1}^{m} |\lambda_t| \leq \prod_{t=1}^{m} \alpha_t, \qquad m = 1, \ldots, n, \tag{19}$$

with equality when $m = n$, in which case both sides are $|\det(A)|$.

In [3] the following useful identity is announced. Let $v_1, \ldots, v_n$ and $e_1, \ldots, e_n$ be two orthonormal bases for V. Then for each $\omega \in \bar{\Delta}(H)$ and each $1 \leq t \leq n$

$$\sum_{i=1}^{n} m_i(\omega)|(e_i, v_t)|^2 = \sum_{\gamma \in \bar{\Delta}(H)} m_t(\gamma) \left| \left(\left(\frac{h}{\nu(\omega)} \right)^{1/2} e_\omega^*, \left(\frac{h}{\nu(\gamma)} \right)^{1/2} v_\gamma^* \right) \right|^2. \tag{20}$$

The importance of the identity (20) is that it relates projections of orthonormal bases in V with projections of the induced orthonormal bases in $V_\chi{}^m(H)$. Using (20) we next state and prove an inequality for subdeterminants of an Hermitian matrix that contains as special cases many of the Hadamard–Fischer inequalities.

Theorem. *Let A be an $n \times n$ positive-definite Hermitian matrix. Let $A_1, \ldots, A_k$ be an arbitrary set of principal submatrices of A in which the main diagonal entry a_{ii} appears in a total of p_i of the indicated submatrices, $i = 1, \ldots, n$ (p_i may be 0). If $\alpha_1 \geq \cdots \geq \alpha_n$ are the eigenvalues of A, then*

$$\prod_{j=1}^{k} \det(A_j) \geq \prod_{t=1}^{n} \alpha_t^{p_{\varphi(t)}}, \tag{21}$$

where $\varphi \in S_n$ is chosen so that $p_{\varphi(1)} \leq \cdots \leq p_{\varphi(n)}$.

Proof. Let R^n be the space of n-tuples and define $T: R^n \to R^n$ by $Tx = A^T x$, $x \in R^n$. Let $v_1, \ldots, v_n$ be an orthonormal basis of eigenvectors of T with corresponding eigenvalues $\alpha_1, \ldots, \alpha_n$.

Let $e_i = (\delta_{i1}, \ldots, \delta_{in}) \in R^n$, $i = 1 \ldots, n$, so that for any $\omega \in Q_{m,n}$

$$\det[(Te_{\omega_i}, e_{\omega_j})] = \det[(A^T e_{\omega_i}, e_{\omega_j})]$$
$$= \det(a_{\omega_i, \omega_j})$$
$$= \det(A[\omega|\omega]).$$

(The matrix $A[\omega|\omega]$ is just the principal submatrix of A lying in rows and columns numbered ω.) Then if $K(T)$ denotes the associated transformation on the Grassman space $\bigwedge^m V$, we have, by (9) and (16),

$$\det(A[\omega|\omega]) = m!(K(T)e_\omega^*, e_\omega^*)$$

$$= m! \sum_{\gamma \in Q_{m,n}} \prod_{t=1}^{n} \alpha_t^{m_t(\gamma)} |(e_\omega^*, (m!)^{1/2} v_\gamma^*)|^2$$

$$= \sum_{\gamma \in Q_{m,n}} \prod_{t=1}^{n} \alpha_t^{m_t(\gamma)} |((m!)^{1/2} e_\omega^*, (m!)^{1/2} v_\gamma^*)|^2. \tag{22}$$

Let $c_{\omega,\gamma} = |((m!)^{1/2}e_\omega{}^*, (m!)^{1/2}v_\gamma{}^*)|^2$ and let $s_{it} = |(e_i, v_t)|^2$. Then, since $\sum_{\gamma \in Q_{m,n}} c_{\omega,\gamma} = 1$ [i.e., $(m!)^{1/2}e_\omega{}^*$ is a unit vector and $(m!)^{1/2}v^*$ is an orthonormal basis of $\bigwedge^m V$], we can use the arithmetic–geometric mean inequality in (22) to obtain

$$\det(A[\omega|\omega]) = \sum_{\gamma \in Q_{m,n}} \prod_{t=1}^{n} \alpha_t^{m_t(\gamma)} c_{\omega,\gamma}$$

$$\geq \prod_{\gamma \in Q_{m,n}} \left(\prod_{t=1}^{n} \alpha_t^{m_t(\gamma)} \right)^{c_{\omega,\gamma}}$$

$$= \prod_{t=1}^{n} \alpha_t^{\sum_{\gamma \in Q_{m,n}} m_t(\gamma) c_{\omega,\gamma}}.$$

We now apply the identity (20) to obtain

$$\det(A[\omega|\omega]) \geq \prod_{t=1}^{n} \alpha_t^{\sum_{i=1}^{n} m_i(\omega) s_{it}}.$$

The hypotheses state that we have k increasing sequences $\omega^1, \ldots, \omega^k$ such that a_{ii} appears p_i times altogether among the $A[\omega^j|\omega^j] = A_j$, $j = 1, \ldots, k$, i.e.,

$$\sum_{j=1}^{k} m_i(\omega^j) = p_i, \qquad i = 1, \ldots, n,$$

and hence

$$\prod_{j=1}^{k} \det(A_j) = \prod_{j=1}^{k} \det(A[\omega^j|\omega^j])$$

$$\geq \prod_{j=1}^{k} \prod_{t=1}^{n} \alpha_t^{\sum_{i=1}^{n} m_i(\omega^j) s_{it}}$$

$$= \prod_{j=1}^{n} \alpha_t^{\sum_{i=1}^{n} s_{it} \sum_{j=1}^{k} m_i(\omega^j)}$$

$$= \prod_{t=1}^{n} \alpha_t^{\sum_{i=1}^{n} p_i s_{it}}. \tag{23}$$

Let L be the left side of (23) so that taking logarithms we have

$$\log L \geq \sum_{t=1}^{n} \log \alpha_t \sum_{i=1}^{n} p_i s_{it}. \tag{24}$$

Now if we regard the right side of (24) as a linear function of the doubly stochastic matrix $S = (s_{it})$, then, by the Birkhoff theorem [7], the minimum is assumed on a permutation matrix. But by the rearrangement theorem [2]

$$\min_{\sigma \in S_n} \sum_{t=1}^{n} p_{\sigma(t)} \log \alpha_t = \sum_{t=1}^{n} p_{\varphi(t)} \log \alpha_t.$$

Hence, from (23) we have

$$\prod_{j=1}^{k} \det(A_j) \geq \prod_{t=1}^{n} \alpha_t^{p \, \varphi(t)}.$$

For example if A_1 and A_2 are nonoverlapping principal submatrices that together include every main diagonal entry of A, then each $p_i = 1$ and hence (21) becomes the Fischer inequality

$$\det(A_1) \det(A_2) \geq \prod_{t=1}^{n} \alpha_t = \det(A).$$

Once again, if every main diagonal entry of A occurs in precisely p of the principal submatrices $A_1, \ldots, A_k$ (i.e. p is the same for every main diagonal entry), then

$$\prod_{t=1}^{k} \det(A_t) \geq \prod_{t=1}^{n} \alpha_t^{p} = \det(A)^p.$$

If A_1 is an $m \times m$ principal submatrix of A, then for m values of i, $p_i = 1$ and $p_i = 0$ for the remaining values. In this case (21) becomes the well-known [4]

$$\det(A_1) \geq \prod_{t=1}^{m} \alpha_{n-t+1}.$$

In [5] it was proved that if A is an $n \times n$ positive-definite Hermitian matrix, then the following analog of the Hadamard determinant theorem holds for the permanent function:

$$\text{per}(A) \geq \prod_{i=1}^{n} a_{ii}. \qquad (25)$$

Of course the inequality (25) is a statement about the length of an element of the symmetry class of symmetric tensors, i.e., if A is a Gram matrix based on $x_1, \ldots, x_n$, then $a_{ij} = (x_i, x_j)$ and by (9), $\text{per}(A) = n! \|x_1 * \cdots * x_n\|^2$. Thus (25) takes the form

$$\|x_1 * \cdots * x_n\|^2 \geq \frac{1}{n!} \|x_1\|^2 \cdots \|x_n\|^2.$$

We are able to substantially improve (25) as follows.

Theorem. *Let A be an $n \times n$ positive-definite Hermitian matrix whose minimum eigenvalue is λ_n. Then*

$$\text{per}(A) \geq \prod_{i=1}^{n} a_{ii} + \lambda_n^{n-2} \left(\sum_{n \geq j > i \geq 1} |a_{ij}|^2 \right). \qquad (26)$$

Similarly,

$$\det(A) \leq \prod_{i=1}^{n} a_{ii} - \lambda_n^{n-2} \left(\sum_{n \geq j > i \geq 1} |a_{ij}|^2 \right)$$

Proof. Use the Laplace expansion theorem to obtain

$$\text{per}(A) = \sum_{j=1}^{n} a_{1j} \, \text{per}[A(1|j)]$$

$$= a_{11} \, \text{per}[A(1|1)] + \sum_{j=2}^{n} a_{1j} \, \text{per}\,[A(1|j)]$$

$$= a_{11} \, \text{per}[A(1|1)] + \sum_{j=2}^{n} a_{1j} \sum_{k=2}^{n} a_{k1} \, \text{per}[A(1, k|1, j)],$$

where $A(i|j)$ is the submatrix obtained from A by deleting row i and column j and $A(1, k|1, j)$ is the $(n-2) \times (n-2)$ submatrix obtained by deleting rows 1 and k and columns 1 and j. Set $c_{kj} = \text{per}[A(1, k|1, i)]$, $C = (c_{kj})$, $u_A = (a_{12}, a_{13}, \ldots, a_{1n})$ so that (25) becomes

$$\text{per}(A) = a_{11} \, \text{per}[A(1|1)] + (Cu_A, u_A). \tag{27}$$

The matrix C consists of $(n-2) \times (n-2)$ subpermanents of the matrix $A(1|1)$. The matrix C is thus an $(n-2) \times (n-2)$ principal submatrix of the $(n-2)$ induced power matrix of $A(1|1)$. Designate this latter matrix by $P_{n-2}[A(1|1)]$ [9]. We remark in passing that the induced power matrix is the matrix representation of the associated transformation on the symmetric space with respect to the basis in example (iii) of Sec. 2. The eigenvalues of $P_{n-2}[A(1|1)]$ are the homogeneous products

$$\prod_{t=1}^{n-1} \mu_t^{m_t(\gamma)}, \qquad \gamma \in G_{n-2, n-1}$$

where $\mu_1 \geq \cdots \geq \mu_{n-1} > 0$ are the eigenvalues of $A(1|1)$. Since C is a principal submatrix of $P_{n-2}[A(1|1)]$ it follows by the Cauchy inequalities and (27) that

$$\mu_{n-1}^{n-2} \|u_A\|^2 \leq \text{per}(A) - a_{11} \, \text{per}[A(1|1)] \leq \mu_1^{n-2} \|u_A\|^2,$$

i.e.,

$$\mu_{n-1}^{n-2} \sum_{j=2}^{n} |a_{1j}|^2 \leq \text{per}(A) - a_{11} \, \text{per}[A(1|1)] \leq \mu_1^{n-2} \sum_{j=2}^{n} |a_{1j}|^2.$$

Hence

$$\text{per}(A) \geq a_{11} \, \text{per}[A(1|1)] + \lambda_n^{n-2} \sum_{j=2}^{n} |a_{1j}|^2. \tag{28}$$

If we apply the inequality (28) to $A(1|1)$ we have

$$\text{per}[A(1|1)] \geq a_{22} \, \text{per}[A(1, 2|1, 2)] + \lambda_n^{n-3} \sum_{j=3}^{n} |a_{2j}|^2. \tag{29}$$

Combining (28) and (29) and using the fact that $a_{11} \geq \lambda_n$, we have

$$\text{per}(A) \geq a_{11}\left(a_{22}\,\text{per}[A(1,2|1,2)] + \lambda_n^{n-3}\sum_{j=3}^{n}|a_{2j}|^2\right) + \lambda_n^{n-2}\left(\sum_{j=2}^{n}|a_{1j}|^2\right)$$

$$\geq a_{11}a_{22}\,\text{per}[A(1,2|1,2)] + \lambda_n^{n-2}\left(\sum_{j=2}^{n}|a_{1j}|^2 + \sum_{j=3}^{n}|a_{2j}|^2\right).$$

Continuing in this way we obtain (26). We omit the similar proof of the generalization of the Hadamard inequality.

As a final example of some of these techniques, we will look at the statement of Parseval's identity in a general symmetry class $V_\chi^m(H)$. As we know, if $e_1, \ldots, e_n$ is an orthonormal basis of V then the tensors

$$\left[\frac{h}{\nu(\omega)}\right]^{1/2} e_\omega^*$$

constitute an orthonormal basis of $V_\chi^m(H)$. Thus for any $x_1, \ldots, x_m$ and $y_1, \ldots, y_m$ in V, we have

$$(x_1 * \cdots * x_m, y_1 * \cdots * y_m)$$

$$= \sum_{\omega \in \bar{\Delta}(H)} \frac{h}{\nu(\omega)}(x_1 * \cdots * x_m, e_\omega^*)(e_\omega^*, y_1 * \cdots * y_m).$$

and, for any $\omega \in \bar{\Delta}(H)$ we have

$$\|x_1 * \cdots * x_m\|^2 \geq \frac{h}{\nu(\omega)}|(x_1 * \cdots * x_m, e_\omega^*)|^2. \tag{30}$$

In particular, suppose that $((x_i, x_j)) = A$ is doubly stochastic, i.e.

$$1 = \sum_{j=1}^{m} a_{ij} = \left(x_i, \sum_{j=1}^{m} x_j\right).$$

Let $x = \sum_{j=1}^{m} x_j$ and let $e_1 = x/\|x\|$ so that in case $V_\chi^m(H) = V^{(m)}$, i.e., $H = S_m$, $\chi \equiv 1$, we have $\omega = (1, \ldots, 1) \in G_{m,n} = \bar{\Delta}(H)$, and (30) becomes

$$\frac{1}{m!}\text{per}(A) \geq \frac{m!}{m!}\left|\frac{1}{m!}\text{per}((x_i, e_1))\right|^2,$$

i.e.,

$$\text{per}(A) \geq m! \prod_{i=1}^{m}|(x_i, e_1)|^2.$$

But,

$$(x_i, e_1) = \left(x_i, \frac{x}{\|x\|}\right) = \frac{1}{\|x\|}\sum_{j=1}^{m}(x_i, x_j) = \frac{1}{\|x\|}.$$

Also,

$$\|x\| = (x, x)^{1/2} = \left[\sum_{i,j=1}^{m} (x_i, x_j) \right]^{1/2} = \left[\sum_{i=1}^{m} \sum_{j=1}^{m} (x_i, x_j) \right]^{1/2} = m^{1/2}.$$

Hence

$$\operatorname{per}(A) \geq m!/m^m. \tag{31}$$

In other words, on the convex body consisting of all positive-semidefinite Hermitian doubly stochastic matrices, the minimum value of the permanent function is assumed at the centroid, i.e.

$$\operatorname{per}(A) \geq \operatorname{per}(J_m) = m!/m^m,$$

where every entry of J_m is $1/m$. The question of whether (31) holds for *any* doubly stochastic matrix is at present unanswered.

REFERENCES

[1] Beckenbach, E. F., and Bellman, R., "Inequalities," Springer, Berlin, 1961.

[2] Hardy, G. H., Littlewood, J. E., and Pólya, G., "Inequalities," Cambridge Univ. Press, London and New York, 1952.

[3] Marcus, M., Matrix applications of a quadratic identity for decomposable symmetrized tensors, *Bull. Amer. Math. Soc.* **71**, 360–364 (1965).

[4] Marcus, M., Convex functions of quadratic forms, *Duke Math. J.* **24**, 321–326 (1957).

[5] Marcus, M., The Hadamard theorem for permanents, *Proc. Amer. Math. Soc.* **15**, 967–973 (1964).

[6] Marcus, M., and Minc, H., Permanents, *Amer. Math. Monthly* **72**, 577–591 (1965).

[7] Marcus, M., and Minc, H., "A Survey of Matrix Theory and Matrix Inequalities," Allyn and Bacon, Boston, 1964.

[8] Mostow, G. D., Sampson, J. H., and Meyer, J. P., "Fundamental Structures of Algebra," Chap. 16. McGraw-Hill, New York, 1963.

[9] Ryser, H. J., Compound and induced matrices in combinatorial analysis, *Proc. Symp. Appl. Math.* **10**, 149–167 (1960) (Amer. Math. Soc.).

[10] Schur, I., Über endliche Gruppen und Hermitesche Formen, *Math. Z.* **1**, 184–207 (1918).

[11] Wedderburn, J. H. M., "Lectures on matrices" (Colloq. Publ. Vol. 17), pp. 75–76. Amer. Math. Soc., Providence, Rhode Island, 1934.

[12] Weyl, H., Inequalities between the two kinds of eigenvalues of a linear transformation, *Proc. Nat. Acad. Sci. USA* **35**, 408–411 (1949).

Monotonicity of Ratios of Means and Other Applications of Majorization

ALBERT W. MARSHALL
Boeing Scientific Research Laboratories
Seattle, Washington

INGRAM OLKIN
Stanford University, Stanford, California and
Boeing Scientific Research Laboratories
Seattle, Washington

and

FRANK PROSCHAN
Boeing Scientific Research Laboratories
Seattle, Washington

1. Introduction and Summary

It is well known that if $a_1, \ldots, a_n$ are positive numbers, then the mean $(\sum_1^n a_i^r/n)^{1/r}$ is increasing in r. In this paper, we first obtain conditions for the monotonicity of the ratio $(\sum_1^n a_i^r/\sum_1^n b_i^r)^{1/r}$ of means (and for its continuous version). The conditions for monotonicity permit $b_1 = \cdots = b_n = 1$, so that $\sum b_i^r = n$, and thus the classical result becomes a special case.

Since monotonicity of a ratio can be viewed as a form of total positivity, the theory of total positivity is exploited (Sec. 3) to obtain more general versions of the result above.

The proof of monotonicity is based on a theorem which gives sufficient conditions for majorization. Because majorization leads to many different forms of inequalities (see Hardy *et al.* [9] and Beckenbach and Bellman [2]), it is not surprising that a diversity of applications of the majorization result are obtained.

One application concerns a stochastic comparison between a function of order statistics from a distribution with increasing failure rate average and the same function of the order statistics from the exponential distribution. The use of these stochastic comparisons in testing certain statistical hypotheses is pointed out (Sec. 5).

Marshall and Olkin [10] compare the condition number of a matrix A

with the condition number of its symmetrized version AA^*. The majorization result is applied (Sec. 6) to obtain a comparison between the condition number of a positive-definite matrix and the condition number of a polynomial in the matrix.

In the final application, several inequalities concerning absolute deviations are obtained (Sec. 7) which generalize known results.

Remark.   To avoid awkward notation we often omit subscripts in sums or in vectors, e.g., $\sum x \log x = \sum_1^n x_i \log x_i$, and

$$\left(\frac{a^r}{\sum a^r}\right) \equiv \left(\frac{a_1^r}{\sum\limits_1^n a_i^r}, \ldots, \frac{a_n^r}{\sum\limits_1^n a_i^r}\right).$$

2. Majorization

To determine conditions on $(a_1, \ldots, a_n)$ and $(b_1, \ldots, b_n)$ such that $g(r) \equiv (\sum a^r / \sum b^r)^{1/r}$ is nondecreasing in r, one might set $d \log g(r)/dr \geq 0$, or equivalently,

$$\sum \left(\frac{a^r}{\sum a^r}\right) \log\left(\frac{a^r}{\sum a^r}\right) \geq \sum \left(\frac{b^r}{\sum b^r}\right) \log\left(\frac{b^r}{\sum b^r}\right). \tag{2.1}$$

Inequalities of this type can be obtained under appropriate conditions using majorization.

Definition 2.1.   *If* $a_1 \geq \cdots \geq a_n$, $b_1 \geq \cdots \geq b_n$, $\sum_1^k a_j \geq \sum_1^k b_j$ *for* $k = 1, 2, \ldots, n-1$, *and* $\sum_1^n a_j = \sum_1^n b_j$, *then* $a = (a_1, \ldots, a_n)$ *is said to majorize* $b = (b_1, \ldots, b_n)$, *written* $a \succ b$.

Remark.   An alternative definition of majorization is sometimes used: A set $\{a\}$ is said to majorize a set $\{b\}$ if, possibly after ordering of the elements of each set, the conditions of Definition 2.1 are satisfied (Hardy *et al.* [9, p. 45]).

Definition 2.2.   *A real function* φ *of n real variables is said to be a* Schur function *if for every pair* $i \neq j$, $(x_i - x_j)(\partial\varphi/\partial x_i - \partial\varphi/\partial x_j) \geq 0$.

These concepts are linked in the basic theorem:

Theorem 2.3.   (Schur [15], Ostrowski [12]).   *Let* $\varphi(x)$ *be defined for* $x_1 \geq \cdots \geq x_n$. *Then* $\varphi(a) \geq \varphi(b)$ *for all* $a \succ b$ *if and only if* φ *is a Schur function.*

Remark. If the alternative definition of majorization is used (see the remark after Definition 2.1), then the requirement that φ be symmetric must be imposed.

Now $\sum x \log x$ is a Schur function since all functions of the form $\sum_1^n g(x_i)$, g convex, are Schur functions. Thus to prove (2.1) it is sufficient that $(\alpha/\sum\alpha) \succ (\beta/\sum\beta)$, where $\alpha_i = a_i^r$ and $\beta_i = b_i^r$ $(r \geq 0)$ and where $\alpha_i = a_{n-i+1}^r$ and $\beta_i = b_{n-i+1}^r$ $(r < 0)$, $i = 1, \ldots, n$.

Theorem 2.4. *If $\alpha_1 > 0, \ldots, \alpha_n > 0, \beta_1 \geq \cdots \geq \beta_n > 0$, and $\beta_1/\alpha_1 \leq \cdots \leq \beta_n/\alpha_n$, then $(\alpha/\sum\alpha) \succ (\beta/\sum\beta)$.*

Proof. Note that the hypotheses imply $\alpha_1 \geq \cdots \geq \alpha_n > 0$. Thus, we must prove that for $k = 1, \ldots, n-1$,

$$\sum_1^k \alpha_j / \sum_1^n \alpha_l \geq \sum_1^k \beta_j / \sum_1^n \beta_l .$$

This follows from

$$\sum_1^k \alpha_j \sum_1^n \beta_l - \sum_1^k \beta_j \sum_1^n \alpha_l = \sum_1^k \alpha_j \sum_{k+1}^n \beta_l - \sum_1^k \beta_j \sum_{k+1}^n \alpha_l$$

$$= \sum_{j=1}^k \sum_{l=k+1}^n \alpha_j \alpha_l \left(\frac{\beta_l}{\alpha_l} - \frac{\beta_j}{\alpha_j} \right) \geq 0.$$

Using Theorems 2.3 and 2.4 with (2.1), we have thus derived the following

Theorem 2.5. *If $a_1 > 0, \ldots, a_n > 0$, $b_1 \geq \cdots \geq b_n > 0$, $b_1/a_1 \leq \cdots \leq b_n/a_n$, then $(\sum a^r / \sum b^r)^{1/r}$ is increasing in r.*

Proof. A more direct though possibly less clearly motivated proof of Theorem 2.5 can be given which is again based upon $(a^r/\sum a^r) \succ (b^r/\sum b^r)$ (after reordering when $r < 0$). Since $\phi(x_1, \ldots, x_n) = \sum x^t$, $t \geq 1$, is a symmetric Schur function, it follows from Theorem 2.3 that $\sum(a^r/\sum a^r)^t \geq \sum(b^r/\sum b^r)^t$. Monotonicity in $r < 0$ and in $r > 0$ is a consequence of choosing $t = s/r$, $|s| \geq |r|$. Monotonicity in all r then follows from $(\sum a^{-r}/\sum b^{-r})^{-1/r} \leq (\sum a^r/\sum b^r)^{1/r}$, $r > 0$, which is obtained by choosing $\phi(x_1, \ldots, x_n) = \sum x^{-1}$.

An important example in which the conditions of Theorem 2.4 are satisfied is obtained by choosing $\alpha_i = \psi(\beta_i)$, where ψ is a nonnegative star-shaped function. (A real function ψ defined on $[0, \infty)$ is said to be *star-shaped* if $\psi(x)/x$ is increasing in x. An interesting example of starshapedness is furnished by every ψ which is convex on $[0, \infty)$ and satisfies $\psi(0) \leq 0$. Note that a nonnegative starshaped function ψ must be increasing and must satisfy $\psi(0) = 0$. Such functions are discussed by Bruckner and Ostrow [5].) With this choice, assuming $\beta_1 \geq \cdots \geq \beta_n > 0$, it follows that $\alpha_1 \geq \cdots \geq \alpha_n \geq 0$, so that by Theorem 2.4,

$$\left(\frac{\beta}{\sum \beta} \right) \prec \left(\frac{\psi(\beta)}{\sum \psi(\beta)} \right) = \left(\frac{\alpha}{\sum \alpha} \right). \tag{2.2}$$

3. An Extension Using Total Positivity

Theorems 2.4 and 2.5 can be viewed as theorems on total positivity and can be proved by the methods of total positivity. A matrix (t_{ij}) of nonnegative numbers is said to be *totally positive of order 2* (TP$_2$) if all its 2×2 minors are nonnegative. Similarly, a nonnegative function $t(x, y)$ of real variables x belonging to $\mathcal{X}$, and y belonging to $\mathcal{Y}$, is said to be totally positive of order 2 if, for all $x_1 < x_2$ in $\mathcal{X}$ and $y_1 < y_2$ in $\mathcal{Y}$, the determinant

$$\det \begin{bmatrix} t(x_1, y_1) & t(x_1, y_2) \\ t(x_2, y_1) & t(x_2, y_2) \end{bmatrix} \geq 0.$$

Suppose the t_{ij} are nonnegative; then (t_{ij}) is clearly TP$_2$ if and only if $t_{i+1,j}/t_{ij}$ is increasing in j for each i.

Let $t_{1j} = \alpha_j > 0$, $t_{2j} = \beta_j > 0$, $j = 1, 2, \ldots, n$; then β_i/α_i being increasing in i is equivalent to (t_{ij}) being TP$_2$. Since it is easily concluded from Theorem 2.4 that $\sum_1^k \alpha_i / \sum_1^l \alpha_j \geq \sum_1^k \beta_i / \sum_1^l \beta_j$ for all $k \leq l$, Theorem 2.4 essentially states that if (t_{ij}) is TP$_2$ and $T_{ik} = \sum_{j=1}^k t_{ij}$, then (T_{ij}) is TP$_2$. Write $T_{ik} = \sum_{j=1}^n t_{ij} H_{jk}$, where H_{jk} is 1 for $j \leq k$, and is 0 for $j > k$. Since (H_{jk}) is TP$_2$, Theorem 2.4 follows from a standard theorem on total positivity which asserts that

$$\varphi(x, z) \equiv \int \varphi_1(x, y) \varphi_2(y, z) \, d\mu(y)$$

is TP$_2$ provided $\varphi_1(x, y)$ and $\varphi_2(y, z)$ are each TP$_2$.

Because monotonicity of ratios can be interpreted as total positivity of order 2, Theorem 2.5 also is a statement of total positivity. This suggests the following generalization.

Theorem 3.1.   *Let $g(x, y)$ be TP$_2$ and decreasing in y for each x. Then*

$$h(x, s) \equiv \left[\int g^{1/s}(x, y) \, d\mu(y) \right]^s$$

is TP$_2$.

Proof.   Define

$$u(x, s) = \log h(x, s) = s \log \int g^{1/s}(x, y)\, d\mu(y).$$

Then

$$-s^2 \left[\int g^{1/s}\, d\mu \right]^2 \frac{\partial^2 u(x, s)}{\partial x\, \partial s}$$

$$= \int g^{1/s}\, d\mu \int g^{1/s-1} g_x \log g\, d\mu - \int g^{1/s-1} g_x\, d\mu \int g^{1/s} \log g\, d\mu$$

$$= \det \begin{bmatrix} \int g^{1/s}\, d\mu & \int g^{1/s-1} g_x\, d\mu \\[2mm] \int g^{1/s} \log g\, d\mu & \int g^{1/s-1} g_x \log g\, d\mu \end{bmatrix}$$

$$= \iint\limits_{y_1 < y_2} \det \begin{bmatrix} g^{1/s}(x, y_1) & g^{1/s-1}(x, y_1) g_x(x, y_1) \\ g^{1/s}(x, y_2) & g^{1/s-1}(x, y_2) g_x(x, y_2) \end{bmatrix}$$

$$\det \begin{bmatrix} 1 & \log g(x, y_1) \\ 1 & \log g(x, y_2) \end{bmatrix} d\mu(y_1)\, d\mu(y_2),$$

from Problem 68 of Pólya and Szegö [13]. The first determinant of the integrand is nonnegative since $g(x, y)$ is TP$_2$. The second determinant is nonpositive since $g(x, y)$ is decreasing in y for each x. The result follows from the fact that a nonnegative function $h(x, s)$ is TP$_2$ if and only if $\partial^2 \log h(x, s)/\partial x\, \partial s \geq 0$.

To obtain Theorem 2.5 from Theorem 3.1, let y range over the values $1, 2, \ldots, n$ and choose $g(1, i) = a_i$, $g(2, i) = b_i$, and $\mu(i) = 1/n$. We can extend Theorem 2.5 slightly by choosing $\mu(i) = p_i > 0$, $\sum p_i = 1$. Under the hypothesis of Theorem 2.5 we conclude that $(\sum p a^r / \sum p b^r)^{1/r}$ is increasing in r. A further extension is obtained in the next section.

4. Monotonicity of Ratios of Means

With Theorem 2.5 in mind, consider right continuous distributions G and F of nonnegative random variables approximated by step functions with jumps $1/n$ at a_i and b_i, respectively, $a_1 \geq \cdots \geq a_n > 0$, $b_1 \geq \cdots \geq b_n > 0$. Then $\bar{G}(a_i) \approx i/n \approx \bar{F}(b_i)$ (where $\bar{F} \equiv 1 - F$, $\bar{G} \equiv 1 - G$), and the condition b_i/a_i increasing in i becomes $\bar{F}^{-1}(i/n)/\bar{G}^{-1}(i/n)$ increasing in i. In the limit, we obtain the condition $\bar{F}^{-1}(p)/\bar{G}^{-1}(p)$ increasing in p.

To avoid the necessity of assuming that the distribution functions are strictly increasing, define

$$\bar{H}^{-1}(p) = \inf\{x \geq 0: \quad \bar{H}(x) \leq p\}, \qquad H^{-1}(p) = \inf\{x \geq 0: \quad H(x) \geq p\},$$

where H is a distribution function.

Theorem 4.1. *If F and G are distribution functions, $F(0) = 0 = G(0)$, and $\bar{F}^{-1}(p)/\bar{G}^{-1}(p)$ is increasing in p, then*

$$\left[\frac{\int x^r \, dG(x)}{\int x^r \, dF(x)}\right]^{1/r}$$

is increasing in r.

Proof. Using the approximations above, a limiting argument may be used to obtain the result from Theorem 2.5. Alternatively, it may be obtained as a special case of Theorem 3.1 by choosing $g(1, y) = \bar{G}^{-1}(y)$, $g(2, y) = \bar{F}^{-1}(y)$ and taking μ to be uniform on $[0, 1]$.

When $F(0) = 0 = G(0)$, F and G are continuous and have continuous inverses, the hypothesis of Theorem 4.1 has the following equivalent formulations:

(i) $\bar{F}^{-1}(p)/\bar{G}^{-1}(p) \equiv F^{-1}(1-p)/G^{-1}(1-p)$ is increasing in p, $0 < p < 1$;
(ii) $\bar{G}^{-1}\bar{F}(x)/x \equiv G^{-1}F(x)/x$ is increasing in x in the support of F;
(iii) $F(x) = G[\psi(x)]$ for some nonnegative starshaped function ψ;
(iv) If X is a random variable with distribution F, then $\psi(X)$ has distribution G for some nonnegative starshaped ψ.

We say that F *is starshaped with respect to G* if (i), (iii), or (iv) holds, because (i), (iii), and (iv) are equivalent even without the continuity restrictions on F and G. Since the equivalence of (iii) and (iv) is easily verified, we need show only that (i) and (iii) are equivalent. Let $\mathscr{S}_F$ be the set of all x such that $x = \inf\{z: \bar{H}(z) \leq p\}$ for some $p \in (0, 1)$.

Theorem 4.2. *If F and G are right continuous distribution functions such that $F(0) = G(0) = 0$, then $F(x) \equiv G[\varphi(x)]$ for some nonnegative, strictly increasing function φ such that $\varphi(x)/x$ is increasing for all $x \in \mathscr{S}_F$ if and only if $\bar{F}^{-1}(p)/\bar{G}^{-1}(p)$ is increasing in p, $0 < p < 1$.*

Proof. Suppose $F(x) \equiv G[\varphi(x)]$ for some nonnegative strictly increasing φ such that $\varphi(x)/x$ is increasing in $x \in \mathscr{S}_F$. Then

$$\frac{\bar{F}^{-1}(p)}{\bar{G}^{-1}(p)} = \frac{\inf\{x: \bar{F}(x) \leq p\}}{\inf\{x: \bar{G}(x) \leq p\}} = \frac{\inf\{x: \bar{F}(x) \leq p\}}{\inf\{x: \bar{F}(\varphi^{-1}(x)) \leq p\}}$$

$$= \frac{\inf\{y: \bar{F}(y) \leq p\}}{\inf\{\varphi(y): \bar{F}(y) \leq p\}} = \frac{y_p}{\varphi(y_p)}.$$

Now $p < p^*$ implies $y_p \geq y_{p*}$. Thus $p < p^*$ implies

$$y_p/\varphi(y_p) \leq y_{p*}/\varphi(y_{p*}), \quad \text{i.e.,} \quad \bar{F}^{-1}(p)/\bar{G}^{-1}(p) \leq \bar{F}^{-1}(p^*)/\bar{G}^{-1}(p^*).$$

Next, suppose $\bar{F}^{-1}(p)/\bar{G}^{-1}(p)$ is increasing in p, let $y \in \mathscr{S}_F$, and define $\varphi(y) = \bar{G}^{-1}\bar{F}(y) = \inf \{z: \bar{G}(z) \leq \bar{F}(y)\}$. Then since

$$\frac{\bar{F}^{-1}(p)}{\bar{G}^{-1}(p)} = \frac{\inf \{z: \bar{F}(z) < p\}}{\inf \{z: \bar{G}(z) \leq p\}} = \frac{y_p}{\varphi(y_p)}$$

is increasing in p, it follows that $\varphi(y)/y$ is increasing in $y \in \mathscr{S}_F$. Also $\varphi(y)$ is strictly increasing because $\bar{F}(y)$ is strictly decreasing in $y \in \mathscr{S}_F$.

Some choices of F and G in Theorem 4.1 are of special interest.

I. Let F be degenerate at 1. Then $\bar{F}^{-1}(p)/\bar{G}^{-1}(p) = 1/\bar{G}^{-1}(p)$ is increasing for all G. In this case, Theorem 4.1 reduces to the well-known fact that $[\int x^r \, dG(x)]^{1/r}$ is increasing in r for every G.

II. Let $\bar{G}(x) = e^{-x}$. Then the condition $\bar{F}^{-1}(p)/\bar{G}^{-1}(p)$ increasing in p becomes $-x^{-1} \log \bar{F}(x)$ increasing in x. A distribution F with this property is said to have an *increasing failure (hazard) rate average* (IFRA), since in case F has a density f, $-\log \bar{F}(x) = \int_0^x q(u) \, du$, where $q(u) = f(u)/\bar{F}(u)$ is the failure rate of F. Similarly, if $x^{-1} \log \bar{F}(x)$ is decreasing, we say F has a *decreasing failure (hazard) rate average* (DFRA). The class of IFRA (DFRA) distributions has applications in reliability theory (see Birnbaum *et al.* [4]). From Theorem 4.1 we see that if F is IFRA (DFRA), $[\int x^r \, dF(x)/\Gamma(r + 1)]^{1/r}$ is decreasing (increasing) in r. This conclusion was obtained for the smaller class of distributions with increasing (decreasing) failure rate by Barlow *et al.* [1].

Properties of order statistics from IFRA (DFRA) distributions are developed in Sec. 5.

Choose $\bar{F}(x) = e^{-x}$ and G a DFRA distribution for which $\int x^r \, dG(x) = r^r$. (A proof that such a distribution exists has been obtained by H. Rubin and is presented in the appendix.) From Theorem 4.1 it follows that $[r^r/\Gamma(r + 1)]^{1/r}$ is an increasing function of r, a result obtained by Minc and Sathre [11].

III. Let $F(x) = G(x^t)$, $t \geq 1$. Then $\bar{G}^{-1}(p) = [\bar{F}^{-1}(p)]^t$ so that $\bar{F}^{-1}(p)/\bar{G}^{-1}(p) = [\bar{F}^{-1}(p)]^{1-t}$ is increasing in p. Thus, the conditions of Theorem 4.1 are satisfied, and so

$$\left[\frac{\int x^r \, dG(x)}{\int x^r \, dF(x)} \right]^{1/r} = \left[\frac{\int x^{rt} \, dF(x)}{\int x^r \, dF(x)} \right]^{1/r}$$

is increasing in r. More generally, if X has distribution F and $Y = \psi(X)$ has distribution G, where $\psi \geq 0$ is starshaped, then

$$\left\{ \int [\psi(x)]^r \, dF(x) \Big/ \int x^r \, dF(x) \right\}^{1/r}$$

is increasing in r.

5. Statistical Applications

In the present section we make some comparisons involving the order statistics from distributions F and G, where F is starshaped with respect to G.

Let $X_1 \geq \cdots \geq X_n$ be order statistics from F. Then from (2.2) we have for any starshaped $\psi \geq 0$ that

$$\left(\frac{X_1}{\sum X}, \ldots, \frac{X_n}{\sum X}\right) \prec \left(\frac{\psi(X_1)}{\sum \psi(X)}, \ldots, \frac{\psi(X_n)}{\sum \psi(X)}\right).$$

Consequently, if F is starshaped with respect to the distribution G, and $X_1 \geq \cdots \geq X_n$ are order statistics from F, $Y_1 \geq \cdots \geq Y_n$ are order statistics from G, then

$$\left(\frac{X_1}{\sum X}, \ldots, \frac{X_n}{\sum X}\right) \overset{st}{\prec} \left(\frac{Y_1}{\sum Y}, \ldots, \frac{Y_n}{\sum Y}\right), \tag{5.1}$$

i.e., $\sum_1^k X_i / \sum_1^n X_i$ is stochastically less than or equal to $\sum_1^k Y_i / \sum_1^n Y_i$ for $k = 1, \ldots, n$. (A random variable U is stochastically greater than or equal to a random variable V, denoted by

$$U \overset{st}{\geq} V, \qquad \text{if} \quad P\{U \geq a\} \geq P\{V \geq a\}$$

for all a.)

With (5.1), Theorem 2.3 yields some interesting applications. For example, choosing the Schur function $\varphi(z_1, \ldots, z_n) = n^{-1}\sum z^2 - 1$, we obtain

$$\sum (X_i - \bar{X})^2 / \bar{X}^2 \overset{st}{\leq} \sum (Y_i - \bar{Y})^2 / \bar{Y}^2. \tag{5.2}$$

Choosing the Schur function $\varphi(z_1, \ldots, z_n) = n\sum a_i z_i / \sum z_i$, $a_1 \geq \cdots \geq a_n$, $z_1 \geq \cdots \geq z_n$, we obtain

$$\sum a_i X_i / \bar{X} \overset{st}{\leq} \sum a_i Y_i / \bar{Y}, \tag{5.3}$$

where $\bar{X} = \sum X / n$, $\bar{Y} = \sum Y / n$.

An important special case where F is starshaped with respect to G (introduced in Sec. 4) is obtained by choosing $\bar{G}(x) = e^{-x}$ and F to be IFRA. We discuss the statistical applications of (5.2) and (5.3) in this case, although the results hold more generally.

I. Consider first the problem of testing the hypothesis that F is exponential versus the alternative that F is IFRA. Because of the stochastic ordering given by (5.2), a test based on the statistic $R(X) = \sum (X_i - \bar{X})^2 / \bar{X}^2$ is unbiased. (By using different Schur functions, alternative statistics could be used yielding unbiased tests.) To carry out the test at the level of significance α, determine k_α such that $P\{R(X) \leq k_\alpha\} = \alpha$ when F is exponential, and reject the hypothesis of exponentiality when $R(X) \leq k_\alpha$.

For a test of the hypothesis that F is exponential versus the alternative that F has increasing failure rate, i.e., $\log \bar{F}(x)$ is concave where finite, see Proschan and Pyke [14].

II. Next, we discuss testing for outliers when the distribution F is known to be IFRA. Suppose that $X_1 \geq \cdots \geq X_n$ are order statistics from F unless possibly that X_1 is an "outlier," i.e., X_1 does not arise as an observation from F, but from $F_1 \leq F$, $F_1 \not\equiv F$.

A natural test of the hypothesis that $X_1 \geq \cdots \geq X_n$ all come from F is to reject the hypothesis if $X_1/\bar{X}$ is too large. If F is unknown, the distribution of this statistic is unavailable, but since F is IFRA, it follows from (5.3) with $a_1 = 1$, $a_2 = \cdots = a_n = 0$ that $X_1/\bar{X} \leq Y_1/\bar{Y}$, where $Y_1 \geq \cdots \geq Y_n$ are the order statistics from an exponential distribution. To control the type I error, note that $P\{X_1/\bar{X} > k_\alpha\} \leq P\{Y_1/\bar{Y} > k_\alpha\} = \alpha$.

Although the type II error cannot be determined without knowing F_1, we can assert that the type II error is smaller under F_2 than under F_1 whenever F_2 is starshaped with respect to F_1.

Similarly, a test can be obtained when X_n is suspected of being an outlier; here the test statistic is $X_n/\bar{X}$, and we use (5.3) with $a_1 = \cdots = a_{n-1} = 0$, $a_n = -1$ to control the type I error as above. More generally, a test against the possibility that $X_1, \ldots, X_r$ and $X_s, \ldots, X_n$ are all outliers makes use of (5.3) with $a_1 = \cdots = a_r = 1$, $a_{r+1} = \cdots = a_{s-1} = 0$, $a_s = \cdots = a_n = -1$. The test statistic is $(X_s + \cdots + X_n - X_1 - \cdots - X_r)/\bar{X}$.

6. Condition Numbers

A commonly used measure of the difficulty of numerically inverting a nonsingular matrix A is its condition number $c_\varphi(A) = \varphi(A)\,\varphi(A^{-1})$, where ordinarily φ is a norm [i.e., $\varphi(A) > 0$ when $A \neq 0$, $\varphi(\gamma A) = |\gamma|\varphi(A)$ for complex γ, $\varphi(A + B) \leq \varphi(A) + \varphi(B)$]. Marshall and Olkin [10] show that

$$c_\varphi(A) \leq c_\varphi(AA^*) \tag{6.1}$$

when φ is a unitarily invariant norm (i.e., $\varphi(A) = \varphi(UA) = \varphi(AU)$ for all unitary matrices U). The proof is based in part on a result of von Neumann [16] that φ is a unitarily invariant norm if and only if there exists a symmetric gauge function Φ such that $\varphi(A) = \Phi(\alpha)$ for all A, where $\alpha_1^2, \ldots, \alpha_n^2$ are the characteristic roots of AA^*. [A function Φ on a complex vector space is called a symmetric gauge function (SGF) if $\Phi(u) > 0$ when $u \neq 0$, $\Phi(\gamma u) = |\gamma|\,\varphi(u)$ for complex γ, $\Phi(u + v) \leq \Phi(u) + \Phi(v)$, and $\Phi(u_1, \ldots, u_n) = \Phi(\varepsilon_1 u_{i_1}, \ldots, \varepsilon_n u_{i_n})$ whenever $\varepsilon_j = \pm 1$ and $i_1, \ldots, i_n$ is a permutation of $(1, \ldots, n)$.] Using this, a more general result than (6.1) is also obtained by Marshall and Olkin [10], namely, that if Φ is a SGF and $\alpha_i > 0$, then

$$\Phi(\alpha_1^r, \ldots, \alpha_n^r)\, \Phi(\alpha_1^{-r}, \ldots, \alpha_n^{-r}) \qquad \text{is increasing in}\quad r > 0. \tag{6.2}$$

The proof of (6.2) rests on the following lemma.

Lemma 6.1. *If $u \prec v$, Φ is a SGF, and g is a nonnegative convex function, then*

$$\Phi[g(u)] \leq \Phi[g(v)]. \tag{6.3}$$

The proof of (6.3) was given by Fan [7] in case (i) $g(x) = x$, and by Marshall and Olkin [10] in case (ii) $g(x) = x^{-1}$. The proof of Lemma 6.1 parallels that of (ii) where the only properties of x^{-1} used are its nonnegativity and convexity.

We note that every SGF is a Schur function. The result (6.3) does not hold for Schur functions Φ without the additional condition that g is increasing.

In Sec. 2 we have shown that if $\psi \geq 0$ is starshaped, then $[\psi(\beta)/\sum\psi(\beta)] \succ (\beta/\sum\beta)$. In the following, we consider nonnegative starshaped functions of the form $\psi(\beta) = \sum c_j \beta^j$ where $c_j \geq 0$. From (6.3) with $g(x) = x$ we obtain

$$\Phi\left(\frac{\beta_1}{\sum\beta}, \ldots, \frac{\beta_n}{\sum\beta}\right) \leq \Phi\left[\frac{\psi(\beta_1)}{\sum\psi(\beta)}, \ldots, \frac{\psi(\beta_n)}{\sum\psi(\beta)}\right].$$

From (6.3) with $g(x) = x^{-1}$ we obtain

$$\Phi\left(\frac{\sum\beta}{\beta_1}, \ldots, \frac{\sum\beta}{\beta_n}\right) \leq \Phi\left[\frac{\sum\psi(\beta)}{\psi(\beta_1)}, \ldots, \frac{\sum\psi(\beta)}{\psi(\beta_n)}\right].$$

By multiplying these inequalities and using $\Phi(\gamma x) = |\gamma|\, \Phi(x)$, we obtain

$$\Phi(\beta_1, \ldots, \beta_n)\Phi(1/\beta_1, \ldots, 1/\beta_n)$$
$$\leq \Phi[\psi(\beta_1), \ldots, \psi(\beta_n)]\Phi[1/\psi(\beta_1), \ldots, 1/\psi(\beta_n)]. \tag{6.4}$$

The special case $\psi(\beta) = \beta^{s/r}$, $r < s$, and $\beta_i = \alpha_i^r$, $i = 1, 2, \ldots, n$, yields (6.2).

If B is a positive-definite matrix with characteristic roots $\beta_1, \ldots, \beta_n$, then the characteristic roots of $\psi(B) = \sum c_j B^j$ are $\psi(\beta_i) = \sum c_j \beta_i^j$. (For any positive-definite matrix C, the square roots of the characteristic roots of CC^* are the characteristic roots of C.) Hence, in terms of condition numbers, (6.4) becomes

$$c_\varphi(B) \leq c_\varphi[\psi(B)] \tag{6.5}$$

for any positive-definite matrix B.

For any matrix A and any unitarily invariant norm, $c_\varphi(A) = c_\varphi[(AA^*)^{1/2}]$. With $B = (AA^*)^{1/2}$ and $\psi(B) = \sum c_j B^j$, it follows from (6.5) that

$$c_\varphi(A) \leq c_\varphi[\psi(AA^*)^{1/2}]. \tag{6.6}$$

This reduces to (6.1) when $\psi(B) = B^2$.

7. Inequalities for Absolute Deviations

If $c_1, \ldots, c_n$ are real numbers satisfying $\sum_1^n c_i = 0$, then

$$\tfrac{1}{2}\sum |c|^s \leq (\tfrac{1}{2}\sum |c|)^s, \qquad s \geq 1. \tag{7.1}$$

This inequality was proved by Gatti [8] for $s = 2$, and in its present form by Birnbaum [3]. Generalizations of (7.1) can be obtained using Theorems 2.3 and 2.4.

Lemma 7.1.   *If $c_1, \ldots, c_n$ satisfy $\sum_1^n c_i = 0, u_i \equiv |c_i|$, and $u_1 \geq \cdots \geq u_n$, then*

$$\left(\frac{u_1}{\sum u}, \ldots, \frac{u_n}{\sum u}\right) \prec (\tfrac{1}{2}, \tfrac{1}{2}, 0, \ldots, 0). \tag{7.2}$$

Proof.   From $c_1 = -\sum_2^n c_i$ we have $u_1 = |\sum_2^n c_i| \leq \sum_2^n u_i$, so that $2u_1 \leq \sum_1^n u_i$, and consequently $u_1/\sum_1^n u_i \leq \tfrac{1}{2}$. Of course, $(u_1 + u_2)/\sum_1^n u_i \leq 1$.

From (2.2), it follows that for $0 \leq r \leq 1$,

$$\left(\frac{u_1^r}{\sum u^r}, \ldots, \frac{u_n^r}{\sum u^r}\right) \prec \left(\frac{u_1}{\sum u}, \ldots, \frac{u_n}{\sum u}\right). \tag{7.3}$$

Since $\varphi(x_1, \ldots, x_n) = \sum x^t, t \geq 1$, is a Schur function, we have from Theorem 2.3 and (7.2),

$$\left(\frac{u^r}{\sum u^r}\right)^t \leq 2\frac{1}{2^t}, \qquad t \geq 1.$$

The choice $t = s/r, s \geq r$, yields

$$(\tfrac{1}{2}\sum u^r)^{1/r} \geq (\tfrac{1}{2}\sum u^s)^{1/s}, \qquad 0 \leq r \leq 1, r \leq s. \tag{7.4}$$

The result (7.1) corresponds to the case $r = 1$. The restriction $0 \leq r \leq 1$ cannot be relaxed to $0 \leq r$, as may be seen from the choice $c_1 = 1, c_2 = \cdots = c_n = -1/(n-1)$ and $r > 1$.

Remark. If in Lemma 7.1 we define $u_i = h(|c_i|)$ where h is nonnegative and subadditive, i.e., $h(x + y) \leq h(x) + h(y)$, then (7.2) remains valid. The function $h(x) = x^r$, $0 \leq r \leq 1$, leads to (7.4). If $h(x)$ is nonnegative and concave for $x \geq 0$, with $h(0) = 0$, then $h(x)$ is subadditive in $x \geq 0$.

As a consequence of (7.1), De Novellis [6] proves that

$$\sum u^{s+1} \leq \tfrac{1}{2}\sum u \sum u^s \qquad \text{for} \quad s \geq 0. \tag{7.5}$$

Using the generalized version (7.4) of (7.1), a generalized version of (7.5) can be obtained, namely,

$$\sum u^{r+s} \leq \tfrac{1}{2}\sum u^r \sum u^s, \qquad 0 \leq r \leq 1. \tag{7.6}$$

From (7.2) and (7.3), we see that $\tfrac{1}{2} \geq u_1{}^r/\sum u^r$, so that

$$\sum u^{r+s}/\sum u^s = \sum u^r \left(\frac{u^s}{\sum u^s}\right) \leq u_1{}^r \leq \tfrac{1}{2}\sum u^r,$$

which yields (7.6).

The role of $\tfrac{1}{2}$ in (7.2) stems from the fact that $c_1, \ldots, c_n$ can be divided into two sets with equal sums (except for sign). Suppose we have three sets of positive numbers $\{x\}, \{y\}, \{z\}$ such that $\sum_1^{n_1} x_i = \sum_1^{n_2} y_j = \sum_1^{n_3} z_k$. Let $u_1 \geq \cdots \geq u_n$ $(n = n_1 + n_2 + n_3)$ be the ordered x's, y's, and z's. Then

$$\left(\frac{u_1}{\sum u}, \ldots, \frac{u_n}{\sum u}\right) \prec (\tfrac{1}{3}, \tfrac{1}{3}, \tfrac{1}{3}, 0, \ldots, 0).$$

By using arguments analogous to those for the case of two sets, we obtain

$$(\tfrac{1}{3}\sum u^r)^{1/r} \geq (\tfrac{1}{3}\sum u^s)^{1/s}, \qquad 0 \leq r \leq 1, r \leq s,$$

which parallels (7.4). The extension to the case of an arbitrary number of sets is immediate.

Appendix

Theorem. *There exists a decreasing failure rate (DFR) distribution with moments* $\mu_r = r^r, r > 0$.

Proof. (H. Rubin). Consider

$$r^r = \int_0^\infty x^r f(x)\, dx = \int_{-\infty}^\infty e^{-yr} f(e^{-y}) e^{-y}\, dy$$

$$\equiv \int_{-\infty}^\infty e^{-yr} g(y)\, dy.$$

From the inversion formula, Widder [17, p. 241],

$$g(y) = \frac{1}{2\pi i} \int_{-\infty}^{\infty} r^r e^{yr} \, dr = \frac{1}{2\pi i} \int_{-\infty}^{\infty} \exp\left[r \log r + y^r\right] dr.$$

Transform from r to θ by $r = \rho(y, \theta) e^{i\theta}$ choosing ρ in such a manner that $r \log r + y^r$ is real. Since

$$r \log r + yr = \rho[\cos \theta (\log \rho + y) - \theta \sin \theta] + i\rho[\sin \theta (\log \rho + y) + \theta \cos \theta]$$

$$\equiv a + bi,$$

we choose $b = 0$, i.e.,

$$\log \rho = -\theta \cot \theta - y. \tag{A.1}$$

Then

$$r \log r + yr = \rho[\cos \theta(-\theta \cot \theta) - \theta \cos \theta] = -\rho\theta \csc \theta$$

$$= -e^{-y}(\theta \csc \theta \, e^{-\theta \cot \theta})$$

$$\equiv -e^{-y} A(\theta).$$

To determine $dr/d\theta$, note that from (A.1), $d \log \rho / d\theta = \theta \csc^2 \theta - \cot \theta$, so that

$$\frac{dr}{d\theta} = \rho \frac{d}{d\theta} (\cos \theta + i \sin \theta) + e^{i\theta} \frac{d\rho}{d\theta}$$

$$= \rho \csc \theta \left[\theta \cot \theta - 1\right] + i\rho\theta \csc \theta \equiv c + di.$$

Hence

$$g(y) = \frac{1}{2\pi i} \int \exp\left[-e^{-y} A(\theta)\right](c + di) \, d\theta \equiv L + Mi.$$

But $g(y)$ is real, so that the right-hand side must be real. This implies that the complex term vanishes, and that

$$g(y) = \frac{1}{2\pi} \int_{-\pi}^{\pi} \exp\left[-e^{-y} A(\theta)\right] e^{-y} A(\theta) \, d\theta$$

$$= \frac{1}{\pi} \int_{0}^{\pi} \exp\left[-e^{-y} A(\theta)\right] e^{-y} A(\theta) \, d\theta.$$

Let $x = e^{-y}$, then

$$f(x) = \frac{g(-\log x)}{x} = \frac{1}{\pi} \int_{0}^{\pi} e^{-xA(\theta)} A(\theta) \, d\theta,$$

which is a mixture of exponential distributions, and is automatically DFR.

REFERENCES

[1] Barlow, R. E., Marshall, A. W., and Proschan, F., Properties of probability distributions with monotone hazard rate, *Ann. Math. Statist.* **34**, 374–389 (1963).

[2] Beckenbach, E. F., and Bellman, R., "Inequalities." Springer, Berlin, 1961.

[3] Birnbaum, Z. W., On an inequality due to S. Gatti, *Metron* **19**, 3–4 (1958).

[4] Birnbaum, Z. W., Esary, J. D., and Marshall, A. W., Stochastic characterization of wearout for components and systems, *Ann. Math. Statist.* **37**, 816–825 (1966).

[5] Bruckner, A. M., and Ostrow, E., Some function classes related to the class of convex functions, *Pacific J. Math.* **12**, 1203–1215 (1962).

[6] De Novellis, M., Some applications and developments of Gatti-Birnbaum inequality, *Metron* **19**, 245–247 (1958).

[7] Fan, K., Maximum properties and inequalities for the eigenvalues of completely continuous operators, *Proc. Nat. Acad. Sci. U.S.A.* **37**, 760–766 (1951).

[8] Gatti, S., Sul massimo di un indice di anormalità, *Metron* **18**, 181–188 (1956).

[9] Hardy, G. H., Littlewood, J. E., and Pólya, G., "Inequalities," 2nd ed. Cambridge Univ. Press, London and New York, 1952.

[10] Marshall, A. W., and Olkin, I., Norms and inequalities for condition numbers, *Pacific J. Math.* **15**, 241–247 (1965).

[11] Minc, H., and Sathre, L., Some inequalities involving $(r!)^{1/r}$, *Proc. Edinburgh Math. Soc. Ser. II* **14**, 41–46 (1964).

[12] Ostrowski, A., Sur quelques applications des fonctions convexes et concaves au sens de I. Schur, *J. Math. Pures Appl.* **31**, 253–292 (1952).

[13] Pólya, G., and Szegö, G., "Aufgaben und Lehrsätze aus der Analysis," Vol. I, Zweiter Abschnitt. Springer, Berlin, 1925.

[14] Proschan, F., and Pyke, R., Tests for monotone failure rate, *Proc. Fifth Berkeley Symp. Math. Statist. and Probability*, to appear.

[15] Schur, I., Über ein Klasse von Mittelbildungen mit Anwendungen auf die Determinantentheorie, *Sitzber. Berl. Math. Ges.* **22**, 9–20 (1923).

[16] von Neumann, J., Some matrix-inequalities and metrization of matric-space, *Tomsk. Univ. Rev.* **1**, 286–300 (1937) (in "Collected Works," Vol. IV. Pergamon Press, Oxford, 1962).

[17] Widder, D. V., "The Laplace Transform." Princeton Univ. Press, Princeton, New Jersey, 1941.

Ratios of Means and Applications

B. MOND and O. SHISHA
Aerospace Research Laboratories
Wright-Patterson Air Force Base
Dayton, Ohio

1

The main purpose of this paper is to survey a number of inequalities dealing with ratios of means, as well as some related inequalities.

Let $q_1, q_2, \ldots, q_n$ be positive numbers with $\sum_{j=1}^{n} q_j = 1$. Throughout this section, n and the q_j will be held fixed. For every sequence $(x_1, x_2, \ldots, x_n)$ with all $x_k > 0$, consider the *mean of order r*, $M_r(x_1, x_2, \ldots, x_n)$, defined as $(\sum_{k=1}^{n} q_k x_k^r)^{1/r}$ if $r \neq 0$, and as $\prod_{k=1}^{n} x_k^{q_k}$ if $r = 0$.

Let r and s be reals (to be held fixed throughout this section), $r < s$. Then it is known (see, e.g. [3, p. 17] or [11, p. 26]) that for every positive $x_1, x_2, \ldots, x_n$, one has $M_r(x_1, x_2, \ldots, x_n) \leq M_s(x_1, x_2, \ldots, x_n)$, and in fact strict inequality holds except when $x_1 = x_2 = \cdots = x_n$.

Cargo and Shisha [4] considered the ratio $M_s(x_1, x_2, \ldots, x_n)/M_r(x_1, x_2, \ldots, x_n)$ (≥ 1) and sought for it an *upper bound*. They proved the following theorem.

Theorem 1. *Let $0 < A < B$, set $\gamma = B/A$, and let I denote the n-dimensional cube $\{(x_1, x_2, \ldots, x_n): A \leq x_k \leq B; k = 1, 2, \ldots, n\}$. Then throughout I:*

$$M_s(x_1, x_2, \ldots, x_n)/M_r(x_1, x_2, \ldots, x_n) \leq \Delta, \tag{1}$$

where Δ is

$$\left\{\frac{r(\gamma^s - \gamma^r)}{(s-r)(\gamma^r - 1)}\right\}^{1/s}\left\{\frac{s(\gamma^r - \gamma^s)}{(r-s)(\gamma^s - 1)}\right\}^{-1/r} \qquad \text{if} \quad rs \neq 0,$$

$$\left\{\frac{\gamma^{s/(\gamma^s - 1)}}{e \log\{\gamma^{s/(\gamma^s - 1)}\}}\right\}^{1/s} \qquad \text{if} \quad r = 0,$$

and

$$\left\{\frac{\gamma^{r/(\gamma^r - 1)}}{e \log\{\gamma^{r/(\gamma^r - 1)}\}}\right\}^{-1/r} \qquad \text{if} \quad s = 0.$$

191

Let θ be

$$\left\{ \frac{r}{\gamma^r - 1} - \frac{s}{\gamma^s - 1} \right\} \bigg/ (s - r) \qquad \textit{if} \quad rs \neq 0,$$

$$(s \log \gamma)^{-1} - (\gamma^s - 1)^{-1} \qquad \textit{if} \quad r = 0,$$

and

$$(r \log \gamma)^{-1} - (\gamma^r - 1)^{-1} \qquad \textit{if} \quad s = 0.$$

Then $0 < \theta < 1$. Equality in (1) for a point $(x_1, x_2, \ldots, x_n) \in I$ holds if and only if there exists a subsequence $(k_1, k_2, \ldots, k_\mu)$ of $(1, 2, \ldots, n)$ such that $\sum_{m=1}^{\mu} q_{k_m} = \theta$, $x_{k_m} = B$ $(m = 1, 2, \ldots, \mu)$, and $x_k = A$ for every k distinct from all k_m.

This theorem has received a great deal of attention in the literature and has motivated considerable amount of further work.

Beckenbach [1] considered the ratio

$$\frac{M_s(c_1, c_2, \ldots, c_m, x_{m+1}, x_{m+2}, \ldots, x_n)}{M_r(c_1, c_2, \ldots, c_m, x_{m+1}, x_{m+2}, \ldots, x_n)}$$

for fixed positive $c_1, c_2, \ldots, c_m$ and variable positive $x_{m+1}, x_{m+2}, \ldots, x_n$. In the following theorem he gave a lower bound for such a ratio.

Theorem 2. *Let $1 \leq m < n$, and let $c_1, c_2, \ldots, c_m, x_{m+1}, x_{m+2}, \ldots, x_n$ be positive numbers. Then*

$$\frac{M_s(c_1, c_2, \ldots, c_m, x_{m+1}, x_{m+2}, \ldots, x_n)}{M_r(c_1, c_2, \ldots, c_m, x_{m+1}, x_{m+2}, \ldots, x_n)}$$

$$\geq \frac{M_s(c_1, c_2, \ldots, c_m, c^*, c^*, \ldots, c^*)}{M_r(c_1, c_2, \ldots, c_m, c^*, c^*, \ldots, c^*)}. \qquad (2)$$

Here c^* [which appears $n - m$ times in the numerator and $n - m$ times in the denominator of the right-hand side of (2)] is given by

$$c^* = \left[\left(\sum_{j=1}^{m} q_j c_j^s \right) \bigg/ \sum_{j=1}^{m} q_j c_j^r \right]^{1/(s-r)}.$$

We have

$$\min_{1 \leq j \leq m} c_j \leq c^* \leq \max_{1 \leq j \leq m} c_j.$$

Equality holds in (2) if and only if each x_j equals c^*.

Note that if all the c_j are equal, the right-hand side of (2) is 1, but otherwise it is larger than 1.

Similarly [1, Theorem 2], Beckenbach gave an upper bound for the left-hand side of (2), where, again $c_1, c_2, \ldots, c_m$ are fixed, while the x_j are variables satisfying for some constants A, B $(0 < A < B)$, $A \leq x_j \leq B$, $j = m + 1, m + 2, \ldots, n$.

2

As an application of Theorem 1, one has the following (cf. [13]) theorem.

Theorem 3. *Let a_1, a_2, $\ldots$, a_n, b_1, b_2, $\ldots$, b_n be positive numbers. Let $p > 1$, $(1/p) + (1/q) = 1$. Let $0 < A < B$, and suppose*

$$A \leq \frac{a_k^{1/q}}{b_k^{1/p}} \leq B \qquad (k = 1, 2, \ldots, n).$$

Set $\gamma = B/A$. Then

$$1 \leq \frac{\left(\sum_{k=1}^{n} a_k{}^p \right)^{1/p} \left(\sum_{k=1}^{n} b_k{}^q \right)^{1/q}}{\sum_{k=1}^{n} a_k b_k} \leq \left[\frac{q}{p+q} \frac{\gamma^p - \gamma^{-q}}{1 - \gamma^{-q}} \right]^{1/p} \left[\frac{p}{p+q} \frac{\gamma^p - \gamma^{-q}}{\gamma^p - 1} \right]^{1/q}.$$

(3)

Equality holds on the left if and only if all the ratios $a_k^{1/q}/b_k^{1/p}$ are equal. Let

$$\theta = \left[\frac{q}{1 - \gamma^{-q}} - \frac{p}{\gamma^p - 1} \right] \Big/ (p+q).$$

Then $0 < \theta < 1$. Equality holds on the right in (3) *if and only if there exists a subsequence $(k_1, k_2, \ldots, k_\mu)$ of $(1, 2, \ldots, n)$ such that $\sum_{m=1}^{\mu} a_{k_m} b_{k_m} = \theta \sum_{k=1}^{n} a_k b_k$, $a_{k_m}^{1/q}/b_{k_m}^{1/p} = B$ $(m = 1, 2, \ldots, \mu)$, and $a_k^{1/q}/b_k^{1/p} = A$ for every k distinct from all k_m.*

We have included, for completeness, Hölder's inequality and the condition for equality in it.

Proof of Theorem 3. Set $s = p$, $r = -q$,

$$x_k = \frac{a_k^{1/q}}{b_k^{1/p}}, \qquad q_k = \frac{a_k b_k}{\sum\limits_{j=1}^{n} a_j b_j} \qquad (k = 1, 2, \ldots, n).$$

Using Theorem 1 we have

$$1 \leq \left(\sum_{k=1}^{n} q_k x_k{}^p \right)^{1/p} \Big/ \left(\sum_{k=1}^{n} q_k x_k^{-q} \right)^{-1/q} \leq \left[\frac{q}{p+q} \frac{\gamma^p - \gamma^{-q}}{1 - \gamma^{-q}} \right]^{1/p}$$

$$\times \left[\frac{p}{p+q} \frac{\gamma^p - \gamma^{-q}}{\gamma^p - 1} \right]^{1/q},$$

(4)

and $0 < \theta < 1$. Equality holds on the left in (4) if and only if all the x_k are equal. Equality holds on the right in (4) if and only if the condition of the last sentence of Theorem 3 holds. Now

$$\left(\sum_{k=1}^{n} q_k x_k{}^p\right)^{1/p} \Big/ \left(\sum_{k=1}^{n} q_k x_k{}^{-q}\right)^{-1/q} = \left(\sum_{k=1}^{n} a_k{}^p\right)^{1/p} \left(\sum_{k=1}^{n} b_k{}^q\right)^{1/q} \Big/ \sum_{k=1}^{n} a_k b_k,$$

which completes the proof.

Theorem 4. *Let* $a_1, a_2, \ldots, a_n, b_1, b_2, \ldots, b_n$ *be positive numbers. Let* $p > 1, (1/p) + (1/q) = 1$. *Let* $0 < A < B$, *and suppose that for* $k = 1, 2, \ldots, n$,

$$A \leq [a_k/(a_k + b_k)]^{1/q} \leq B,$$
$$A \leq [b_k/(a_k + b_k)]^{1/q} \leq B.$$

Let

$$\gamma = B/A, \qquad \theta = \left(\frac{q}{1 - \gamma^{-q}} - \frac{p}{\gamma^p - 1}\right)\Big/(p + q).$$

Then

$$1 \leq \frac{\left(\sum_{k=1}^{n} a_k{}^p\right)^{1/p} + \left(\sum_{k=1}^{n} b_k{}^p\right)^{1/p}}{\left[\sum_{k=1}^{n} (a_k + b_k)^p\right]^{1/p}}$$

$$\leq \left[\frac{q}{p+q} \frac{\gamma^p - \gamma^{-q}}{1 - \gamma^{-q}}\right]^{1/p} \left[\frac{p}{p+q} \frac{\gamma^p - \gamma^{-q}}{\gamma^p - 1}\right]^{1/q}. \qquad (5)$$

We have $0 < \theta < 1$. *Equality holds on the right in (5) if and only if: (i) there exists a subsequence* $(j_1, j_2, \ldots, j_\mu)$ *of* $(1, 2, \ldots, n)$ *such that*

$$\sum_{m=1}^{\mu} a_{j_m}(a_{j_m} + b_{j_m})^{p-1} = \theta \sum_{k=1}^{n} a_k(a_k + b_k)^{p-1},$$

$$[a_{j_m}/(a_{j_m} + b_{j_m})]^{1/q} = B \qquad (m = 1, 2, \ldots, \mu)$$

and $[a_k/(a_k + b_k)]^{1/q} = A$ *for every* k *distinct from all* j_m; *and (ii) there exists a subsequence* $(k_1, k_2, \ldots, k_\nu)$ *of* $(1, 2, \ldots, n)$ *such that*

$$\sum_{m=1}^{\nu} b_{k_m}(a_{k_m} + b_{k_m})^{p-1} = \theta \sum_{k=1}^{n} b_k(a_k + b_k)^{p-1},$$

$$[b_{k_m}/(a_{k_m} + b_{k_m})]^{1/q} = B \qquad (m = 1, 2, \ldots, \nu),$$

and $[b_k/(a_k + b_k)]^{1/q} = A$ *for every* k *distinct from all* k_m.

The left inequality in (5) is Minkowski's inequality.

Proof of Theorem 4. Set

$$Q = \left[\frac{q}{p+q} \frac{\gamma^p - \gamma^{-q}}{1 - \gamma^{-q}} \right]^{1/p} \left[\frac{p}{p+q} \frac{\gamma^p - \gamma^{-q}}{\gamma^p - 1} \right]^{1/q}.$$

Observe that for $k = 1, 2, \ldots, n$,

$$A \leq a_k^{1/q}/[(a_k + b_k)^{p-1}]^{1/p} \leq B, \qquad A \leq b_k^{1/q}/[(a_k + b_k)^{p-1}]^{1/p} \leq B.$$

By Theorem 3, $0 < \theta < 1$ and

$$\sum_{k=1}^{n} (a_k + b_k)^p = \left[\sum_{k=1}^{n} a_k(a_k + b_k)^{p-1} \right] + \sum_{k=1}^{n} b_k(a_k + b_k)^{p-1}$$

$$\geq Q^{-1} \left\{ \left(\sum_{k=1}^{n} a_k^p \right)^{1/p} \left[\sum_{k=1}^{n} (a_k + b_k)^p \right]^{1/q} \right.$$

$$\left. + \left(\sum_{k=1}^{n} b_k^p \right)^{1/p} \left[\sum_{k=1}^{n} (a_k + b_k)^p \right]^{1/q} \right\},$$

equality on the right holding if and only if (i) and (ii) of Theorem 4 hold. Consequently

$$\frac{\left(\sum_{k=1}^{n} a_k^p \right)^{1/p} + \left(\sum_{k=1}^{n} b_k^p \right)^{1/p}}{\left[\sum_{k=1}^{n} (a_k + b_k)^p \right]^{1/p}} \leq Q,$$

equality holding if and only if (i) and (ii) hold. This completes the proof.

3

If in Theorem 1 we take $r = -1$, $s = 1$, then (1) reduces to

$$\left(\sum_{j=1}^{n} q_j x_j \right) \left(\sum_{j=1}^{n} \frac{q_j}{x_j} \right) \leq \frac{(A+B)^2}{4AB},$$

a well-known inequality due to Kantorovich [12]. In particular, taking each q_j to be $1/n$, one gets

$$\left(\sum_{j=1}^{n} x_j \right) \left(\sum_{j=1}^{n} x_j^{-1} \right) \leq \frac{(A+B)^2}{4AB} n^2,$$

an inequality due to Schweitzer [19].

Let $0 < m_1 \leq a_k \leq M_1$, $0 < m_2 \leq b_k \leq M_2$, $k = 1, 2, \ldots, n$, $n \geq 1$, $m_1 m_2 < M_1 M_2$, and let $\xi_1, \xi_2, \ldots, \xi_n$ be positive numbers. Then $(m_1/M_2)^{1/2} \leq (a_k \xi_k)^{1/2}/(b_k \xi_k)^{1/2} \leq (M_1/m_2)^{1/2}$ $(k = 1, 2, \ldots, n)$. By (3),

$$\frac{\left(\sum_{k=1}^{n} a_k^2 \xi_k^2\right)^{1/2} \left(\sum_{k=1}^{n} b_k^2 \xi_k^2\right)^{1/2}}{\sum_{k=1}^{n} a_k b_k \xi_k^2}$$

$$\leq \left[\frac{1}{2} \frac{\dfrac{M_1 M_2}{m_1 m_2} - \dfrac{m_1 m_2}{M_1 M_2}}{1 - \dfrac{m_1 m_2}{M_1 M_2}}\right]^{1/2} \left[\frac{1}{2} \frac{\dfrac{M_1 M_2}{m_1 m_2} - \dfrac{m_1 m_2}{M_1 M_2}}{\dfrac{M_1 M_2}{m_1 m_2} - 1}\right]^{1/2}$$

Hence,

$$\left(\sum_{k=1}^{n} a_k^2 \xi_k^2\right)\left(\sum_{k=1}^{n} b_k^2 \xi_k^2\right) \leq \frac{(m_1 m_2 + M_1 M_2)^2}{4 m_1 m_2 M_1 M_2}\left(\sum_{k=1}^{n} a_k b_k \xi_k^2\right)^2,$$

an inequality due to Greub and Rheinboldt [10]. In particular, if we take each ξ_k to be 1, we have

$$\left(\sum_{k=1}^{n} a_k^2\right)\left(\sum_{k=1}^{n} b_k^2\right) \leq \frac{(m_1 m_2 + M_1 M_2)^2}{4 m_1 m_2 M_1 M_2}\left(\sum_{k=1}^{n} a_k b_k\right)^2,$$

an inequality due to Pólya and Szegö [17].

REFERENCES

[1] Beckenbach, E. F., On the inequality of Kantorovich, *Amer. Math. Monthly* **71**, 606–619 (1964).
[2] Beckenbach, E. F., A "workshop" on Minkowski's inequality, these Proceedings.
[3] Beckenbach, E. F., and Bellman, R., "Inequalities," 2nd revised printing. Springer, New York, 1965.
[4] Cargo, G. T., and Shisha, O., Bounds on ratios of means, *J. Res. Nat. Bur. Standards* **66B**, 169–170 (1962).
[5] Diaz, J. B., Goldman, A. J., and Metcalf, F. T., Equivalence of certain inequalities complementing those of Cauchy–Schwarz and Hölder, *J. Res. Nat. Bur. Standards* **68B**, 147–149 (1964).
[6] Diaz, J. B., and Metcalf, F. T., Stronger forms of a class of inequalities of G. Pólya–G. Szegö, and L. V. Kantorovich, *Bull. Amer. Math. Soc.* **69**, 415–418 (1963).
[7] Diaz, J. B., and Metcalf, F. T., Complementary inequalities I: Inequalities complementary to Cauchy's inequality for sums of real numbers, *J. Math. Anal. Appl.* **9**, 59–74 (1964).

[8] Diaz, J. B., and Metcalf, F. T., Inequalities complementary to Cauchy's inequality for sums of real numbers, these Proceedings.

[9] Goldman, A. J., A generalization of Rennie's inequality, *J. Res. Nat. Bur. Standards* **68B**, 59–63 (1964).

[10] Greub, W., and Rheinboldt, W., On a generalization of an inequality of L. V. Kantorovich, *Proc. Amer. Math. Soc.* **10**, 407–415 (1959).

[11] Hardy, G. H., Littlewood, J. E., and Pólya, G., "Inequalities," 2nd ed. Cambridge Univ. Press, London and New York, 1952.

[12] Kantorovich, L. V., Functional analysis and applied mathematics (in Russian), *Uspehi Mat. Nauk* **3**, 89–185 (1948).

[13] Marshall, A. W., and Olkin, I., Reversal of the Lyapunov, Hölder, and Minkowski inequalities and other extensions of the Kantorovich inequality, *J. Math. Anal. Appl.* **8**, 503–514 (1964).

[14] Mond, B., A matrix inequality including that of Kantorovich, *J. Math. Anal. Appl.* **13**, 49–52 (1966).

[15] Mond, B., An inequality for operators in a Hilbert space, *Pacific J. Math.* **18**, 161–163 (1966).

[16] Mond, B., and Shisha, O., A difference inequality for operators in Hilbert space, *in* "Blanch Anniversary Volume" (B. Mond, ed.). Aerospace Research Laboratories, Wright-Patterson Air Force Base, Ohio, 1967.

[17] Pólya, G., and Szegö, G., "Aufgaben und Lehrsätze aus der Analysis," Vol. 1, pp. 57, 213–214. Springer, Berlin, 1925.

[18] Rennie, B. C., On a class of inequalities, *J. Austral. Math. Soc.* **3**, 442–448 (1963).

[19] Schweitzer, P., An inequality concerning the arithmetic mean (in Hungarian), *Math. Phys. Lapok* **23**, 257–261 (1914).

[20] Shisha, O., and Cargo, G. T., On comparable means, *Pacific J. Math.* **14**, 1053–1058 (1964).

[21] Shisha, O., and Mond, B., Bounds on differences of means, these Proceedings.

[22] Shisha, O., and Mond, B., Differences of means, *Bull. Amer. Math. Soc.* **73**, 328–333 (1967).

Algebraic Inequalities*

T. S. MOTZKIN
University of California
Los Angeles, California

1. Introduction

Realizing the multitude of problems arising when linear inequalities are mixed with, or replaced by, quadratic inequalities (see, e.g., [*11*]), one can foresee the scope of a theory of polynomial inequalities of arbitrary degree which, as a special case, would have to include the theory of systems of real algebraic equations and thus all of algebraic geometry over the reals. Though algebraic inequalities are still largely *terra incognita*, a few of the characteristic aspects of the theory are emerging and are presented here briefly along with a view to their application in the succeeding papers [*7*] and [*8*].

2. Problems

Consider the solution set $S = S(\Sigma)$ of a system Σ of N nonstrict real polynomial inequalities $g_k \geq 0$ of degree $\leq n$ in real d-space, that is, with d real unknowns. In analogy with other theories of systems of relations we ask:

(1) To which systems Σ (*solution-equivalent systems*) does S belong? and to which *minimal* systems (with smallest N)?

(2) When does deletion of an inequality produce a solution-equivalent system? (The *superfluous* inequality is *de facto* implied by the others. A system without superfluous inequalities is nonredundant.)

(3) When is an inequality solution-equivalent to the empty system? (Identical fulfillment.)

(4) When is S empty? (Solvability.)

(5) If S is not empty, what is its dimension?

(6) Which systems Σ^* belong to the projection S^* of S on a coordinate hyperplane? (Elimination.)

(7) How can we find S? (Solution procedure.)

(8) What properties do the sets S have?

* Sponsored, in part, by NSF Grants GP-2480 and GP-4519.

199

3. Simplest Paradigms

All these questions have been answered in the linear case $n = 1$. Concerning (8) we mention only that here S when nonempty is [3, p. 40] the convex sum of

　　a nonempty convex polyhedron P,
　　a nonempty convex O-polyhedrant (polyhedral cone with the origin O as apex) C, and
　　a nonempty linear space L.

In this *canonical decomposition*, L is uniquely determined by S. Ordinarily (i.e., almost always in the algebro-geometric sense) L is merely O, and then P and C are uniquely determined, and Σ contains a subsystem Σ_0 that is, but for multiplication of each inequality by a positive factor, the only minimal solution-equivalent system, namely the set of inequalities (for $d = 1$ at most 2) that correspond to the faces of S. The other extreme, where L is the entire ambient d-space [(3) above], occurs only when all inequalities have the form $O \geq 0$.

If n is arbitrary but $d = 1$, then Σ is solution-equivalent with a system of degree 2 and, alternatively, with a single equation σ of minimal degree ν that is, but for a positive factor, uniquely given by S. The equation σ need not be part of Σ, and knowledge of n does not imply a bound for ν, unless $n = 1$, when $\nu \leq 2$.

4. Characteristic Features

If both $n > 1$ and $d > 1$, then four fundamental complications are apt to arise. Here, "apt" means that for none of these complications is it true that ordinarily it does not arise.

First, the convex set $\bigcirc\!\!\bigcirc$ bounded by half a lemniscate λ is the solution set S of a minimal system with $d = N = 2$, $n = 4$. Of the members of Σ, only the *essential* inequality corresponding to λ is determined by S (but for a positive factor), not so the other *subsidiary* inequality, even when its degree is required to be minimal, namely one. For unbounded S this complication occurs already for $n = 2$: $\succ\!\!\prec$.

Secondly, the convex set Γ $\;\chi\;$ where the curves γ and γ' are algebraic would seem to be a solution set $S(\Sigma)$; but if γ crosses Γ as in $\oslash$, then Γ cannot be an $S(\Sigma)$, since an inequality belonging to γ is both needed and excluded. This, too, occurs for $n = 2$: $\ominus$, ϕ .

Thirdly, S is apt to be *all of space*; as this must then hold for each inequality separately, we can assume $N = 1$. While for $n = 2$ a polynomial that is always nonnegative is the sum of squares of linear functions, for arbitrary n it need not be the sum of squares of polynomials [2], but only of *rational functions* [1]; their appearance in this role is the fourth complication.

5. Solvability

A polynomial that is always positive is the sum of squares of rational functions and of a positive constant and this, constitutes a criterion for solvability of a system S with $N = 1$.

A more general criterion for implication or redundancy is the following result on conditional nonnegativity ([9], p. 220).

Theorem 1. *If* $f \geq 0$ *whenever* $g_1, \ldots, g_k \geq 0$, *then there exist rational functions* ρ_λ *and products* h_λ *of different* g_i *such that* $f = \Sigma \rho_\lambda^2 h_\lambda$.

(There are 2^k such products, including 1, but the sum may have more than 2^k terms since the h_λ need not be distinct.)

In special cases (see, e.g., [7] and [8]) stronger results hold. In particular, for $n = 1$ the ρ_λ may be chosen as constants and the h_λ as g_λ or 1 [3, p. 51].

The position of Theorem 1 in the theory of nonstrict algebraic inequalities is similar to that of the Hilbert zero theorem (Nullstellensatz) in the theory of algebraic equations over an algebraically closed field.

For $f \equiv -1$ (Theorem 1), the particular linear case mentioned and the zero theorem become solvability criteria for arbitrary N. The linear result, together with its variants when strict inequalities are admitted, is equivalent ([3, p. 53] and [4]) to various transposition or alternative theorems, to minimax theorems, and to separation theorems for convex sets. Theorem 1 and the zero theorem can be so regarded only when sharpened so as to give bounds for the degrees of the numerators and denominators of the ρ_λ and of the p_i (see, e.g., [6] and [9, p. 223]).

The linear result has important generalizations to infinite-dimensional spaces; such generalizations are still desiderata for algebraic inequalities or equations.

6. Algebraic Sets

Theorem 1 concerns solvability and implication. As to the class of possible solution sets, the second of the four phenomena mentioned in

Sec. 3 suggests the study of "algebraic domains," finite unions of solution sets. For this purpose we also consider solution sets of strict algebraic inequalities, and in general fields, the solution sets of algebraic equations and the complements of such sets (cf. [10], p. 52.).

Given a polynomial $g(x)$, $x = (x_1, \ldots, x_d)$, with coefficients in a field F, we denote by $a(g)$, $b(g)$, and $c(g)$, respectively, the set of all x with $g(x) = 0$, $g(x) \neq 0$, and if F is the field of reals, $g(x) \geq 0$. Let A, B, C, and D be, respectively, a set obtainable by union and intersection from finitely many sets a, sets a and b, sets c, sets c and b. For $m \geq 1$, let A_m in the space $\{(x_1, \ldots, x_d)\}$ of all points x be the projection of an A in $\{(x_1, \ldots, x_d, t_1, \ldots, t_m)\}$, and let $A_{(m)}$ be the same, using only polynomials homogeneous in $t = (t_1, \ldots, t_m)$ and excluding $t = 0$. Similarly define B_m, etc. Then the following basic results hold ([5]; proofs will be given elsewhere).

Theorem 2. *For algebraically closed F,*

$$\{A_{(m)}\} = \{A\},$$
$$\{A_m\} = \{B_{(m)}\} = \{B_m\} = \{B\},$$

while $\{A\} \neq \{B\}$.

Theorem 3. *Over the field of reals,*

$$\{A_{(1)}\} = \{A\},$$
$$\{B_{(1)}\} = \{B\},$$
$$\{A_{(m+1)}\} = \{C_{(m)}\} = \{C\},$$
$$\{A_m\} = \{B_m\} = \{B_{(m+1)}\} = \{C_m\} = \{D_{(m)}\} = \{D_m\} = \{D\},$$

while $\{A\}$, $\{B\}$, $\{C\}$, $\{D\}$ *are all different.*

REFERENCES

[1] Artin, E., Über die Zerlegung definiter Funktionen in Quadrate, *Abh. Math. Sem. Univ. Hamburg* **5**, 100–115 (1927).

[2] Hilbert, D., Über die Darstellung definiter Formen als Summe von Formenquadraten, *Math. Ann.* **32**, 342–350 (1888); and *Gesamm. Abh.* **2**, 154–161 (1933).

[3] Motzkin, T. S., "Beiträge zur Theorie der linearen Ungleichungen." Jerusalem, 1936.

[4] Motzkin, T. S., Two consequences from the transposition theorem on linear inequalities, *Econometrica* **19**, 184–185 (1951).

[5] Motzkin, T. S., Elimination theory of algebraic inequalities. *Bull. Amer. Math. Soc.* **61,** 326 (1955).

[6] Motzkin, T. S., A proof of Hilbert's Nullstellensatz, *Math. Z.* **63,** 341–344 (1955).

[7] Motzkin, T. S., The arithmetic–geometric inequality, these Proceedings.

[8] Motzkin, T. S., Signs of minors, these Proceedings.

[9] Robinson, A., "Introduction to Model Theory and to the Metamathematics of Algebra." Amsterdam, 1963.

[10] Tarski, A., and McKinsey, J. C. C., "A Decision Method for Elementary Algebra and Geometry." Santa Monica, 1948.

[11] Taussky, O., Positive-definite matrices, these Proceedings.

The Arithmetic–Geometric Inequality*

T. S. MOTZKIN
University of California
Los Angeles, California

1. General Setting

The numerous proofs of the arithmetic–geometric inequality fall naturally into two categories: those that hold for arbitrary positive weights, and the others. The algebraic proofs presented here belong to the second category.

According to [5, Theorem 1], it is possible to prove the (unweighted) arithmetic–geometric inequality by exhibiting the difference of its two members as a sum

$$\sum_{\lambda=1}^{L} \rho_\lambda{}^2 h_\lambda \tag{1}$$

where the ρ_λ are rational functions and the h_λ products of the variables.

This can, in effect, be done in many ways, and one may ask for a sum (1) such that L, or the degrees of the h_λ or of the numerators or of the denominators of the ρ_λ, or some of the numerical coefficients or their denominators are small or minimal and in particular, if possible, such that the ρ_λ are polynomials. These considerations apply to all algebraic inequalities.

2. Special Features

In the case of the arithmetic–geometric inequality, however, two additional points of view arise. First, one may require the sum to be formally symmetric in the variables. This can be achieved by permuting the variables in (1) and averaging. Of course, the symmetrization may increase L or the numerical coefficients.

Secondly, the arithmetic–geometric inequality in the form

$$(x_1 \cdots x_n)^{1/n} \leq (x_1 + \cdots + x_n)/n \qquad (\text{all } x_k \geq 0) \tag{2}$$

* Sponsored, in part, by NSF Grants GP-2480 and GP-4519.

205

is not a polynomial inequality. There are several simple ways to make it one:

(i) The simplest: raise (2) to the power n

$$\left(\frac{x_1 + \cdots + x_n}{n}\right)^n - x_1 \cdots x_n \geq 0 \qquad \text{(all } x_k \geq 0). \tag{3}$$

(ii) Substitute $x_k = y_k{}^n$ (and subsequently replace y_k by x_k):

$$\frac{x_1{}^n + \cdots + x_n{}^n}{n} - x_1 \cdots x_n \geq 0 \qquad \text{(all } x_k \geq 0). \tag{4}$$

(iii) Introduce the left member of (2) as a new variable:

$$x_1 + \cdots + x_n - ny \geq 0 \qquad (y^n - x_1 \cdots x_n = 0, \quad \text{all} \quad x_k \geq 0); \tag{5}$$

(iv) Or, after the nonsymmetric substitution

$$x_n = y^n/(x_1 \cdots x_{n-1}), \qquad \text{for} \quad n \geq 2,$$

$$(x_1 + \cdots + x_{n-1} - ny)x_1 \cdots x_{n-1} + y^n \geq 0 \qquad (y \geq 0, \qquad \text{all} \quad x_k \geq 0). \tag{6}$$

The conditional inequality (m), $m = 3, 4, 5, 6$, is dealt with in Sec. m. A related inequality is considered in Sec. 7. Each section contains results or procedures that seem to be new.

One can more generally substitute $x_k = y_k^{\delta r}$ in (2) where δ is a (positive or negative) divisor of n, and r a positive integer, and then raise to the power n/δ. One may assume $r = 1$ since the corresponding sum representation (1) furnishes a representation for every r. Negative δ correspond to the harmonic–geometric inequality; $\delta = 1$ gives (3), $\delta = n$ gives (4). For $n = 2$ all choices ($\delta = 1, 2, -1, -2$) as well as (6) coincide with

$$(x - y)^2 \geq 0.$$

For $n = 1$ the inequalities become identities. For arbitrary n the equality sign holds if and only if $x_1 = \cdots = x_n = y$; in (6) also for $x_1 \cdots x_{n-1} = 0$, $y = 0$.

3. Power of the Average

3.1. Composite Degree. We first wish to bring

$$\Delta_n = \left(\frac{x_1 + \cdots + x_n}{n}\right)^n - x_1 \cdots x_n$$

into the form (1). We have of course

$$\Delta_2 = \left(\frac{x_1 - x_2}{2}\right)^2$$

and hence

$$(x_1 + x_2 + x_3 + x_4)^4 = 2^4\left[(x_1 + x_2)(x_3 + x_4) + \left(\frac{x_1 + x_2 - x_3 - x_4}{2}\right)^2\right]^2$$

$$= 2^4(x_1 + x_2)^2(x_3 + x_4)^2 + S$$

$$= 2^4 2^2\left[x_1 x_2 + \left(\frac{x_1 - x_2}{2}\right)^2\right]2^2\left[x_3 x_4 + \left(\frac{x_3 - x_4}{2}\right)^2\right] + S$$

$$= 4^4 x_1 x_2 x_3 x_4 + 4^3[x_1 x_2(x_3 - x_4)^2 + x_3 x_4(x_1 - x_2)^2]$$

$$+ 4^2(x_1 - x_2)^2(x_3 - x_4)^2 + S,$$

$$S = 8(x_1 + x_2)(x_3 + x_4)(x_1 + x_2 - x_3 - x_4)^2$$

$$+ (x_1 + x_2 - x_3 - x_4)^4;$$

proceeding in the same manner, we generate lengthy expressions for Δ_{2^k}. More generally, if Δ_j and Δ_k are in the form (1) then, setting $y_1 = x_1 + \cdots + x_k, \ldots, y_j = x_{(j-1)k+1} + \cdots + x_{jk}$, we obtain

$$(x_1 + \cdots + x_{jk})^{jk} = j^{jk}[y_1 \cdots y_j + \Delta_j(y)]^k$$

$$= j^{jk} y_1^k \cdots y_j^k + S$$

$$= j^{jk} k^k(x_1 \cdots x_k + \Delta_k) \cdots + S$$

$$= (jk)^{jk}(x_1 \cdots x_{jk} + \Delta_{jk}),$$

where S and thus also Δ_{jk} have the form (1); and if only polynomials occur in Δ_j and Δ_k, then the same holds for Δ_{jk}.
    We have

$$\Delta_n = \frac{\Delta_{n+1}(x_1, \ldots, x_n, (x_1 + \cdots + x_n)/n)}{(x_1 + \cdots + x_n)/n}, \tag{7}$$

which gives, e.g.,

$$\Delta_3 = \frac{1}{4} x_3(x_1 - x_2)^2 + \frac{1}{108}(4x_1 + 4x_2 + x_3)(x_1 + x_2 - 2x_3)^2; \tag{8}$$

it is, however, not obvious that for $n > 4$ expressions of the form (1) result.

3.2. Inductive Procedure. A sequence of expressions for Δ_n, $n = 1, 2, \ldots$, in the form (1) generalizing (8), but involving fewer squares than those in 3.1 for $n \geq 4$, can be found inductively as follows.

Let

$$\lambda(x) = \left(\frac{x+1}{n+1}\right)^{n+1} - \left(\frac{x}{n}\right)^n.$$

Since

$$\lambda'(x) = \left(\frac{x+1}{n+1}\right)^n - \left(\frac{x}{n}\right)^{n-1}$$

also vanishes for $x = n$, the function

$$\mu(x) = \lambda(x)/(x-n)^2$$

is a polynomial. The coefficients of λ except that of the next to the leading term are positive; hence (beginning the division at the constant term) we see that the coefficients of $\lambda(x)/(n-x)$ except that of the leading term are positive, and similarly that μ has only positive coefficients. We homogenize to

$$\left(\frac{x+y}{n+1}\right)^{n+1} - \left(\frac{x}{n}\right)^n y = \frac{[(x/n) - y]^2 M_{n-1}(x, y)}{n^{n-2}(n+1)^{n+1}}, \tag{9}$$

where M_{n-1} is a binary form whose coefficients are positive integers. The coefficients of $M_0, \ldots, M_6$ are

$$\begin{array}{ccccccc}
 & & & 1 & & & \\
 & & 4 & & 1 & & \\
 & & 27 & & 14 & & 3 \\
 & 256 & & 203 & & 88 & & 16 \\
 3125 & & 3344 & & 2190 & & 800 & & 125 \\
46656 & & 62921 & & 55212 & & 30348 & & 9504 & & 1296 \\
823543 & 1340730 & 1475817 & 1084076 & 510041 & 139258 & 16807
\end{array}$$

Setting $x = x_1 + \cdots + x_n$, $y = x_{n+1}$ in (9), and replacing $(x/n)^n$ by $x_1 \cdots x_n + \Delta_n$, we obtain, by induction, the following result.

Theorem 1. *With the notations*

$$a_1 = x_1, \quad a_2 = (x_1 + x_2)/2, \ldots, a_n = (x_1 + \cdots + x_n)/n,$$

$$g_1 = x_n, \quad g_2{}^2 = x_{n-1}x_n, \ldots, g_n{}^n = x_1 \cdots x_n,$$

we have

$$a_n{}^n = g_n{}^n$$
$$+ g_{n-2}^{n-2}(a_1 - x_2)^2 M_0/2^2$$
$$+ g_{n-3}^{n-3}(a_2 - x_3)^2 M_1(a_2, x_3)/3^3$$
$$+ \cdots$$
$$+ \frac{g_2{}^2(a_{n-3} - x_{n-2})^2 M_{n-4}[(n-3)a_{n-3}, x_{n-2}]}{(n-3)^{n-5}(n-2)^{n-2}}$$
$$+ \frac{g_1(a_{n-2} - x_{n-1})^2 M_{n-3}[(n-2)a_{n-2}, x_{n-1}]}{(n-2)^{n-4}(n-1)^{n-1}}$$
$$+ \frac{(a_{n-1} - x_n)^2 M_{n-2}[(n-1)a_{n-1}, x_n]}{(n-1)^{n-3}n^n}, \tag{10}$$

where M_0, M_1, ... are binary forms with positive coefficients defined by (9).

For instance we obtain

$$\Delta_4 = \frac{1}{4} x_3 x_4 (x_1 - x_2)^2 + \frac{1}{108} x_4 [4(x_1 + x_2) + x_3](x_1 + x_2 - 2x_3)^2$$

$$+ \frac{1}{6912} [27(x_1 + x_2 + x_3)^2 + 14(x_1 + x_2 + x_3)x_4 + 3x_4{}^2]$$

$$\times (x_1 + x_2 + x_3 - 3x_4)^2.$$

For positive x_k, formula (10) exhibits the positivity of Δ_n unless $x_1 = \cdots = x_n$.

Dividing by $g_n{}^n$, (10) becomes

$$q_n = \frac{[(x_1 + \cdots + x_n)/n]^n}{x_1 \cdots x_n} = 1 + \frac{(x_1 - x_2)^2}{4x_1 x_2}$$

$$+ \frac{[4(x_1 + x_2) + x_3](x_1 + x_2 - 2x_3)^2}{108 x_1 x_2 x_3} + \cdots; \tag{11}$$

hence for positive x_k, $1 = q_1 \leq \cdots \leq q_n$ with $q_{n-1} < q_n$ unless $x_n = a_{n-1}$. For $n \to \infty$ and $x_n \to x > 0$, the series (11) converges if and only if

$$\sum_n \left(1 - \frac{x_n}{x}\right)^2 < \infty.$$

3.3. Attempt for Symmetry. We may prefer a symmetric expression for Δ_n, e.g.,

$$\sum_k (x_k - \bar{x})^2 p(x_k, x_1, \ldots, x_{k-1}, x_{k+1}, \ldots, x_n), \tag{12}$$

where $\bar{x}$ is the arithmetic mean $\sum x_k/n$ and p is a polynomial with positive coefficients (or at least ≥ 0 for $x_1 \geq 0, \ldots, x_n \geq 0$), and symmetric in all but the first one of its variables.

However, at least for Δ_3 such an expression does not exist. For if d is the highest degree of terms in (12), then for $d > 3$ and large positive $x_k \neq \bar{x}$ we see that these terms are 0, hence $d = 3$. Again, letting $x_k \neq \bar{x}$, $x_k = \lambda y_k$, $\lambda \to \infty$, we see that (12) subsists after omission of all terms of degree < 3. Hence we may set $p(x_1, x_2, x_3) = \alpha x_1 + \beta(x_2 + x_3)$; by comparison of coefficients we have $\alpha = -3/2$, $\beta = 7/2$.

3.4. Symmetric Expressions.

Another symmetric expression that vanishes for $x_1 = \cdots = x_n$ is

$$\sum_{j,k} (x_j - x_k)^2 p(x_j, x_k, \text{ the other } x_i), \qquad 1 \leq j < k \leq n, \qquad (13)$$

where $p(x_1, \ldots, x_n)$ is a polynomial with positive coefficients (or at least ≥ 0 for $x_1 \geq 0, \ldots, x_n \geq 0$) and symmetric in x_1 and x_2 as well as in $x_3, \ldots, x_n$.

For Δ_n, the polynomial p can as in Sec. 3.3 be assumed to be homogeneous. All such polynomials with positive coefficients are (by comparison of coefficients) for

$$n = 2: \quad \frac{1}{4}$$

$$n = 3: \quad \frac{1}{27} \cdot \frac{1}{2}(x_1 + x_2 + 7x_3)$$

$$n = 4: \quad \frac{1}{256} \cdot \frac{1}{3}(x_1^2 + x_2^2 + 2\alpha x_1 x_2 + (7 - \alpha)(x_1 + x_2)(x_3 + x_4)$$

$$+ (4 + \alpha)(x_3^2 + x_4^2) + 58 x_3 x_4), \qquad 0 \leq \alpha \leq 7, \quad (14)$$

$$n = 5: \quad \frac{1}{3125} \cdot \frac{1}{4} \{x_1^3 + x_2^3 + \alpha(x_1^2 x_2 + x_1 x_2^2)$$

$$+ [\beta(x_1^2 + x_2^2) + \beta' x_1 x_2](x_3 + x_4 + x_5)$$

$$+ (x_1 + x_2)[\gamma(x_3^2 + x_4^2 + x_5^2) + \gamma'(x_3 x_4 + x_3 x_5 + x_4 x_5)]$$

$$+ \delta(x_3^3 + x_4^3 + x_5^3) + \delta'(x_3^2 x_4 + \cdots + x_4 x_5^2) + 601 x_3 x_4 x_5\},$$

$$\alpha = 3\gamma + 3\delta - 39 \geq 0, \quad \beta = 61/3 - \gamma - \delta \geq 0,$$

$$\beta' = 2\delta' - 2\gamma - \delta - 119/3 \geq 0, \quad \gamma \geq 0, \quad \gamma' = 361/3 - 2\delta' \geq 0, \quad \delta \geq 0.$$

$$(15)$$

This last system of inequalities defines a polyhedron of the combinatorial type of the three-dimensional cube.

The expressions become simpler for special choices, e.g., $\alpha = 7$ $(n = 4)$ and for $\gamma = 0$, $\delta = 61/3$, $\delta' = 30$ $(n = 5)$.

For arbitrary n we have ([2], p. 77), denoting by $x^{(r)}$ the set of all $\binom{n}{r}$ products of r of the n variables, by x' the variables other than x_j and x_k, and by a bar (—) the average (arithmetic mean) of a set, the following theorem.

Theorem 2.

$$\Delta_n = \sum_{j,k} (x_j - x_k)^2 \sum_r \frac{r \bar{x}^{n-r-1} \overline{x'^{(r-1)}}}{n^2(n-1)},$$

$$1 \leq j < k \leq n, \quad 1 \leq r \leq n-1.$$

(16)

Proof.   Obviously

$$\Delta_n = \bar{x}^n - \overline{x^{(n)}} = \sum_r \bar{x}^{n-r-1}(\overline{\bar{x}x^{(r)}} - \overline{x^{(r+1)}}).$$

To establish

$$\overline{\bar{x}x^{(r)}} - \overline{x^{(r+1)}} = r \sum_{j,k} \frac{(x_j - x_k)^2 \overline{x'^{(r-1)}}}{n^2(n-1)}$$

we verify that in both members the coefficients are

$$\frac{1}{n\binom{n}{r}} \qquad \text{for} \quad x_1^2 x_2 x_3 \cdots x_r,$$

$$\frac{-r}{n\binom{n}{r+1}} \qquad \text{for} \quad x_1 x_2 \cdots x_{r+1}.$$

The expression (16) is for $n = 4$, the case $\alpha = 1$ of (14); for $n = 5$, the case $\gamma = 29/3$, $\delta = 13/3$, $\delta' = 38$ of (15).

However, like (12), (13) also does not encompass all symmetric homogeneous polynomials that are nonnegative in the posant (positive orthant); e.g.,

$$x_1^3 + x_2^3 + x_3^3 - x_1^2 x_2 - \cdots - x_3^2 x_2 + 3x_1 x_2 x_3$$

$$= \tfrac{1}{2} \sum_{j,k} (x_j - x_k)^2 (x_j + x_k - x_i)$$

$$= x_1(x_2 - x_1)(x_3 - x_1) + (x_3 + x_2 - x_1)(x_3 - x_2)^2$$

is nonnegative for $0 \leq x_1 \leq x_2 \leq x_3$ and by symmetry for $x_1 \geq 0$, $x_2 \geq 0$, $x_3 \geq 0$.

3.5. Square-Free Expressions on Part of the Posant. The form (1) is called square-free if the ρ_λ are constants, i.e., if the sum is a polynomial with positive coefficients. Since Δ_n is symmetric we can assume $x_1 \leq \cdots \leq x_n$, and $\Delta_n \geq 0$ for $x_1 \geq 0, \ldots, x_n \geq 0$ follows from Theorem 3.

Theorem 3. Δ_n *has positive coefficients as a polynomial in*

$$x_1, \quad x_2 - x_1, \quad x_3 - x_2, \ldots, x_n - x_{n-1} \qquad (17)$$

and as a polynomial in

$$x_1, \quad x_2 - a_1, \quad x_3 - a_2, \ldots, x_n - a_{n-1} \qquad [a_k = (x_1 + \cdots + x_k)/k] \qquad (18)$$

and can be written as a polynomial with positive coefficients in

$$x_2, \quad x_3, \ldots, x_n, \quad a_1 - x_2, \quad a_2 - x_3, \ldots, a_{n-1} - x_n. \qquad (19)$$

Proof. Theorem 1 implies the assertion concerning (19) directly, and concerning (18) because of

$$x_{k+1} = x_1 + \frac{1}{2}(x_2 - a_1) + \frac{1}{3}(x_3 - a_2) + \cdots + \frac{1}{k}(x_k - a_{k-1}) + (x_{k+1} - a_k).$$

From the latter assertion follows the one concerning (17) by

$$x_{k+1} - a_k = x_{k+1} - x_k + \frac{k-1}{k}(x_k - x_{k-1}) + \cdots + \frac{1}{k}(x_2 - x_1).$$

Another proof [6, Dβ] of (18) uses induction and

$$x_1 \cdots x_n + \Delta_n = a_n{}^n = \left(a_{n-1} + \frac{x_n - a_{n-1}}{n}\right)^n = a_{n-1}^n + na_{n-1}^{n-1}\frac{x_n - a_{n-1}}{n}$$

$$+ S_n = x_n a_{n-1}^{n-1} + S_n = x_1 \cdots x_n + x_n\Delta_{n-1} + S_n,$$

where S_n has positive coefficients in a_{n-1} and $x_n - a_{n-1}$.

Similarly, (19) follows also [6, Dγ] from

$$S_n = \Delta_n - x_n \Delta_{n-1} = \left[x_n + \frac{n-1}{n}(a_{n-1} - x_n)\right]^n$$

$$- x_n[x_n + (a_{n-1} - x_n)]^{n-1}$$

$$= \sum_r x_n^{n-r}(a_{n-1} - x_n)^r \left(\frac{n}{n} \cdots \frac{n-r+1}{n} - \frac{n-1}{n-1} \cdots \frac{n-r}{n-1}\right)\Big/ r!$$

with positive coefficients in x_n and $a_{n-1} - x_n$. The positive coefficients of $S_n/(a_{n-1} - x_n)^2$ in x_n and a_{n-1} are those implied by (9).

Under the normalization $x_1 + \cdots + x_n = 1$, the content of the posant and of its parts given by setting the linear forms (17), (18), or (19) > 0, is, respectively,

$$\tau = \frac{\sqrt{n}}{(n-1)!}, \quad \frac{\tau}{n!}, \quad \frac{\tau \cdot n!}{n^n}, \quad \tau \cdot \frac{1}{2} \cdot \frac{5}{9} \cdots \left[1 - \left(\frac{n-1}{n} \right)^{n-1} \right].$$

The posant can also be subdivided into parts (convex polyhedral cones) π by the $2^{n-1} - 1$ hyperplanes $\sum_j (x_j - \bar{x}) = 0$, $j \in N$, where N is an arbitrary proper subset of $\{1, \ldots, n\}$. The number of these parts, for $n = 1, 2, \ldots$, is 1, 2, 6, 32, 370, $\ldots$. We establish the following result.

Theorem 4. *In each π, Δ_n can be written as a polynomial with positive coefficients in the $|\sum_j (x_j - \bar{x})|$ and the x_k.*

Proof.   If

$$x_1^* = \bar{x}, \quad x_2^* = x_1 + x_2 - \bar{x}, \quad x_3^* = x_3, \ldots, x_n^* = x_n,$$

then

$$\Delta_n - \Delta_n^* = (x_1 - \bar{x})(\bar{x} - x_2) x_3 \cdots x_n.$$

Hence we obtain the required sum by replacing some difference $x_j - \bar{x}$ by 0 and another (of opposite sign) by the sum of the two differences, and repeating until all differences are 0 (cf. [6, Bβ]).

4. Average of the Power

4.1. Inductive Form; Square-Free Form; First Symmetric Form.
Let

$$\Delta_{n,n} = \frac{x_1^n + \cdots + x_n^n}{n} - \left(\frac{x_1 + \cdots + x_n}{n} \right) = \overline{x^n} - \bar{x}^n;$$

(4) becomes $D_n = \Delta_n + \Delta_{n,n} \geq 0$. To bring D_n in a form similar to (10) for Δ_n, it suffices therefore to do this for $\Delta_{n,n}$, as in 7.1. For square-free expressions, combine 3.5 and 7.5. The form (12) is realizable at least for $n = 3$: comparison of coefficients gives

$$D_3 = \frac{3}{2} \sum_k (x_k - \bar{x})^2 \bar{x}.$$

4.2. Second Symmetric Form.   The homogeneous polynomials in (13) for D_n, $n = 2, 2, 4$, are

$$n = 2: \quad \frac{1}{2}$$

$$n = 3: \quad \frac{1}{6}(x_1 + x_2 + x_3)$$

$$n = 4: \quad \frac{1}{24}\,[2(x_1{}^2 + x_2{}^2) + (4 - 2\alpha)x_1 x_2 + \alpha(x_1 + x_2)(x_3 + x_4)$$

$$+ (1 - \alpha)(x_3{}^2 + x_4{}^2) + 2x_3 x_4], \qquad 0 \le \alpha \le 1.$$

The case $\alpha = 0$ can be written

$$\frac{x_1{}^4 + \cdots + x_4{}^4}{4} - x_1 x_2 x_3 x_4 = \frac{1}{12} \sum_{j,k} (x_j{}^2 - x_k{}^2)^2 + \frac{1}{24} \sum_{j,k} (x_j - x_k)^2 (x_i - x_l)^2,$$

$$1 \le j < k \le 4, \qquad i < l, \ \{i, j, k, l\} = \{1, 2, 3, 4\}. \tag{20}$$

For $\alpha > 0$ the quadratic form is not semidefinite. For $\alpha = 1$ we obtain p_4 as defined below.

For $n = 2, 3, 4, \ldots$, and $r = 1, \ldots, n - 1$, let

$$\varphi_{n,r} = P(x_1 - x_2)(x_1{}^{n-r} - x_2{}^{n-r})x_3 x_4 \cdots x_{r+1}$$

$$= 2(r - 1)!(n - r - 1)!Q(x_1 - x_2)^2$$

$$\times (x_1{}^{n-r-1} + x_1{}^{n-r-2}x_2 + \cdots + x_2{}^{n-r-1})x_3 x_4 \cdots x_{r+1},$$

where P means summation over all $n!$ similar terms formed by permuting $x_1, \ldots, x_n$, while only one out of each set of equal terms appears in Q. Since

$$\varphi_{n,r} = 2Px_1{}^{n-r+1}x_2 x_3 \cdots x_r - 2Px_1{}^{n-r}x_2 x_3 \cdots x_{r+1}$$

we see [4] that

$$\varphi_{n,1} + \cdots + \varphi_{n,n-1} = 2Px_1{}^n - 2Px_1 \cdots x_n = 2 \cdot n! D_n$$

which gives D_n in the form (13) as follows.

Theorem 5.   *With*

$$p_n(x_1, \ldots, x_n) = \sum_{r=1}^{n-1} \frac{(x_1{}^{n-r-1} + x_1{}^{n-r-2}x_2 + \cdots + x_2{}^{n-r-1})x_3 x_4 \cdots x_{r+1}}{n(n-1)\binom{n-2}{r-1}}$$

we have

$$D_n = \sum_{j,k} (x_j - x_k)^2 p_n(x_j, x_k, \text{ the other } x_i), \qquad 1 \le j < k \le n.$$

4.3. Even Degree. For even n, $D_n \geq 0$ for all real $x_1, \ldots, x_n$. We obtain [4] by writing

$$D^n = \tfrac{1}{2}D_{n/2}(x_1^2, \ldots, x_{n/2}^2) + \tfrac{1}{2}D_{n/2}(x_{n/2+1}^2, \ldots, x_n^2)$$

$$+ \tfrac{1}{2}(x_1 \cdots x_{n/2} - x_{n/2+1} \cdots x_n)^2, \qquad (21)$$

where $D_{n/2}$ is expressed polynomially as in (1), e.g. using Sec. 4.1 or Theorem 6, the following theorem.

Theorem 6. *For even n, D_n is a sum of squares of polynomials.*

Note that a formula similar to (21) holds whenever $n = n_1 n_2$, $n_1 > 1$, $n_2 > 1$, and can be used to obtain further forms for D_n.

For $n = 4$, (21) becomes

$$D_4 = \tfrac{1}{4}(x_1^2 - x_2^2)^2 + \tfrac{1}{4}(x_3^2 - x_4^2)^2 + \tfrac{1}{2}(x_1 x_2 - x_3 x_4)^2;$$

averaging over the three partitions of $x_1, \ldots, x_4$ into pairs, we obtain the symmetric form

$$D_4 = \frac{1}{12} \sum_6 (x_j^2 - x_k^2)^2 + \frac{1}{6} \sum_3 (x_i x_j - x_k x_l)^2.$$

Comparison with (20) leads to

$$\sum_3 (x_i - x_j)^2 (x_k - x_l)^2 = 2 \sum_3 (x_i x_j - x_k x_l)^2.$$

It would be desirable to determine whether D_n, n even, can be written as in (13) with a polynomial p that is a sum of squares of polynomials [as in (20) for $n = 4$], or at least is nonnegative for all $x_1, \ldots, x_n$.

Ascending from $D_1 = 0$, formula (21) gives a polynomial square-sum expression for D_n if n is a power of 2. Given such an expression for D_n, one has ([1], cf. [6, Cα]) a similar expression for $D_m(x_1^n, \ldots, x_m^n)$, $m < n$, by virtue of

$$mD_m(x_1^n, \ldots, x_m^n) = nD_n(x_1^m, \ldots, x_m^m, x_1 \cdots x_m, \ldots, x_1 \cdots x_m).$$

5. Additional Variable

5.1. Not a Polynomial Square-Sum

Theorem 7. *The left member g of (5) cannot be written in the form (1), where the h_λ are products of x_k (with $x_{n+1} = y^n - x_1 \cdots x_n$, $x_{n+2} = -x_{n+1}$) and the ρ_λ polynomials in $x_1, \ldots, x_n, y$.*

Proof. Let

$$g = s_1 + x_{n+1} s_2 + x_{n+2} s_3 + x_{n+1} x_{n+2} s_4,$$

where the $s_j \geq 0$ (formally) for $x_1 \geq 0, \ldots, x_n \geq 0$. Set $x_1 = \cdots = x_n = x$, $y = 2x$; then

$$x_{n+1} = (2^n - 1)x^n, \qquad g = -nx,$$

$$s_1 = -nx + x_{n+1}(x_{n+1}s_4 + s_3 - s_2).$$

Hence (for $n > 1$) we would have $s_1 < 0$ for small $x > 0$.

Note that the need for rational functions occurs already for $n = 2$. The same proof holds if $y \geq 0$ is added to the conditions in (5).

5.2. General Remark. The word "formally" is used in Sec. 5.1 because the form (1) implies nonnegativity of the polynomial considered only under strict-inequality conditions. A simple example shows the need for this distinction.

Since

$$x - 1 = (1/x)^2(x^3 - x^2),$$

we have $x - 1 \geq 0$ for $x^3 - x^2 > 0$. But ≥ 0 in the condition is inadmissible, as seen by taking $x = 0$.

6. Trinomial Inequality

6.1. Rational Square-Sum. Evidently

$$h = zx_1 \cdots x_{n-1} + y^n, \qquad z = x_1 + \cdots + x_{n-1} - ny \qquad (22)$$

is nonnegative for $x_1 \geq 0, \ldots, x_{n-1} \geq 0$, $y \geq 0$, $z \geq 0$. For fixed $z \leq 0$, fixed $y \geq 0$, and varying $x_1 \geq 0, \ldots, x_{n-1} \geq 0$, h becomes smallest when $x_1 = \cdots = x_{n-1} = x$, namely

$$s = (n-1)x^n - nx^{n-1}y + y^n$$

$$= (x - y)^2[(n-1)x^{n-2} + x^{n-3}y + \cdots + y^{n-2}];$$

and for arbitrary $x_1 \geq 0, \ldots, x_{n-1} \geq 0$, we have, letting $x = (x_1 + \cdots + x_{n-1})/(n - 1)$,

$$h = s - z \Delta_{n-1}. \qquad (23)$$

Eliminating z from (22) and (23) we obtain

$$h = \frac{sx_1 \cdots x_{n-1} + y^n \Delta_{n-1}}{x_1 \cdots x_{n-1} + \Delta_{n-1}}$$

which has the form (1) when written as

$$h = \frac{(sx_1 \cdots x_{n-1} + y^n \Delta_{n-1})(x_1 \cdots x_{n-1} + \Delta_{n-1})}{(x_1 \cdots x_{n-1} + \Delta_{n-1})^2},$$

with Δ_{n-1} itself in polynomial form (1), e.g. as indicated in Sec. 3.

The above elimination can always be effected when for some z an expression (1) involving $z \geq 0$ and another involving $-z \geq 0$ are given.

6.2. Not a Polynomial Square-Sum. However, we have the following result.

Theorem 8. *For $n \geq 3$, h cannot be written as in (1), with h_λ products of, and p_λ polynomials in, $x_1, \ldots, x_{n-1}, y$.*

Proof. Setting $x_j = t_j^2$, $y = u^2$, this would imply a representation of

$$h(t_1^2, \ldots, t_{n-1}^2, u^2) = (t_1^2 + \cdots + t_{n-1}^2 - nu^2)t_1^2, \ldots, t_{n-1}^2 + u^{2n}$$

as a sum of squares $\sum_k s_k^2$ of polynomials in $t_1, \ldots, t_{n-1}, u$. Let d be the highest degree of terms occurring in this sum; then, writing only the terms of degree d, we have

$$h^* = \sum_k s_k^{*2}.$$

If $d > 2n$, then $h^* = 0$, hence all $s_k^* = 0$; thus $d = 2n$, $h = h^*$. Let $s_k^* = c_{0k} + c_{1k}u + \cdots + c_{nk}u^n$. Then $\sum c_{0k}^2 = (t_1^2 + \cdots + t_{n-1}^2)t_1^2 \cdots t_{n-1}^2$, and the squares of the coefficients of t_1^n in the c_{0k} add up to zero, hence these coefficients are zero. Now the coefficients of $t_1^{n-1}t_2$ must be zero, etc., until only terms divisible by $t_1, \ldots, t_{n-1}$ remain. At this stage $\sum c_{1k}^2$ is divisible by $t_1^2 \cdots t_{n-1}^2$, and therefore similarly $c_{1k} = b_k t_1 \cdots t_{n-1}$. Finally also $c_{2,k}$ is divisible by $t_1 \cdots t_{n-1}$; since its degree is $n - 2$, $c_{2,k} = 0$. But this implies $\sum_k b_k^2 = -n$.

In particular we have in

$$(t_1^2 + t_2^2 - 3u^2)t_1^2 t_2^2 + u^6$$

an (albeit only *semidefinite*) *ternary form of degree 6 that is not a sum of squares of forms*. The extreme simplicity of this example contrasts with the reconditeness of ternary forms with the same property given in [3].

6.3. Stronger Result in Special Cases. For $n = 3$ and $n = 4$ we can show that h cannot be written as a sum of products of $x_1, \ldots, x_{n-1}, y$ and polynomials s_k that are nonnegative for all $x_1, \ldots, x_{n-1}, y$, without assuming that the s_k themselves are sums of squares of polynomials. Again, if the highest degree occurring were $d > n$, the s_k^* would vanish for $x_1 > 0, \ldots,$ $x_{n-1} > 0$, $y > 0$ and therefore for all $x_1, \ldots, x_{n-1}, y$. Hence $d = n$; since the s_k^* of odd degree are zero, we set

$$h = s_1^* x_1 + s_2^* x_2 + s_0^* x_1 x_2 y, \qquad n = 3$$

$$h = s_1^* + s_2^* x_1 x_2 + s_3^* x_1 x_3 + s_4^* x_2 x_3 + s_5^* x_1 y$$
$$+ s_6^* x_2 y + s_7^* x_3 y + s_0^* x_1 x_2 x_3 y, \qquad n = 4.$$

For $x_1 = x_2 = y > 0$, $h = 0$; hence $s_0^* = 0$. Now consider $n = 3$ and $n = 4$ separately.

For $n = 3$, the semidefinite quadratic form s_1^* is without x_1^2 (as h is without x_1^3), hence without $x_1 x_2$ and $x_1 y$. Likewise s_2^* does not involve x_2. Further, s_3^* involves neither x_1 (since otherwise h would have a term $x_1^2 y$) nor x_2, thus $s_3^* = y^2$. As h has no $x_1 y^2$, s_1^* has no y, so that $s_1^* = x_2^2$; similarly $s_2^* = x_1^2$. But now there is no provision for $-3x_1 x_2 y$.

For $n = 4$, $h = 0$ for $x_3 = y = 0$, so that $s_1^* = 0$ and $s_2^* = 0$ for $x_1 > 0$, $x_2 > 0$, $x_3 = y = 0$. Hence s_2^* is free of x_1 and x_2, and similarly for s_3^* and s_4^*. Also $\hat{s}_1$, the y-free part of s_1^*, is free of terms containing only x_1 and x_2, thus each term of $\hat{s}_1$ is divisible by x_3 and similarly by x_1 and x_2. But if we fix $x_1 \neq 0$ and $x_2 \neq 0$, and let $x_3 \to \infty$, then $\hat{s}_1 = x_1 x_2 x_3 (\alpha_1 x_1 + \alpha_2 x_2 + \alpha_3 x_3) \geq 0$ implies $x_1 x_2 x_3 \geq 0$, hence $\alpha_3 = 0$ and similarly $\alpha_1 = 0$ and $\alpha_2 = 0$; thus y divides s_1^*. The terms of s_1^* containing only the first power of y would preponderate for small y; but a nonvanishing multiple of y changes sign with y, hence these terms vanish. Therefore s_2^* cannot contain x_3^2, hence y divides s_2^*, s_3^*, s_4^*, and thus h, which is not the case.

7. Commutator of Power and Average

7.1. Inductive Procedure. Consider the difference

$$\Delta_{m,n} = \frac{x_1^m + \cdots + x_n^m}{n} - \left(\frac{x_1 + \cdots + x_n}{n}\right) = \overline{x^m} - \bar{x}^m$$

the special case $\Delta_{n,n}$ of which occurs in Sec. 4. By the method used in Sec. 3 we establish the following theorem.

Theorem 9. $\Delta_{m,n}$ *can be expressed polynomially in the form* (1).

Proof. Note that for $m = 0$, $m = 1$, $n = 0$, or $n = 1$, we have $\Delta_{m,n} = 0$, and that for $x_{n+1} = \bar{x}$,

$$\Delta_{m,n+1} = \frac{n}{n+1} \Delta_{m,n}$$

[compare (7)]. Hence we introduce

$$\Delta_{m,n+1} - \frac{n}{n+1} \Delta_{m,n} = \frac{x_{n+1}^m + n\bar{x}_m}{n+1} - \left(\frac{x_{n+1} + n\bar{x}}{n+1}\right)^m = F(x_{n+1}, \bar{x})$$

and

$$f(x) = F(x, 1) = \frac{x^m + n}{n+1} - \left(\frac{x+n}{n+1}\right)^m$$

Since $f(x)$ and

$$f'(x) = m\left(\frac{x^{m-1}}{n+1} - \frac{(x+n)^{m-1}}{(n+1)^m}\right)$$

vanish for $x = 1$, we have $f(x) = (x-1)^2 g(x)$ and obtain (for $m \geq 2$, $n \geq 1$) exactly as in 3.2 that all coefficients of $g(x)$ are positive. Thus

$$\Delta_{m,n+1} = \frac{n}{n+1} \Delta_{m,n} + (x_{n+1} - \bar{x})^2 G(x_{n+1}, \bar{x}),$$

where $G(x, 1) = g(x)$ and G is homogeneous, leads inductively to the desired expression.

In particular we obtain, with $a_k = (x_1 + \cdots + x_k)/k$,

$$\frac{\Delta_{2,n}}{n} = \sum_{k=2}^{n} (x_k - a_{k-1})^2 \frac{k-1}{k^3},$$

$$\frac{\Delta_{3,n}}{n} = \sum_{k=2}^{n} (x_k - a_{k-1})^2 \left[(k+1)x_k + (2k-1)a_{k-1}\right] \frac{k-1}{k^4},$$

$$\frac{\Delta_{4,n}}{n} = \sum_{k=2}^{n} (x_k - a_{k-1})^2 [(k^2 + k + 1)x_k^2$$

$$+ 2(k^2 + k + 1)x_k a_{k-1} + (3k^2 - 3k + 1)a_{k-1}^2] \frac{k-1}{k^5}.$$

It would be desirable to find square-sum expressions for

$$\Delta_{l,m,n} = \left(\frac{x_1^l + \cdots + x_n^l}{n}\right)^m - \left(\frac{x_1^m + \cdots + x_n^m}{n}\right)^l$$

for integers $l \geq m > 0$, $m > 0 > l$, and $0 > l \geq m$. This would give a square-sum type proof of the monotonicity of

$$\left(\frac{x_1^p + \cdots + x_n^p}{n}\right)^{1/p}$$

as a function of the (rational) exponent.

7.2. First Symmetric Form. Assume p in (12) homogeneous; then we obtain by comparison of coefficients

$$\Delta_{2,n} = \sum (x_k - \bar{x})^2/n,$$
$$\Delta_{3,n} = \sum (x_k - \bar{x})^2(x_k + 2\bar{x})/n,$$

with positive coefficients. Note that already $x_1 \geq -2\bar{x}, \ldots, x_n \geq -2\bar{x}$ implies $\Delta_{3,n} \geq 0$.

7.3. Second Symmetric Form. The homogeneous polynomials in (13) are for

$\Delta_{2,2}$: $\dfrac{1}{4}$,

$\Delta_{3,3}$: $\dfrac{1}{27}(4x_1 + 4x_2 + x_3)$,

$\Delta_{4,4}$: $\dfrac{1}{256}[21(x_1^2 + x_2^2) + (2\alpha + 24)x_1x_2 + (7 - \alpha)(x_1 + x_2)(x_3 + x_4)$

$$+ \alpha(x_3^2 + x_4^2) + 2x_3x_4], \qquad 0 \leq \alpha \leq 7.$$

This quadratic form is semidefinite for $1 \leq \alpha \leq 7$. For $\alpha = 1$ we obtain $p_{4,4}$ as defined below.

While a sum product $\sum x_j \sum y_j$ for $x_1 \geq 0, \ldots, x_n \geq 0, y_1 \geq 0, \ldots, y_n \geq 0$ is trivially greater than or equal to the product sum $\sum x_j y_j$ formed from the same numbers, we have $\sum x_j \sum y_j \leq n \sum x_j y_j$ if $x_1 \leq \cdots \leq x_n$ and $y_1 \leq \cdots \leq y_n$. In fact, the identity

$$n \sum x_j y_j - \sum x_j \sum y_j = \sum_{j<k} (x_j - x_k)(y_j - y_k),$$

which can also be written

$$\overline{xy} - \bar{x}\,\bar{y} = \tfrac{1}{2}\overline{\Delta x\, \Delta y}, \tag{24}$$

where the bar (—) means averaging and Δx means the sequence of the n^2 differences $x_j - x_k$, shows that an average–product is smaller than or equal to the corresponding product–average if y_j is monotone to x_j [i.e., $(x_j - x_k)(y_j - y_k) \geq 0$], but greater than or equal to the corresponding product–average if y_j is monotone to $-x_j$. This fact, as well as (24), holds also for integrals.

From (24) we deduce

$$\overline{xyz} - \bar{x}\,\overline{yz} = \overline{xyz} - \overline{x}\,\overline{yz} + \overline{x(yz - \bar{y}\bar{z})} = \tfrac{1}{2}\overline{\Delta x\, \Delta yz} + \tfrac{1}{2}\bar{x}\,\overline{\Delta y\, \Delta z}$$

and similarly

$$\overline{xyzu} - \bar{x}\,\overline{yzu} = \tfrac{1}{2}\overline{\Delta x\, \Delta yzu} + \tfrac{1}{2}\bar{x}\,\overline{\Delta y\, \Delta zu} + \tfrac{1}{2}\overline{xy}\,\overline{\Delta z\, \Delta u},$$

etc. In the special case $x = y = \cdots$ we obtain

$$\overline{x^m - \bar{x}^m} = \tfrac{1}{2}[\overline{\Delta x\, \Delta x^{m-1}} + \overline{x\, \Delta x\, \Delta x^{m-2}} + \cdots + \overline{\bar{x}^{m-2}(\Delta x)^2}];$$

for $x_1 \geq 0, \ldots, x_n \geq 0$, because of the monotonicity of the powers, each term is nonnegative:

$$\overline{\Delta x\, \Delta x^r} = \overline{(x_j - x_k)^2(x_j^{r-1} + x_j^{r-2}x_k + \cdots + x_j^{r-1})}.$$

Theorem 10 follows.

Theorem 10. *With*

$$p_{m,n}(x_1, \ldots, x_n) = \sum_{r=1}^{m=1} (x_1^{r-1} + x_1^{r-2}x_2 + \cdots + x_2^{r-1})$$

$$\times (x_1 + \cdots + x_n)^{m-r-1}/n^{m-r+1}$$

we have

$$\Delta_{m,n} = \sum_{j,k} (x_j - x_k)^2 p_{m,n}(x_j, x_k, \quad \text{the other} \quad x_i), \qquad 1 \leq j < k \leq n.$$

7.4. Even Degree. For $m = 2, 3, 4$ we obtain

$$p_{2,n} = 1/n^2,$$

$$p_{3,n} = (x_1 + x_2 + \bar{x})/n^2,$$

$$p_{4,n} = \left[\left(\frac{x_1 + x_2}{2} + \bar{x}\right)^2 + 2\left(\frac{x_1 + x_2}{2}\right)^2 + \left(\frac{x_1 - x_2}{2}\right)^2\right]/n^2.$$

The formula for $p_{3,n}$ implies $\Delta_{3,n} \geq 0$ for $x_j + x_k \geq -\bar{x}\ (1 \leq j < k \leq n)$, and, for $n \geq 4$, a stronger condition (thus a weaker result) than $x_j \geq -2\bar{x}$ in Sec. 7.2.

Using (24) differently than in Sec. 7.3 we have

$$\overline{xyzu} - \overline{xy}\overline{zu} = \overline{xyzu} - \overline{xy}\overline{zu} + \overline{xy}\overline{zu} - \overline{xy}\overline{zu}$$

$$= \tfrac{1}{2}\overline{\Delta xy\, \Delta zu} + \overline{(xy + \tfrac{1}{2}\Delta x\, \Delta y)(zu + \tfrac{1}{2}\Delta z\, \Delta u)} - \overline{xy}\overline{zu}$$

$$= \tfrac{1}{2}\overline{\Delta xy\, \Delta zu} + \tfrac{1}{4}\overline{\Delta x\, \Delta y\, \Delta z\, \Delta u} + \tfrac{1}{2}\overline{xy\, \Delta z\, \Delta u} + \tfrac{1}{2}\overline{zu\, \Delta x\, \Delta y}$$

$$\overline{x^4 - \bar{x}^4} = \tfrac{1}{2}\overline{(\Delta x^2)^2} + \tfrac{1}{4}\overline{(\Delta x)^2}^2 + \overline{x^2(\Delta x)^2}. \tag{25}$$

For even m, $\Delta_{m,n} \geq 0$ for all real $x_1, \ldots, x_n$. We prove the following theorem.

Theorem 11. *For even m,*

$$\Delta_{m,n} = \sum_{j,k} (x_j - x_k)^2 q_{m,n}(x_j, x_k, \quad \text{the other} \quad x_i), \qquad 1 \leq j < k \leq n,$$

where $q_{m,n}$ is a sum of squares of polynomials.

To show this we write

$$\Delta_{m,n} = \Delta_{m/2,n}(x_1^2, \ldots, x_n^2) + \tfrac{1}{2}\,\overline{\Delta x^2}(x^{2^{\overline{m/2-1}}} + x^{2^{\overline{m/2-2}}}\,\bar{x}^2 + \cdots + \bar{x}^{m-2}), \tag{26}$$

with $\Delta_{m/2,n}$ expressed polynomially as in (1), e.g. by Theorem 9.

Note that a formula similar to (26) holds whenever $n = n_1 n_2$, $n_1 > 1$, $n_2 > 1$, and can be used to obtain further representations for $\Delta_{m,n}$.

For $n = 4$, (26) becomes (25), and

$$q_{4,n} = [\bar{x}^2 + \overline{x^2} + (x_1 + x_2)^2]/n^2.$$

7.5. Square-Free Expression by Consecutive Differences. Since $\Delta_{m,n}$ is symmetric, we can assume $x_1 \leq \cdots \leq x_n$; thus $\Delta_{m,n} \geq 0$ for $x_1 \geq 0, \ldots,$ $x_n \geq 0$ follows from Theorem 12.

Theorem 12. $\Delta_{m,n}$ *is a polynomial with positive coefficients in*

$$y_1 = x_1, \quad y_2 = x_2 - x_1, \ldots, y_n = x_n - x_{n-1}.$$

Proof. In view of $x_k = y_1 + \cdots + y_k$, $\sum x_k = ny_1 + (n-1)y_2 + \cdots + y_n$, the coefficient of

$$y_1^{\lambda_1} \cdots y_r^{\lambda_r}, \quad \lambda_r > 0, \quad \lambda_1 + \cdots + \lambda_r = m$$

in

$$n^{m-1} \sum x_k^m - \left(\sum x_k\right)^m$$

is

$$\frac{m!}{\lambda_1! \cdots \lambda_r!}\,[n^{m-1}(n-r+1) - n^{\lambda_1}(n-1)^{\lambda_2} \cdots (n-r+1)^{\lambda_r}] \geq 0.$$

As in the proof of Theorem 3 it follows from the proof of Theorem 9 that $\Delta_{m,n}$ can even be written as a polynomial with positive coefficients in the variables (18) as well as in the variables (19).

7.6. Small Number of Squares versus Symmetry. The functions Δ_n, $\Delta_n + \Delta_{n,n}$, $\Delta_{m,n}$ are all positive for $x_1 > 0, \ldots, x_n > 0$, except when $x_1 = \cdots = x_n$. If such a function is a sum of squares of linear functions multiplied by polynomials that are positive for $x_1 > 0, \ldots, x_n > 0$, then it vanishes for $x_1 > 0, \ldots, x_n > 0$ exactly when all the linear functions vanish. Hence these must be homogeneous with a coefficient matrix of rank $n-1$. Sums involving only $n-1$ linear functions are given in Theorems 1 and 9.

However, the rather natural choices

$$x_1 - x_2, \quad x_1 - x_3, \ldots, x_1 - x_n$$

and

$$x_1 - x_2, \quad x_2 - x_3, \ldots, x_{n-1} - x_n$$

are excluded at least for

$$\Delta_{2,n}(n \geq 3), \quad \Delta_{3,n}, \quad \Delta_3, \quad D_3,$$

as seen from the fact that $\sum a_{jk}(x_j - x_k)^2$, $1 \leq j < k \leq n$, where the a_{jk} are constants, is a symmetric function if and only if all a_{jk} are equal, and from the following theorem.

Theorem 13. *The function*

$$f = \sum_j (x_1 - x_j)^2 \sum_k a_{jk} x_k, \qquad j = 2, \ldots, n, \quad k = 1, \ldots, n$$

is symmetric if and only if

for $n = 2$: $f = a(x_1^3 + x_2^3 - x_1^2 x_2 - x_1 x_2^2) = a(x_1 - x_2)^2(x_1 + x_2)$

for $n = 3$: $f = a(2Qx_1^3 - 3Qx_1^2 x_2 - 12x_1 x_2 x_3)$

$$= a[(x_1 - x_2)^2(x_1 + 2x_2 - 3x_2) + (x_1 - x_3)^2(x_1 - 3x_2 + 2x_3)]$$

for $n \geq 4$: $f = 0$;

while

$$g = \sum_j (x_{j-1} - x_j)^2 \sum_k a_{jk} x_k, \qquad j = 2, \ldots, n, \quad k = 1, \ldots, n$$

is symmetric if and only if

for $n = 4$: $g = a(Qx_1^3 - Qx_1^2 x_2 + 2Qx_1 x_2 x_3)$

$$= a[(x_1 - x_2)^2 - (x_3 - x_4)^2](x_1 + x_2 - x_3 - x_4),$$

otherwise as for f. (For the meaning of Q see Sec. 4.2.)

Note that f for $n = 3$ changes sign in the posant [>0 for $(1, 0, 0)$, <0 for $(1, 1, 0)$] and that g [>0 for $(1, 0, 0, 0)$, <0 for $(1, 0, 1, 1)$] is the product of three linear functions.

Proof. Let $n \geq 3$. As the coefficients of all x_j^3 in f must be equal, we can set $a_{jj} = \alpha$; similarly, because of the $x_j^2 x_{j'}$ terms, $a_{jj'} = \beta$, $j \neq j'$. Now the $x_1 x_j^2$ terms give $a_{j1} = 2\alpha + \beta$, the coefficient of x_1^3 gives $(n-1)(2\alpha + \beta) = \alpha$, and the coefficient of $x_1^2 x_j$ gives $(n-2)\beta + \alpha - 2(2\alpha + \beta) = \beta$. The determinant of these two equations for α and β vanishes exactly for $n = 2$

and $n = 3$. For $n = 3$ we obtain $\beta = -\frac{3}{2}\alpha$, whence f as indicated. (For $n \geq 4$ either equation already shows that $\alpha = 0$ if $\beta = 0$, and $\beta = 0$ follows from the equality of the coefficients of $x_1 x_j x_{j'}$ and $x_j x_{j'} x_{j''}$.) For $n \geq 5$, g contains no $x_1 x_3 x_5$, hence also no $x_{j-1} x_j x_k$, $k = j - 2, j - 1, j, j + 1$, hence $a_{jk} = 0$ for these values of k. Now g contains no $x_1^2 x_4$, hence no $x_j^2 x_k$ for $k = j - 2, j + 2$, hence $a_{j,j-2} = 0$ and $a_{j,j+1} = 0$; and since g must also be without $x_j^2 x_{j+1}$ and $x_j^2 x_{j-1}$, we have $a_{j,j+1} - 2a_{j,j} = 0$, $a_{j,j} - 2a_{j,j-1} = 0$, hence $g = 0$. For $n = 4$, equality of all terms $x_j^2 x_{j'}$ gives $a_{31} = 0$, $a_{34} = 0$, $a_{23} = a_{24} = a_{41} = a_{42} = -a_{21} = -a_{22} = -a_{43} = -a_{44}$, $a_{32} = a_{33} = 0$. For $n = 3$, g differs from f only by a permutation.

REFERENCES

[1] de Bruijn, N. G., private communication, 1965.
[2] Dougall, J., Quantitative proofs of certain algebraic inequalities, *Proc. Edinburgh Math. Soc.* **24**, 61–77 (1906).
[3] Hilbert, D., Über die Darstellung definiter Formen als Summe von Formenquadraten, *Math. Ann.* **32**, 342–350 (1888); *Gesamm. Abh.* **2**, 154–161 (1933).
[4] Hurwitz, A., Über den Vergleich des arithmetischen und des geometrischen Mittels, *J. Reine Angew. Math.* **108**, 266–268 (1891); *Werke* **2**, 505–507 (1933).
[5] Motzkin, T. S., Algebraic inequalities, these Proceedings.
[6] Muirhead, R. F., Proofs that the arithmetic mean is greater than the geometric mean, *Math. Gaz.* **2**, 283–287 (1904).

Signs of Minors*

T. S. MOTZKIN
University of California
Los Angeles, California

1. Introduction

Many matrix inequalities concern sign of minors; the two well-known ones that do not, the C-B-S inequality and Hadamard's inequality, are immediate consequences of one that does (see Sec. 5).

The following brief survey encompasses a general discussion (Sec. 2); facts related to the signs of elements (Sec. 3); and results involving diagonal elements and principal minors (Sec. 4), in particular of symmetric and skew-symmetric matrices (Sec. 5). Many results of Sec. 5, including the application to Hadamard's inequality, generalize immediately to Hermitian matrices.

2. The Minor Hypersurface Dissection

2.1.   Let

$$a = (a_{jk}), \qquad j = 1, \ldots, J, \quad k = 1, \ldots, K.$$

For $j_1 < \cdots < j_m$, $k_1 < \cdots < k_m$, let $j^{(m)} = (j_1, \ldots, j_m)$, $k^{(m)} = (k_1, \ldots, k_m)$, $a_{j^{(m)}k^{(m)}} = \det_{\mu, \nu} a_{j_\mu k_\nu}$, and $a^{(m)} = (a_{j^{(m)}k^{(m)}})$ be the mth compound matrix of a. Further let A_m be the product of all elements of $a^{(m)}$, and A the product of all A_m, $m = 1, \ldots, \min(J, K)$.

Then A is a homogeneous polynomial in the a_{jk} of degree

$$d_{J,K} = \sum_m m \binom{J}{m}\binom{K}{m}$$
$$= J \sum_m \binom{K}{m}\binom{J-1}{J-m} = J\binom{J+K-1}{J}$$
$$= (J+K-1)!/[(J-1)!(K-1)!],$$

whose $\sum_{m \geq 0} \binom{J}{m}\binom{K}{m} - 1 = \binom{J+K}{J} - 1$ irreducible factors are the $a_{j^{(m)}k^{(m)}}$. [The average degree of the factors, counting $A_0 = 1$ as a factor, is $(J^{-1} + K^{-1})^{-1}$.]

* Sponsored, in part, by NSF Grants GP-2480 and GP-4519.

For a singular point of the hypersurface $a_{j^{(m)}k^{(m)}} = 0$ in JK-space, lower degree minors of a must vanish; hence the singular points of the *minor hypersurface* $A = 0$ *for* J *by* K *matrices* are exactly the points where more than one minor of a vanishes.

For real a_{jk}, each component hypersurface $a_{j^{(m)}k^{(m)}} = 0$ has $JK - 1$ (real) dimensions, whereas the set of all singular points of $A = 0$ has $JK - 2$ dimensions.

Two real J by K matrices a and b are *combinatorially equisign* if, for each $j^{(m)}$ and $k^{(m)}$, the sign (1, -1, or 0) of $a_{j^{(m)}k^{(m)}}$ is the same as that of $b_{j^{(m)}k^{(m)}}$. They are *continuously equisign* if a continuous deformation, i.e., a matrix $c(t)$ of continuous functions of t, $0 \leq t \leq 1$, exists such that $c(0) = a$, $c(1) = b$, and all $c(t)$ are combinatorially equisign.

The classes of continuously equisign matrices are the finitely many regions of dimension 0, $\ldots, JK$ determined by the minor hypersurface; the set of these regions is the *minor hypersurface dissection* of the JK-space of J by K matrices.

There is a trivial correspondence between these regions and between those defined by K by J matrices. Furthermore, we obtain a correspondence with certain regions of $J(J + K)$-space as follows. Consider the matrix $(1, a)$ obtained by juxtaposition of the J by J unit matrix and of a; then the elements of $(1, a)^{(J)}$ are equal to the minors of a [including the empty minor $A_0 = a^{(0)} = 1$], multiplied by numbers $\varepsilon(j^{(m)}, k^{(m)}) = 1$ or -1 that do not depend on a. If p is a J by J matrix with det $p > 0$, then the signs of the J-minors of (p, pa) are the same as those of $(1, a)$. Since there exists a continuous $q(t)$, $0 \leq t \leq 1$, $q(0) = 1$, $q(1) = p$, det $q(t) > 0$, we obtain the following result.

Theorem 1. *Those (combinatorial or continuous) classes of* $(J + K)$-*ads* [ordered $(J + K)$-tuples] *of points in real* J-*space, with respect to the signs of all* J-*minors, for which the first* J-*minor is positive, are in a natural one-to-one correspondence with the classes of equisign* J *by* K *matrices, and thus also with the classes of* $(J + K)$-*ads of points in* K-*space.*

The number of continuous classes with nonzero J-minors is therefore twice that of the JK-dimensional regions of the minor hypersurface dissection of the space of J by K matrices. Indeed, to a there corresponds not only $(1, a)$ but also $(1^*, a)$, where we denote, in general, by b^* the matrix obtained from a matrix b after multiplying its last row by -1.

2.2. Multiplication of a row or column by a positive number leaves a matrix in the same class. Classes obtainable from each other by multiplication of rows and/or columns by -1 constitute together a $(\pm)$-*class*. Points in real J-space obtainable from each other by multiplication by a nonzero number constitute together a projective $(J-1)$-point (in this context, 0 is one such point in addition to the usual ones). One easily verifies the following theorem.

Theorem 2. *Those classes of $(J+K)$-ads of projective $(J-1)$-points, with respect to the signs of all J-minors, for which the first J-minor is nonzero, are in a natural almost one-to-one correspondence with the $(\pm)$-classes of J by K matrices, and thus also with the classes of $(J+K)$-ads of projective $(K-1)$-points.*

Here "almost one-to-one" means one-to-one if J is odd, but if J is even, then the $(\pm)$-class containing a corresponds both to the class of ads of projective points that contains $(1, a)$ and to the class that contains $(1, a^*)$; these two classes coincide if and only if a has a vanishing row, or two complementary vanishing submatrices with an odd number of rows.

If a has a nonzero column, then the two classes differ in the sign of the product of the elements of that column.

In general, the transition from $(1, a)$ to $(1, a^*)$ corresponds to an orientation-changing projective transformation in odd-dimensional space; the ad remains in the same class if its points are on two complementary even-dimensional subspaces.

If the columns represent hyperplanes instead of points, the ad represents an ordered hyperplane dissection of real projective space.

2.3 From ads we obtain tuples (nonordered sets with multiplicities) by permuting the members and forming the union; we do the same with classes of ads. Interchange of two columns of $(1, a)$ induces in a

(1) if both columns belong to a, an interchange of columns;

(2) if both belong to 1, an interchange of rows (and multiplication of one row by -1);

(3) if one, say k, belongs to a and the other, j, to 1, and if $a_{jk} \neq 0$, replacement of a_{jk} by -1 and of every $a_{j'k'}$, $j' \neq j$, $k' \neq k$, by $a_{jk}a_{j'k'} - a_{jk'}a_{j'k}$ (and multiplication of the j-row by sgn a_{jk}).

All $(\pm)$-classes obtainable from a given class without vanishing minors form together an *exchange class*, and the following result, more explicit than in [11], can be established.

Theorem 3. *Those classes of $(J+K)$-tuples of projective $(J-1)$-points, with respect to the signs of all J-minors, for which no J-minor is zero, are in a natural almost one-to-one correspondence with the exchange classes of J by K matrices, and thus also with the classes of $(J+K)$-tuples of projective $(K-1)$-points.*

Here "almost one-to-one" means one-to-one if J is odd, but if J is even then the exchange class containing a corresponds both to the class of tuples of projective points that contains $(1, a)$ and to the one that contains $(1, a^*)$; these two classes may or may not coincide.

The tuples can also be interpreted as nonordered, nondegenerate, hyperplane dissections of projective space.

Between tuples and ads are ads with the identifying stipulation that all members but one may be permuted. Interpreting the fixed member as the hyperplane at infinity, we obtain the nonordered, nondegenerate, hyperplane dissections of affine space, and their classes.

2.4   Finally we mention several important sets of matrices that are unions of regions in the minor hypersurface dissection.

(1) The set of those a for which the system $xa > 0$ of linear inequalities in $x = (x_1, \ldots, x_J)$ is solvable [8].

(2) The set of those a for which $xa \geq 0$ implies $x \geq 0$ [4].

(3) The set of those a for which the matrix game a is zero-sum [9].

(4) The set of those a (variation-diminishing matrices) for which $v(xa) \leq v(x)$ for every x, where $v(x) + 1$ is the largest m such that $x_{j_1} x_{j_2} < 0$, $x_{j_2} x_{j_3} < 0, \ldots, x_{j_{m-1}} x_{j_m} < 0$ for some $j_1 < \cdots < j_m$ [8].

3. Restricted Elements

3.1.   For $J > 1$, $K > 1$, not every combination of signs of minors is realizable. For $J = K$ and given sgn $a_{jk} = \varepsilon_{jk}$ ($= 0, 1, -1$), where $j = 1, \ldots, J$; $k = 1, \ldots, K$, the set of all the $D = \det_{j,k} a_{jk}$ is

(1) $\{0\}$,

(2) the set of positive numbers,

(3) the set of negative numbers, or

(4) the set of real numbers.

Of these, case (1) occurs iff all J' terms are 0 (by the Frobenius–König theorem, iff for some $j_1, \ldots, j_m, k_1, \ldots, k_n$ ($m + n > J$), all $a_{j_\mu k_\nu} = 0$—we say: iff some ($>J$)-submatrix of zero elements exists), case (2) if all terms are ≥ 0, but not all 0 (see Sec. 3.3), case (3) analogously, case (4) otherwise.

3.2.   If, on the other hand, instead of sgn $a_{jk} = \varepsilon_{jk}$ the inequalities $|a_{jk}| \leq \alpha_{jk}$ are given, then the set of all $D = \det a$ is $|D| \leq \delta$, for some $\delta = \delta(\alpha_{11}, \ldots, \alpha_{nn})$. If $|D| = \delta$, then any a_{jk} whose minor is $\neq 0$ must fulfill $|a_{jk}| = \alpha_{jk}$, any other a_{jk} (can there be such, for $\delta > 0$?) can be replaced by an a'_{jk} with $|a'_{jk}| = \alpha_{jk}$. Hence δ is one of the 2^{J^2} values of det a with

$|a_{jk}| = \alpha_{jk}$, and is thus piecewise polynomial in the a_{jk}. If the product of a_{jk} and its minor has a constant sign $\neq 0$ for all j and k, then the same holds for the inverse matrix. If, in addition, $|a_{jk}| = \alpha_{jk}$ for all j and k, then det a is at least a local extremum.

By Hadamard's inequality, $\delta^2 \leq (\alpha_{11} + \cdots + \alpha_{1n}^2) \cdots (\alpha_{n1}^2 + \cdots + \alpha_{nn}^2)$. Equality occurs iff an orthogonal matrix a_{jk} with $|a_{jk}| = \alpha_{jk}$ exists; e.g., if $\alpha_{11} = \alpha_{12} = \cdots = \alpha_{nn} = 1$, for the Hadamard matrices (e.g., [2]).

3.3. Within the above case (2) where all terms of det a are ≥ 0 we mention two subcases.

(1) One term is >0, all others 0. Then a is a (possibly row- and column-permuted) triangular matrix with nonzero diagonal [5]. Thus one nonzero term requires more zeros than none!

(2) All terms are >0. This implies $J \leq 2$, since for $J = 3$ the product P of all terms is ≤ 0, so that the six terms cannot be all >0 or all <0 (also, replacing each element by 1 or -1, since by Hadamard's inequality such a determinant must be absolutely $<3^{3/2} < 6$).

It is, of course, not only the case of only positive terms that cannot be realized for $J \geq 3$. *Out of the $2^{J!}$ combinations of prescribed nonzero signs for the terms, exactly $2^{(J-1)^2+1}$ are realizable.* For by multiplying rows and columns by -1 an even number of times (which does not change the terms), one can make $a_{11} > 0, \ldots, a_{1J} > 0, a_{21} > 0, \ldots, a_{J-1,1} > 0$. The signs of the remaining $(J-1)^2 + 1$ elements determine the signs of the terms, and conversely, the signs of two otherwise identical terms containing $a_{11}a_{jk}$ and $a_{1k}a_{j1}$, $j < J$, determine the sign of a_{jk}, and after the signs of the elements of the first $J - 1$ rows are fixed, those of the last row follow from the signs of the terms.

The number $\rho(J)$ of realizable sign combinations out of $3^{J!}$, if 0 is admitted, is evidently $\leq 3^{J^2}$. We have $\rho(2) = 9$, $\rho(3) = 393$ (namely 1, 12, 60, 144, 144, 32 for $0, \ldots, 6$ nonzero terms), $\rho(J) \leq 2^{2J} \cdot 3^{(J-1)^2}$.

For $J \geq 4$, $P \geq 0$, hence if all $a_{jk} \neq 0$, then the number ν of positive terms is even; knowledge of the possible values of ν for every J would imply knowledge of the set of all J for which Hadamard matrices exist.

3.4. Concerning the nature of the bound on the determinant if bounds are given for the absolute value of each term, we know even less than in the case of bounded elements. However, the combinatorial part of the Frobenius–König theorem implies that *if each term is absolutely $\leq \varepsilon$, then a contains a $(>J)$-submatrix of elements that are absolutely $\leq \varepsilon^{1/J}$.* Note the case $\varepsilon = 1$. Of course, if $\varepsilon > 0$, the condition is not sufficient.

If a term is called a $(1, 1, \ldots, 1)$-partitional term, the product of an element by its minor a $(1, J - 1)$-partitional term, and the determinant itself the only J-partitional term, the definition of the $(\pi_1, \ldots, \pi_s)$-*partitional term* becomes obvious. We shall not consider the many questions on the signs and absolute values of these terms; we merely prove the following theorem.

Theorem 4. *All* $(2, 1, \ldots, 1)$-*terms vanish iff either all* $(1, \ldots, 1)$-*terms vanish or all* 2 *by* 2 *minors vanish.*

Proof. Each $(2, 1, \ldots, 1)$-term is the difference of two products of J elements that differ only by a transposition of the column subscripts. If the term is zero, the two products are equal; if all terms are zero, all such products are equal (as any two can be obtained from each other by a sequence of transpositions). Thus all products are zero or none is; in the latter case no element is zero, hence the minors involved in the $(2, 1, \ldots, 1)$-terms must vanish. The converse implication is trivial.

3.5. Most problems, and some results, of this section can be extended to matrices with complex elements. Again the consideration of determinants each of whose elements has a bound on its absolute value leads to that of determinants each of whose elements has a given absolute value. But here the set of these determinants is not finite; because of connectedness and rotational symmetry it is either a disk or an annulus. The maximum and minimum are attained by certain real matrices; thus the maximum, as before, is connected with Hadamard's inequality, while the minimum is zero unless one term is absolutely greater than the sum of the absolute values of all the others (the *dominant* case, see Sec. 4.2).

For matrices whose elements have the same absolute value, cf. [6, 12].

Further determinants of interest are those each of whose elements has a given real part, or lies on a given, possibly the same, circle (not about 0).

4. Diagonal Elements and Minors

4.1. In many results on determinants (e.g. Secs. 3.3 and 3.5) one term is emphasized; this term can be assumed to be the diagonal term. The diagonal elements of the compound matrices are called *diagonal, principal,* or *coaxial minors.*

In Sec. 3.3 we noted that for $J \geq 3$ no choice of nonzero signs for the elements will force det a to have a given sign, and mentioned the obvious case of a determinant, necessarily positive, for which all elements times their minors are positive. It suffices to assume this for the elements of a single row or column to see that the sign of a determinant can be determined by the signs of its 1- and $(n-1)$-minors. However, it can also be determined by the signs of 1- and 2-minors; this is implicit in a result of [3] on certain matrices with $a_{jk} > 0$ for $j \le k$, <0 otherwise.

Results on matrices with many vanishing diagonal minors are given in [7]. To give an example, the proof of [7, Lemma 3.1] shows that if all diagonal minors vanish, then all cycles $a_{j_1 j_2} \cdots a_{j_{\nu-1} j_\nu} a_{j_\nu j_1}$ vanish. The directed graph of all (j, k) with $a_{jk} \ne 0$ is thus cycle-free and therefore part of an ordering of $(1, \ldots, J)$, and we have Theorem 5 [7, 1.31].

Theorem 5. *All diagonal minors of a matrix vanish if and only if, after a simultaneous permutation of rows and columns, the matrix is triangular with vanishing diagonal elements.*

4.2. We now prove the dominance (Levy–Minkowski–Hadamard) inequality which states that if $a_{jj} > \sum_{k \ne j} |a_{jk}|$ for each j, then $\det a > 0$, and the sharper Ostrowski inequality, $\det a \ge \prod_j (a_{jj} - \sum_{k \ne j} |a_{jk}|)$ for the same matrices ([16], see also [17]) by writing the difference of the two members as a square-sum [15, Eq. (1)], albeit without squares.

Let $a_{jk} = \varepsilon_{jk} \alpha_{jk}$, $\varepsilon_{jk} = 1$ or -1, $j \ne k$, and $a_{jj} = \alpha_{jj} + \sum_k \alpha_{jk}$. Then the coefficient of any product $\alpha_{1k_1} \cdots \alpha_{Jk_J}$ in $\det a$ is the determinant of a matrix $\eta = \eta(k_1, \ldots, k_J)$ that has in each row a 1 on the diagonal and at most one nonzero ε_{jk_j} not on the diagonal. The mapping $j \to k_j$ splits into cycles with incoming appendages, and $\det \eta$ is the product of the determinants corresponding to the cycles. These determinants are obviously equal to 0, 1, or 2.

Examination of this proof shows (1) that for complex a_{jk} the inequality becomes Re $\det a > 0$; (2) that the conclusion (also for complex a_{jk}) persists for *generalized determinants*, defined as follows. For every cycle $\gamma = (j_1 j_2, j_2 j_3, \ldots, j_{\nu-1} j_\nu, j_\nu j_1)$, $\nu > 1$, let $\delta(\gamma)$ be given with $|\delta(\gamma)| \le 1$; in the complex statement $\delta(\gamma)$ need not be real. For each permutation $\pi = (p_1, \ldots, p_n)$, let $\delta(\pi)$ be the product of the $\delta(\gamma)$ with $\gamma \subset \pi$; for the identical permutation 1, $\delta(1) = 1$. Then $\det_\delta a$ is defined as $\sum_\pi \delta(\pi) a_{1, p_1} \cdots a_{n, p_n}$. If all $\delta(\gamma) = 1$, $\det_\delta a$ is the permanent of a. We have proved Theorem 6.

Theorem 6. *If $a_{jj} > \sum_{k \ne j} |a_{jk}|$ for each j, then*

$$\text{Re } \det_\delta a \ge \prod_j (a_{jj} - \sum_{k \ne j} |a_{jk}|) > 0.$$

In the complex case the proof of Theorem 6 does not provide a square-sum representation in the sense of [15, Eq. (1)]; in the real case it does, but separately for each choice of ε_{jk}. From this one can obtain a single formula expressing $\det_\delta a$ in terms of sums $\sum_k \varepsilon_{jk} a_{jk}$, $\varepsilon_{kk} = 1$, by the method of [*15*, Sec. 6.1]; however, the expression will in general contain denominators. In particular, this is the case for $\det a$ itself when $J \geq 3$. Only for the permanent we prove the following.

Theorem 7.   *The permanent of a equals*

$$\sum_{\varepsilon_1 = \pm 1, \ldots, \varepsilon_J = \pm 1} \prod_j \sum_k \varepsilon_j \varepsilon_k a_{jk} / 2^J,$$

and is thus positive if $a_{jj} > \sum_{k \neq j} |a_{jk}|$ for each j.

Indeed, each term of the permanent occurs in each term of the above sum with coefficient $(\prod_j \varepsilon_j)^2 = 1$; on the other hand, each product $\prod_j a_{jk_j}$ that is not a term of the permanent omits some column, say h, and occurs, therefore, in the sum terms corresponding to $\varepsilon_1, \ldots, \varepsilon_h, \ldots,$ ε_J and $\varepsilon_1, \ldots, -\varepsilon_h, \ldots, \varepsilon_J$ with opposite signs.

4.3.   Nonnegativity of all principal minors holds also for the following class of matrices. The condition involves a cyclic ordering of the rows (and columns).

Theorem 8.   *If*

$$a_{jj} \geq a_{j,j+1} \geq \cdots \geq a_{jJ} \geq a_{j1} \geq a_{j2} \geq \cdots \geq a_{j,j-1} \geq 0, \qquad j = 1, \ldots, J,$$

then $\det a \geq 0$, *and if the inequalities are strict then* $\det a > 0$.

Proof.   Let $b_{1J} = a_{1J}$, $b_{j,j-1} = a_{j,j-1}$, $b_{jJ} = a_{jJ} - a_{j1}$ for $j > 1$, $b_{jk} = a_{jk} - a_{j,k+1}$ for $k \neq j - 1$; then the jth row of a is a linear combination, with coefficients $b_{jk} \geq 0$, of rows fulfilling the same inequalities but consisting of ones and zeros only. Hence a is a linear combination, with coefficients that are products of some b_{jk}, of zero-one matrices fulfilling the above inequalities. Now if $\det a = 0$, then there exist $z_1, \ldots, z_J$ not all 0 such that $\sum_k a_{jk} z_k = 0$, $j = 1, \ldots, J$; we may assume $z = \sum z_j / J \geq 0$. Let $z_j - z = y_j$, then $\sum y_j = 0$. A cyclic permutation of the rows and columns leaves the inequalities in effect and permutes the z_j and the y_j cyclically; hence by determining the smallest among $y_1, y_1 + y_2, \ldots, \sum y_j = 0$, we can choose the permutation so that, after its execution, all of $y_1, y_1 + y_2, \ldots$ are ≥ 0. In view of $\sum a_{1k} z_k = \sum b_{1k}(y_1 + \cdots + y_k) + z \sum a_{1k} = 0$ we see that, if the inequalities are strict, then all y_j as well as z vanish; hence $\det a \neq 0$ in that case. Since the matrices fulfilling the strict inequalities form a convex and thus connected part of J^2-space, $\det a$ has the same sign for all these matrices; choosing a close to 1 we see that $\det a > 0$. For nonstrict inequalities we obtain det $a \geq 0$, and the representation as a linear combination of zero-one matrices is seen to be of the type [15, Eq. (1)], and again square-free.

5. Symmetric and Skew-Symmetric Matrices

5.1. We recall that every two of the following five statements are equivalent.

(1) There is a $z = (z_1, \ldots, z_J) \neq 0$ with $za = 0$.
(2) det $a = 0$.
(3) The rank of $a^{(J-1)}$ is ≤ 1.
(4) The bilinear form $xa^{(J-1)}y^T$ splits into linear factors.
(5) The bilinear function $\begin{vmatrix} \zeta & y \\ x^T & a \end{vmatrix}$ splits into linear factors.

Theorem 9.   *The skew-bordered determinant*

$$\begin{vmatrix} 0 & x \\ -x^T & a \end{vmatrix} = Q(x)$$

is a constant γ times a square of a linear form iff either

(1) det $a \neq 0$, *and the rank of $a^{-1} + a^{T-1}$ is ≤ 1; or*
(2) det $a = 0$, *and $a^{(J-1)}$ is symmetric.*

Case (2) *occurs iff either*

(i) $a^{(J-1)} = 0, J \geq 4$, *or*
(ii) *there is a z with $za = 0, za^T = 0$.*

In case (2), *any diagonal element* $(\neq 0$, *if such exists*) *of $a^{(J-1)}$ can be chosen as γ.*

Proof.   Obviously Q is a constant γ times a square of a linear form iff the rank of the symmetric part of $a^{(J-1)}$ is ≤ 1. If det $a \neq 0$, this can be written as in (1). If det $a = 0$, then the rank of $a^{(J-1)}$ is ≤ 1; looking at any principal 2-minor of $a^{(J-1)}$ we see easily that if its rank and the rank of its symmetric part are ≤ 1, then the 2-minor is symmetric. Further, any nonzero row of $a^{(J-1)}$ can serve as z with $za = 0, za^T = 0$; and if $a^{(J-1)} = 0$, $J = 2$ or 3, then the rank of (a, a^T) is $< J$, and thus there is a z with $za = 0, za^T = 0$. Finally, if $a^{(J-1)}$ is symmetric and of rank 1, then for any nonzero row x of $a^{(J-1)}$ we have $a^{(J-1)} = z^T z / \gamma$, where γ is the diagonal element of x.

Note that if the degree of a skew-symmetric matrix a is even, then the symmetric part of $a^{(J-1)}$ is 0, hence $Q = 0$; while if it is odd, then (e.g., from the previous statement) $\det a = 0$, and $a^{(J-1)}$ is symmetric. Hence Q is γ times a square of a linear form; by induction, γ and Q are squares of polynomials in the elements.

Theorem 10. *The skew-bordered determinant*

$$\begin{vmatrix} 0 & x \\ -x^T & a \end{vmatrix} = Q(x)$$

is semidefinite iff either

(1) $\det a \neq 0$, *and* $a^{-1} + a^{T\,-1}$ *is semidefinite, or*
(2) $\det a = 0$, *and* $a^{(J-1)}$ *is symmetric.*

Proof. Obviously Q is semidefinite iff the symmetric part of $a^{(J-1)}$ is semidefinite. If $\det a \neq 0$, this can be written as (1). If $\det a = 0$, then the rank of $a^{(J-1)}$ is ≤ 1; looking at any principal 2-minor of $a^{(J-1)}$ we see easily that if its rank is ≤ 1 and its symmetric part semidefinite, then the 2-minor is symmetric. On the other hand, (2) implies semidefiniteness by Theorem 9.

5.2. We now define, for an arbitrary J by J matrix a, $a_{j,k}^{\backslash}$ as the minor of a formed by the rows $1, \ldots, j$ and the columns $1, \ldots, j-1, k$; then $a^{\backslash}$ is an upper triangular matrix. Further, let $a^{\wedge} = a^{T\,\backslash T}$ (lower triangular). Finally, if all $a_{jj}^{\backslash} \neq 0$, let $a^{\backprime}$ be the diagonal matrix for which $a_{11}^{\backprime} = 1/a_{11}^{\backslash} = 1/a_{11}$, $a_{jj}^{\backprime} = 1/(a_{jj}^{\backslash} a_{j-1,j-1}^{\backslash})$, $j > 1$. Then we have Theorem 11.

Theorem 11. *If all* $a_{jj}^{\backslash} \neq 0$, *then*

$$a = a^{\wedge} a^{\backprime} a^{\backslash} \tag{1}$$

and consequently

$$\sum_{j,k} a_{jk} x_j y_k = \sum_l \left(\sum_j a_{lj}^{\wedge} x_j \right) \left(\sum_k a_{lk}^{\backslash} y_k \right) a_{jj}^{\backprime}. \tag{2}$$

Proof. The identity

$$a_{l-1,l-1}^{\backslash} a_{l+1,j,k} = a_{ll}^{\backslash} a_{l,j,k} - a_{jl}^{\wedge} a_{lk}^{\backslash},$$

where $a_{l,j,k}$ is the minor of a formed by the rows $1, \ldots, l-1, j$ and the columns $1, \ldots, l-1, k$, implies

$$\frac{a_{jl}^{\wedge} a_{lk}^{\backslash}}{a_{l-1,l-1}^{\backslash} a_{ll}^{\backslash}} = \frac{a_{l,j,k}}{a_{l-1,l-1}^{\backslash}} - \frac{a_{l+1,j,k}}{a_{l,l}^{\backslash}} \qquad \text{(with } a_{1,j,k} = a_{jk}, \quad a_{00}^{\backslash} = 1\text{)};$$

adding over $l = 1, \ldots, \min(j, k)$ gives (1).

The decomposition (1) is closely related to that obtained by repeated pivoting (elimination method).

5.3. For symmetric a, (1) gives the transformation to diagonal form, a proof of the necessity and sufficiency of $a_{jj}^\natural > 0,\ j = 1, \ldots, J$, for positive definiteness, and in the latter case a matrix $b = a^\natural \sqrt{a^\natural}$ such that $bb^T = a$.

The fact that $a_{jj}^\natural > 0,\ j = 1, \ldots, J$ implies positive-definiteness for symmetric a can be based, in the sense of [15, Eq. (1)], on (2) with $x = y$; to obtain a strict representation by squares, replace each $1/a_{jj}^\natural$ by $a_{jj}^\natural (1/a_{jj}^\natural)^2$.

Already for $J = 2$ a representation without denominators does not exist, since $\sum a_{jk}x_jx_k$, which is linear in the a_{jk}, cannot be written polynomially so as to involve the second-order expression $a_{22}^\natural$.

That conversely every positive-definite symmetric matrix a has a positive determinant, and thus positive principal minors, follows also by induction from the cases $J = 1$ and $J = 2$: regard $\sum a_{jk}x_jx_k$ as a quadratic function

$$a_{11}x_1{}^2 + 2x_1 \sum_{k>1} a_{1k}x_k + \sum_{j>1,k>1} a_{jk}x_jx_k$$

of x_1; if it is positive for all x_1, then the two-by-two determinant $a_{11}\sum_{>1} a_{jk}x_jx_k - (\sum_{>1} a_{1k}x_k)^2 > 0$, which by the induction hypothesis implies the positivity of the determinant

$$\det_{j>1,k>1}(a_{11}a_{jk} - a_{j1}a_{1k}) = a_{11}^{2-J} \det_{j,k} a_{jk}.$$

5.4. If S and T are equinumerous nonempty subsets of $1, \ldots, J$, then a_{ST} shall mean the minor of a formed by the S-rows and the T-columns. That, for positive-definite symmetric a, $\det a \le a_{SS}a_{S'S'}$ where $S' = \{1, \ldots, J\}\backslash S$ follows from Theorem 12.

Theorem 12.   For $a = a^T$, $a_{jj}^\natural > 0, j = 1, \ldots, J$, we have

$$a_{SS}a_{S'S'} - a_{JJ}^\natural = \sum_{T,U \neq T'} (a_{ST}^\natural)^2 (a_{S'U}^\natural)^2 a_{TT}^\natural a_{UU}^\natural$$

$$+ \tfrac{1}{2}\sum_{T,U} (a_{ST}^\natural - a_{S'U}^\natural)^2 a_{JJ}^\natural.$$

Proof.   By the multiplicative homomorphism property of compound matrices, $a_{ST} = \sum_{U,V} a_{SU}^\natural a_{UV}^\natural a_{VT}^\natural$; but $a_{UV}^\natural = 0$, $U \neq V$, hence $a_{ST} = \sum_U a_{SU}^\natural a_{UU}^\natural a_{UT}^\natural$. Thus if $a = a^T$, then

$$a_{SS}a_{S'S'} = \sum_{T,U} (a_{ST}^\natural)^2 a_{TT}^\natural (a_{S'U}^\natural)^2 a_{UU}^\natural,$$

and

$$\sum_T (a_{ST}^\natural)^2 (a_{S'T'}^\natural)^2 a_{TT}^\natural a_{T'T'}^\natural = a_{JJ} + \tfrac{1}{2}\sum_{T,U} (a_{ST}^\natural - a_{S'U}^\natural)^2 a_{JJ}^\natural$$

because of $a_{TT}^\natural a_{T'T'}^\natural = a_{JJ}^\natural$, $a_{JJ} = (a_{JJ}^\natural)^2 a_{JJ}^\natural$, $a_{JJ}^\natural = \sum_T a_{ST}^\natural a_{S'T'}^\natural$ (Laplace) and of the C-B-S inequality (Sec. 5.5).

Formulas showing that not only for positive-definite symmetric a, but for any matrix a with $a_{jj}^\mathsf{y} > 0$, $a_{jj}^\mathsf{b} a_{jj}^\mathsf{y} \geq 0$, $j = 1, \dots, J$, one has $\det a \leq a_{J-1,J-1}^\mathsf{y} a_{JJ}$ and that $a_{jj}^\mathsf{y} > 0$, $a_{jk}^\mathsf{b} a_{kj}^\mathsf{y} \geq 0$, $j, k = 1, \dots, J$, imply $\det a \leq a_{11} a_{22} \cdots a_{JJ}$ are given in Theorem 13.

Theorem 13. *If all $a_{jj}^\mathsf{y} \neq 0$ then*

$$a_{J-1,J-1}^\mathsf{y} a_{JJ} - a_{JJ}^\mathsf{y} = a_{J-1,J-1}^\mathsf{y} \sum_{j=1}^{J-1} a_{Jj}^\mathsf{b} a_{jj} a_{jJ}^\mathsf{y} \tag{1}$$

and

$$\delta_J = \delta_{J-1} a_{JJ}^\mathsf{y} / a_{J-1,J-1}^\mathsf{y} + (\delta_{J-1} + a_{J-1,J-1}^\mathsf{y}) \sum_{j=1}^{J-1} a_{Jj}^\mathsf{b} a_{jj} a_{jJ}^\mathsf{y}, \tag{2}$$

where $\delta_k = a_{11} a_{22} \cdots a_{kk} - a_{kk}^\mathsf{y}$.

Proof. (2) follows from (1), and (1) from the expression for a_{JJ} according to (1), Theorem 11.

If $\det a \geq 0$, we call $(\det a)^{1/J} \geq 0$ the *length* of a. If all principal k-minors of a are ≥ 0, we call the geometric mean of their lengths the *mean k-length* of a and denote it by $\lambda_k(a)$. Then $\det a \leq a_{11} a_{22} \dots a_{JJ}$ can, if $\det a \geq 0$, $a_{11} \geq 0, \dots, a_{JJ} \geq 0$, be written $\lambda_J(a) \leq \lambda_1(a)$. A refinement of this inequality is stated in Theorem 14.

Theorem 14. *For positive-definite symmetric a we have*

$$\lambda_J(a) \leq \lambda_{J-1}(a) \leq \cdots \leq \lambda_1(a).$$

Proof. Since also a^{-1} is positive-definite, Theorem 13 implies $\det a^{-1} \leq a^{-1}_{11} \cdots a^{-1}_{JJ}$. Multiplying by $(\det a)^J$ we see that $(\det a)^{J-1}$ is not greater than the product of the principal $(J-1)$-minors, i.e., $\lambda_J(a) \leq \lambda_{J-1}(a)$. Applying this inequality to every k-minor of a and taking the geometric mean we obtain $\lambda_k(a) \leq \lambda_{k-1}(a)$.

If a is diagonal then all $\leq$ signs become $=$; otherwise all are $<$.

5.5. Three particularly important quadratic forms are

$$f_J = \sum a_k^2 \sum x_k^2 - \left(\sum a_k x_k\right)^2,$$

$$g_J = \sum a_k^2 b_k \sum x_k^2 / b_k - \left(\sum a_k x_k\right)^2, \qquad b_k > 0,$$

$$h_J = \sum x_k a_k \sum x_k / a_k - \sum x_k^2, \qquad x_k a_k > 0;$$

the positive-semidefiniteness of f_J or g_J constitutes the C-B-S inequality. Of the expressions $f_J = \sum_{j,k>j} (a_j x_k - a_k x_j)^2$, $g_J = \sum_{j,k>j} (a_j x_k b_j / b_k - a_k x_j)^2 b_k / b_j$, $h_j = \sum_{j,k>j} (a_k / a_j - 1)^2 x_j a_j x_k / a_k$, as sums of $\binom{J}{2}$ squares, the first was used in the proof of Theorem 12; in it, all $\binom{J}{2}$ terms are needed for general a_j and x_j. But if, e.g., $a_1 \neq 0$, we have the following representation by $J - 1$ squares.

Theorem 15. *If $a_1 \neq 0$, then*

$$\sum a_k^2 \sum x_k^2 - \sum (a_k x_k)^2 = s_J \sum_1^{J-1} (s_k x_{k+1} - a_{k+1} y_k)^2/(s_k s_{k+1})$$

where $s_k = \sum_1^k a_j^2$, $y_k = \sum_1^k a_j x_j$.

Proof. We have $s_k \neq 0$ and $f_J = s_J \sum x_k^2 - y_j^2$. We verify easily that $s_{k-1} f_k - s_k f_{k-1} = (s_{k-1} x_k - a_k y_{k-1})^2$; hence

$$\frac{f_k}{s_k} - \frac{f_{k-1}}{s_{k-1}} = \frac{(s_{k-1} x_k - a_k y_{k-1})^2}{s_k s_{k-1}} .$$

Letting $k = 2, \ldots, J - 1$, adding, and noting $f_1 = 0$, we obtain the contention of the theorem.

The identity

$$[x^2 y^2 - (xy)^2] x^2 = (x \cdot xy - x^2 \cdot y)^2$$

where $x = (x_1, \ldots)$, $y = (y_1, \ldots)$ and the products and squares are scalar products (or products with scalars), gives for $x^2 \neq 0$ the representation

$$x^2 y^2 - (xy)^2 = x^2 \sum (x_k \cdot xy/x^2 - y_k)^2$$

as a product of two sums of J squares, which exhibits the proportionality condition for vanishing. The same condition results by writing $\sum (x_k t - y_k)^2$, which is ≥ 0 for all t, as a sum of two squares, and substituting $t = xy/x^2$ so that the nonconstant square vanishes.

5.6. For a J by K matrix b, let $|b| = (\det bb^T)^{1/2} = (b^{(J)} b^{(J)T})^{1/2} \geq 0$ (necessarily $= 0$ for $J > K$) and b_S the matrix formed by the S-rows of b, $S < \{1, \ldots, J\}$. We have:

Theorem 16. *If S_1, S_2, $\ldots$ is a partition of $\{1, \ldots, J\}$ into pairwise disjoint nonempty subsets, then*

$$|b_S| \leq |b_{S_1}| \, |b_{S_2}| \cdots .$$

Proof. We can assume that the partition consists of two subsets. Let $a = bb^T$; then

$$|b_{S_1}|^2 |b_{S_2}|^2 - |b_S|^2 = a_{S_1 S_1} a_{S_2 S_2} - a_{JJ}^\wedge \geq 0$$

by Theorem 11 since $a_{jj}^\wedge = |b_{\{1, \ldots, j\}}|^2 \geq 0$.

Hadamard's inequality is the case of J 1-sets, $J = K$. On the other hand, the case $J = 2$ of Theorem 16 says that the sine of the angle of two vectors is between -1 and 1, and the first member of the corresponding inequality in the proof, written as a square (namely, involving the remaining cosine square) yields again the C-B-S inequality.

If the length of an edge of a hypercube whose volume equals that of a given parallel box b is called the *length* of b, and the geometric mean of the lengths of the k-faces of b is called the k-*length* of b, then Theorem 14 and the proof of Theorem 16 imply the following result.

Theorem 17. *The k-length of a parallel box is greater than or equal to its $(k + 1)$-length.*

Equality occurs only for rectangular boxes.

5.7. That a skew determinant is nonnegative and that a positive-semi-definite symmetric determinant is smaller than or equal to the product of complementary principal minors, are both special cases of Theorem 18.

Theorem 18. *If $a + b = c$ where a is positive-semidefinite symmetric and b skew-symmetric, then $\det a + \det b \leq \det c$. Hence if $\sum c_{jk} x_j x_k \geq 0$ for all x, then all principal minors of c are ≥ 0.*

Proof. If a is diagonal the contention follows by expansion of $\det c$ by products of elements of a. Otherwise write $a = t\hat{a}t^T$, $\det t \neq 0$, where $\hat{a}$ is diagonal, e.g. $a = a^{\backslash}a^{\backslash}a^{\backslash}$ if all $a_{jj}^{\backslash} \neq 0$, and $b = t\hat{b}t^T$.

Making c triangular, $\det a \leq$ the product of its diagonal elements; it is $\leq$ the product of complementary principal minors by selection of an appropriate block-triangular c.

5.8. A quadratic form $\sum a_{jk} x_j x_k$ is *copositive* if it is positive for $x_1 \geq 0$, $\ldots, x_J \geq 0$, except $x_1 = \cdots = x_J = 0$. We establish the following necessary and sufficient condition for copositivity [10, 13].

Theorem 19. *A symmetric matrix is copositive iff each principal minor for which the cofactors of its last row are all positive is positive. (This is meant to include positivity of the diagonal elements.)*

Proof. The contention is trivial for $J = 1$; assume it holds for $J - 1$. Then if the condition given is fulfilled we have $f = \sum a_{jk} x_j x_k > 0$ for $x_1 \geq 0, \ldots, x_J \geq 0$, $x_1^2 + \cdots + x_J^2 = 1$, whenever $x_1 \cdots \cdot x_J = 0$, hence also whenever $x_k^2 \leq \varepsilon \sum x_j^2$ for some ε. We now replace each point on

$x_1^2 + \cdots + x_J^2 = 1$ by the proportional point on $x_J = 1$. On this hyperplane there remains, in the positive orthant, a bounded region where f
might have nonpositive values; if such values exist consider the minimum
of f, say, at $\xi_1, \ldots, \xi_J$. As a nonpositive minimum can occur only in the
interior of the region, the derivatives $\sum a_{jk}\xi_k$, $j < J$, must vanish, and the
minimum must be unique. Thus the cofactors α_{Jk} of a_{Jk} are not all zero,
and the ξ_k are proportional to the α_{Jk}; because of $\xi_J = 1$ we have $\xi_k =
\alpha_{Jk}/\alpha_{JJ}$, $\sum a_{jk}\xi_j\xi_k = \xi_J \sum a_{Jk}\xi_k = \det a/\alpha_{JJ}$. Hence to exclude this
possibility we must require that if all α_{Jk} have the same sign, $\det a$ has that
sign too. But if the quadratic function f in a $(J-1)$-dimensional region
of the hyperplane $x_J = 1$ has a unique minimum, then f plus a constant is
positive on $x_J = 1$, hence $\alpha_{JJ} > 0$.

We see that Theorem 19 holds in various other versions: the words
"positive is positive" may be replaced by "of one sign has the same sign,"
and the words "last row" may be replaced by "one row" or by "elements."
The theorem can further be modified to take account of the fact that not
only α_{JJ} but all principal minors would have to be positive; accordingly,
a check on copositivity proceeds from any positive-definite principal
k-minor to a $(k+1)$-minor containing it; this is either positive and therefore positive-definite, or nonpositive, and then one examines the cofactors
of one row.

Altogether, however, it can be shown that the set $\mathscr{S}_2$ of all copositive
matrices, as a subset of the $\binom{J+1}{2}$-space of all symmetric matrices, is
bounded by $[\binom{J+1}{2}-1]$-dimensional parts of all $2^J - 1$ hypersurfaces
$a_{SS} = 0$, $S \subset \{1, \ldots, J\}$, $S \neq \{\}$, in contrast to the set $\mathscr{S}_1$ of all positive-
definite matrices, which is bounded by part of the single hypersurface
$\det a = 0$. And whereas the interior of $\mathscr{S}_1$ is the solution set of the system
$a_{jj}^k > 0$, $j = 1, \ldots, J$, the interior of $\mathscr{S}_2$, for $J \geq 2$, is not the solution set
of any system of finitely many polynomial inequalities (cf. [14]).

5.9. Among other sets of matrices or of pairs of matrices defined by
inequalities, not to be investigated further at the present occasion, we
mention:

$\mathscr{S}_2'$ (the dual of 2; $\mathscr{S}_1$ is self-dual), the set of all "completely positive"
matrices cc^T where $\det c \neq 0$ and all $c_{jk} > 0$. Its boundary, or equivalently,
the set of extreme points of $\mathscr{S}_2$, is more complicated than the boundary of
$\mathscr{S}_2$; for some results see [1]. A positive-definite matrix bb^T is completely
positive iff $b = co$, c as above, o orthogonal.

$\mathscr{M}_1$, the set of all matrices $b = co$ (cones congruent to simplicial cones
in the positive orthant).

$\mathscr{M}_{2,r}$, the set of all J by K matrices of *positivity rank* $\leq r$, i.e., products
of a J by r and an r by K matrix with nonnegative elements.

$\mathscr{P}_1$, the set of all pairs of matrices representing simplicial cones one of which is congruent to part of the other. The cones determine spherical simplices; letting the radius of the sphere become infinite we obtain

$\mathscr{P}_2$, like $\mathscr{P}_1$, with simplices instead of simplicial cones. Even for the elementary question when a triangle is congruent to part of another it is easy to state necessary conditions, but the exact polynomial inequalities are surprisingly complicated.

For all these sets, as well as for the set of all J by K matrices of rank $\leq r$, there are derived sets defined by the approximation problem of determining those matrices, or pairs of matrices, whose (e.g., orthogonal) distance from the set is below a given bound.

REFERENCES

[1] Baumert, L. D., Extreme copositive quadratic forms, I, II. *Pacific J. Math.* **19**, 197–204 (1966); **20**, 1–20 (1967).

[2] Baumert, L. D., and Hall, M., Jr., Hadamard matrices of the Williamson type, *Math. Comp.* **19**, 442–447 (1965).

[3] Braumann, P., A theorem about systems of linear equations, *Univ. Lisboa. Revista Fac. Ci. A.* (2) **5**, 103–112 (1956).

[4] Collatz, L., Über monotone Systeme linearer Ungleichungen, *J. Reine Angew. Math.* **194**, 193–194 (1955).

[5] Gordon, B., and Motzkin, T. S., A combinatorial problem on determinants: the number of nonzero terms, to be published.

[6] Motzkin, T. S., Bemerkung über Singularitäten gewisser mit Lücken behafteter Potenzreihen, *Math. Ann.* **109**, 95–100 (1933).

[7] Motzkin, T. S., On vanishing coaxial minors, *Proc. Edinburgh Math. Soc.* (2) **4**, 210–217 (1935).

[8] Motzkin, T. S., "Beiträge zur Theorie der linearen Ungleichungen." Jerusalem, 1936.

[9] Motzkin, T. S., Two consequences of the transposition theorem on linear inequalities, *Econometrica* **19**, 184–185 (1951).

[10] Motzkin, T. S., in *Nat. Bur. Standards Rept.* 1818, 11–12 (1952).

[11] Motzkin, T. S., Types of dissections, *Bull. Amer. Math. Soc.* **63**, 35 (1957).

[12] Motzkin, T. S., Determinants whose elements have equal norm, *Proc. Amer. Math. Soc.* **11**, 871–874 (1960).

[13] Motzkin, T. S., Quadratic forms positive for nonnegative variables not all zero, *Notices Amer. Math. Soc.* **12**, 224 (1965).

[14] Motzkin, T. S., Algebraic inequalities, these Proceedings.

[15] Motzkin, T. S., The arithmetic-geometric inequality, these Proceedings.

[16] Ostrowski, A., Sur la détermination des bornes inférieures pour une classe des déterminants, *Bull. Sci. Math.* (2) **61**, 19–32 (1937).

[17] Ostrowski, A., Note on bounds for determinants with dominant principal diagonal, *Proc. Amer. Math. Soc.* **3**, 26–30 (1952).

A Priori Bounds in Problems of Steady Subsonic Flow*

L. E. PAYNE

Department of Mathematics
Cornell University, Ithaca, New York

1. Introduction

The problem of compressible potential flow of an inviscid fluid has been well studied in the literature (see e.g. [1, 7, 9]). If the fluid is enclosed in a bounded domain, the flux is prescribed at each point of the boundary, and if the flow is subsonic, then the questions of existence, uniqueness, and stability have for the most part been settled. However, there are to my knowledge no known methods for computing or estimating with computable error the solution of such a flow problem.

In this paper we obtain upper and lower bounds of a priori type for the L_2 integral of the velocity of the flow. If an approximating function can be chosen which approximates well in mean square the data of the flow problem, then close upper and lower bounds in L_2 norm are obtained. The particular flow problem which we treat leads to an interior Neumann problem for a nonlinear second-order elliptic partial differential equation. We consider also in Sec. 4 the exterior Neumann problem for the compressible flow equations and in particular the problem of a fixed body in a uniform stream. For completeness we also derive L_2 bounds in the Dirichlet problem for the compressible flow equations. However, the interest here is more mathematical than physical.

Some of the results of Sec. 3 are essentially contained in the interesting paper of Finn and Gilbarg [4] on the uniqueness of steady subsonic flows in exterior domains. Maximum principles and uniqueness theorems based on inequalities similar to those used in Sec. 3 were also established by Levin [6].

The bounds in this paper are dependent on knowledge of an upper bound for the maximum velocity on the boundary of the domain. This bound need not be sharp if the flow nowhere approaches sonic velocity; thus the bound may frequently be obtained by observation or measurement. It is shown in Secs. 3 and 4 that if measurements must be taken they may be confined to certain portions of the boundary.

* This research was supported in part by NSF Grant GP-4216.

2. Definitions and Notation

Let R denote a bounded domain with smooth boundary ∂R. In the potential flow problem for a compressible inviscid fluid, the components v_i of the velocity may be expressed as the gradient of a potential function, i.e.

$$v_i = \partial \Phi / \partial x_i, \qquad i = 1, 2, 3. \tag{2.1}$$

If the flux is prescribed at each point of ∂R, then the function Φ satisfies

$$\frac{\partial}{\partial x_i} \left(\rho \frac{\partial \Phi}{\partial x_i} \right) = 0 \quad \text{in} \quad R,$$

$$\rho \frac{\partial \Phi}{\partial n} = g \quad \text{on} \quad \partial R. \tag{2.2}$$

In (2.2) we have used the summation convention on the repeated index i, ρ denotes the fluid density, and $\partial/\partial n$ denotes the outward normal derivative on ∂R. From Bernoulli's law it follows that ρ is a function of the square of the velocity vector, i.e.

$$\rho = \rho(q^2); \qquad q^2 = v_i v_i. \tag{2.3}$$

The local speed of sound C is given by

$$C^2 = -\rho/2\rho', \tag{2.4}$$

where

$$\rho' \equiv d\rho/dq^2. \tag{2.5}$$

Let us denote by C_S the quantity

$$C_S = -\frac{\rho(0)}{2\rho'(0)}, \tag{2.6}$$

i.e. the value of C at stagnation velocity. We shall assume that our flow is entirely subsonic which means that

$$q^2 \leq -\rho/2\rho'. \tag{2.7}$$

We shall be concerned for the most part with the isentropic flow of perfect gases. In this case the pressure p and the density ρ satisfy the relation

$$p = K\rho^\gamma, \qquad 1 < \gamma < 2. \tag{2.8}$$

It is easily shown then that the flow will be everywhere subsonic if at each point of the flow domain

$$q^2 \leq \frac{2}{\gamma + 1} C_S^2. \tag{2.9}$$

3. An Auxiliary Inequality

Let $\rho(\sigma^2)$ be an arbitrary continuously differentiable function defined in R which satisfies

$$\rho > 0, \qquad \rho' < 0 \tag{3.1}$$

for all q, and let φ and ψ be arbitrary smooth functions in R. We seek then conditions on ρ which are sufficient to insure that $I(\varphi, \psi)$ defined by

$$I(\varphi, \psi) = \int_R \left[\rho(\sigma^2) \frac{\partial \varphi}{\partial x_i} - \rho(\xi^2) \frac{\partial \psi}{\partial x_i} \right] \frac{\partial}{\partial x_i} (\varphi - \psi) \, dx \tag{3.2}$$

should be nonnegative. Here of course

$$\sigma^2 = \frac{\partial \varphi}{\partial x_i} \frac{\partial \varphi}{\partial x_i}, \qquad \xi^2 = \frac{\partial \psi}{\partial x_i} \frac{\partial \psi}{\partial x_i}. \tag{3.3}$$

Clearly from (3.2)

$$2I = \int_R [\rho(\sigma^2) + \rho(\xi^2)] \frac{\partial}{\partial x_i} (\varphi - \psi) \frac{\partial}{\partial x_i} (\varphi - \psi) \, dx$$

$$+ \int_R [\rho(\sigma^2) - \rho(\xi^2)] \frac{\partial}{\partial x_i} (\varphi + \psi) \frac{\partial}{\partial x_i} (\varphi - \psi) \, dx. \tag{3.4}$$

Since ρ is a differentiable function of its argument, we have by the mean-value theorem

$$\rho(\sigma^2) - \rho(\xi^2) = \rho'(t^2)(\sigma^2 - \xi^2), \tag{3.5}$$

where t is some value between σ and ξ. Inserting (3.5) into (3.4) we have

$$2I = \int_R \Big\{ [\rho(\sigma^2) + \rho(\xi^2)] \, \delta_{ij}$$

$$+ \rho'(t^2) \frac{\partial}{\partial x_i} (\varphi + \psi) \frac{\partial}{\partial x_i} (\varphi + \psi) \Big\} \frac{\partial}{\partial x_j} (\varphi - \psi) \frac{\partial}{\partial x_j} (\varphi + \psi) \, dx. \tag{3.6}$$

We now investigate the matrix

$$A_{ij} = \Big\{ [\rho(\sigma^2) + \rho(\xi^2)] \, \delta_{ij} + \rho'(t^2) \frac{\partial}{\partial x_i} (\varphi + \psi) \frac{\partial}{\partial x_j} (\varphi - \psi) \Big\}. \tag{3.7}$$

A simple computation shows that the eigenvalues of A_{ij} are given by

$$\lambda_1 = \lambda_2 = \rho(\sigma^2) + \rho(\xi^2)$$

$$\lambda_3 = \rho(\sigma^2) + \rho(\xi^2) + \rho'(t^2) \frac{\partial}{\partial x_i} (\varphi + \psi) \frac{\partial}{\partial x_i} (\varphi + \psi). \tag{3.8}$$

Clearly if $\rho > 0$ and $\rho' > 0$, all three eigenvalues are positive and no further condition need be imposed on ρ to insure that $I > 0$. We are, however, assuming (3.1), the physically meaningful condition. In any case it will follow that $I > 0$ provided $\lambda_3 > 0$.

Using (2.4) we may rewrite λ_3 as

$$\lambda_3 = \rho(\sigma^2) + \rho(\xi^2) - \frac{\rho(t^2)}{2C(t^2)} \frac{\partial}{\partial x_i}(\varphi + \psi)\frac{\partial}{\partial x_i}(\varphi + \psi). \tag{3.9}$$

Now let us assume that at a point P in R

$$\rho(\sigma^2) \geq \rho(\xi^2). \tag{3.10}$$

Then at P

$$\xi^2 \geq t^2 \geq \sigma^2 \tag{3.11}$$

and

$$\rho(\sigma^2) \geq \rho(t^2) \geq \rho(\xi^2). \tag{3.12}$$

From (3.5) and (2.4) we know that

$$\rho(\xi^2) = \rho(\sigma^2) - \frac{\rho(t^2)}{2C(t^2)}(\xi^2 - \sigma^2). \tag{3.13}$$

Thus at such a point

$$\lambda_3 = 2\rho(\sigma^2) - \frac{\rho(t^2)}{2C^2(t^2)}\left\{\frac{\partial}{\partial x_i}(\varphi + \psi)\frac{\partial}{\partial x_i}(\varphi + \psi) + (\xi^2 - \sigma^2)\right\}$$

$$\geq 2\rho(t^2)\left\{1 - \frac{1}{4}\frac{(\sigma^2 + 3\xi^2)}{C^2(t^2)}\right\}. \tag{3.14}$$

Here we have used (3.12) and the arithmetic–geometric mean inequality. Thus $\lambda_3 > 0$ provided

$$\sigma^2 + 3\xi^2 < 4C^2(t^2). \tag{3.15}$$

For a perfect gas it follows that

$$C^2(t^2) = C_S^2 - \frac{\gamma - 1}{2}t^2. \tag{3.16}$$

Thus (3.15) will be satisfied provided

$$\sigma^2 + 2(\gamma - 1)t^2 + 3\xi^2 < 4C_S^2. \tag{3.17}$$

Since $\sigma^2 \leq t^2 \leq \xi^2$, (3.17) will hold if

$$\xi^2 \leq \frac{2C_S^2}{1 + \gamma}. \tag{3.18}$$

In particular, if at P the speed ξ is subsonic [(3.18) is satisfied], $I > 0$.

If, on the other hand, at the point under consideration $\xi^2 \leq \sigma^2$, then $\lambda_3 > 0$ at that point if σ is subsonic. Thus I will certainly be positive, and, in fact, the integrand will be positive at every point in R if ξ and σ are everywhere subsonic.

For a perfect gas (2.8) it follows that $\rho'' > 0$ which implies that if $\sigma^2 \leq t^2$,

$$\frac{\rho(t^2)}{C^2(t^2)} \leq \frac{\rho(\sigma^2)}{C^2(\sigma^2)}. \tag{3.19}$$

In this case (3.14) leads directly to

$$\lambda_3 \geq 2\rho(\sigma^2)\left[1 - \frac{1}{4}\frac{(\sigma^2 + 3\xi^2)}{C^2(\sigma^2)}\right] \tag{3.20}$$

from which it follows that $\lambda_3 > 0$ provided (3.18) is satisfied.

Suppose now that we are able to determine a number $\alpha < 1$ such that in R

$$\max[\sigma_m{}^2, \xi_m{}^2] \leq \frac{2\alpha}{1+\gamma}C_S^2. \tag{3.21}$$

(Here σ_m and ξ_m denote the least upper bounds for σ and ξ in R.) Then from (3.20) using (3.19) it follows that

$$\lambda_3 \geq 2(1 - \alpha)\rho(0). \tag{3.22}$$

Since

$$C_S^2 = K\gamma[\rho(0)]^{\gamma-1}, \tag{3.23}$$

inequalities (3.21) and (3.22) could be expressed in terms either of C_S or of $\rho(0)$. From (3.22) it follows that

$$I \geq (1 - \alpha)\rho(0)\int_R \frac{\partial}{\partial x_i}(\varphi - \psi)\frac{\partial}{\partial x_i}(\varphi - \psi)\,dx. \tag{3.24}$$

We use this result in the next section to derive bounds for the solution of (2.2).

It seems to be known that if the flow is subsonic and g vanishes over a portion Σ of the boundary, the maximum velocity can occur at a point P on Σ only if at P the surface ∂R has negative Gaussian curvature. However, the author has been unable to find in the literature the theorem established below.

Theorem 1. *Let g and its tangential derivatives vanish at a point P of ∂R; let Φ have continuous second derivatives in the intersection of $\bar{R}$ and a spherical neighborhood of P; then if the flow is subsonic and nonconstant, the maximum velocity can occur at P only if the Gaussian curvature of ∂R is negative at P.*

Proof. By the strong form of the Hopf maximum principle [5], it follows that if the flow is subsonic the maximum value q_m of q occurs at some point on the boundary ∂R of R, and further that unless q is constant, then at the point of maximum velocity $\partial q/\partial n > 0$. Let us now suppose that q_m is attained at a point P of ∂R at which g and its tangential derivatives vanish. Note that we have assumed ∂R to be smooth. However, for the proof of the theorem we require only that ∂R be smooth in the neighborhood of P. Thus at P we have

$$\frac{\partial \Phi}{\partial x_i} \frac{\partial^2 \Phi}{\partial x_i \partial x_k} n_k > 0 \tag{3.25}$$

where n_k denotes the kth component of the unit normal. But this condition may be rewritten as

$$-\left(n_l \frac{\partial \Phi}{\partial x_j} - n_j \frac{\partial \Phi}{\partial x_i}\right)\left(n_l \frac{\partial \Phi}{\partial x_k} - n_k \frac{\partial \Phi}{\partial x_l}\right)\frac{\partial n_j}{\partial x_k} + \frac{\partial \Phi}{\partial n}\frac{\partial^2 \Phi}{\partial x_j \partial x_k}n_j n_k$$
$$+ n_l \frac{\partial \Phi}{\partial x_i}\left(n_l \frac{\partial}{\partial x_i} - n_i \frac{\partial}{\partial x_l}\right)\left(\frac{\partial \Phi}{\partial n}\right) > 0. \tag{3.26}$$

Now $(n_l \, \partial/\partial x_i - n_i \, \partial/\partial x_l)$ is a tangential derivative on ∂R and at the point P

$$\left(n_l \frac{\partial \rho}{\partial x_i} - n_i \frac{\partial \rho}{\partial n_l}\right) = \rho'\left(n_l \frac{\partial}{\partial x_i} - n_i \frac{\partial}{\partial x_l}\right)q^2 = 0. \tag{3.27}$$

Thus (3.27) reduces to

$$-\left(n_l \frac{\partial \Phi}{\partial x_j} - n_j \frac{\partial \Phi}{\partial x_l}\right)\left(n_l \frac{\partial \Phi}{\partial x_k} - n_k \frac{\partial \Phi}{\partial x_l}\right)\frac{\partial n_j}{\partial x_k} + \frac{g}{\rho}\frac{\partial^2 \Phi}{\partial x_j \partial x_k}n_j n_k$$
$$+ \frac{n_l \, \partial \Phi/\partial x_i}{\rho}\left(n_l \frac{\partial g}{\partial x_i} - n_i \frac{\partial g}{\partial x_l}\right) > 0. \tag{3.28}$$

By assumption the last two terms vanish at P. The first term on the right will be nonpositive if the Gaussian curvature is nonnegative (see [10, p. 138]) and the theorem is proved.

It follows from the theorem that if a portion Σ of ∂R is fixed (i.e. $\partial \Phi/\partial n = 0$) and has nonnegative Gaussian curvature, the maximum velocity cannot occur on Σ.

Remark. We note from the proof of this theorem that the result has very little to do with the fact that Φ satisfies the subsonic flow equations. This merely insured that $\partial q/\partial n > 0$ at the point on the boundary where q assumed its maximum value. The same proof may be used to establish the fact that if ∂R and an arbitrary function v are sufficiently smooth and

$|\text{grad } v|$ assumes a local maximum at a point P of ∂R at which $\partial v / \partial n$ and its tangential derivatives vanish, then either grad v vanishes identically in R or the curvature of ∂R must be nonpositive at P.

4. Bounds for the Solution of (2.2)

In the inequality (3.24) we take φ to be the unknown solution Φ of (2.2), and ψ to be some chosen approximating function. Since ψ (and hence ξ) are at our disposal we can easily choose approximating functions which satisfy $(1 + \gamma)\xi_m{}^2 \leq 2\alpha C_s{}^2$. However, we must also have a similar bound for $q_m{}^2$. Since q_m occurs on the boundary ∂R, we may in an actual physical problem obtain such a bound by measurement. If the flow does not approach sonic velocity at any point on the boundary, a constant α in (3.21) should be quite easily obtained, since the optimal α is not required. We may in fact be able to eliminate from our consideration certain points of ∂R since we know by the previous theorem that if g vanishes over a portion Σ of ∂R, then the maximum velocity cannot occur at points on Σ where the Gaussian curvature is nonnegative.

We assume now that α has been determined.

Then from (3.24) we have

$$\int_R \frac{\partial}{\partial x_i}[\Phi - \psi] \frac{\partial}{\partial x_i}[\Phi - \psi] \, dx \leq [(1 - \alpha)\rho(0)]^{-1} I(\Phi, \psi). \qquad (4.1)$$

But by Green's identity

$$I(\Phi, \psi) = \oint_R \left[g - \rho(\xi^2) \frac{\partial \psi}{\partial n} \right] (\Phi - \psi) \, ds$$
$$+ \int_R \frac{\partial}{\partial x_i} \left[\rho(\xi^2) \frac{\partial \psi}{\partial x_i} \right] (\Phi - \psi) \, dx. \qquad (4.2)$$

Using Schwarz's inequality we obtain

$$I(\Phi, \psi) \leq \left\{ \oint_R \left[g - \rho(\xi^2) \frac{\partial \psi}{\partial n} \right]^2 ds \oint_R (\Phi - \psi)^2 \, ds \right\}^{1/2}$$
$$+ \left\{ \int_R \left(\frac{\partial}{\partial x_i} \left[\rho(\xi^2) \frac{\partial \psi}{\partial x_i} \right] \right)^2 ds \int_R (\Phi - \psi)^2 \, dx \right\}^{1/2}. \qquad (4.3)$$

Since the left-hand side of (4.1) is unaffected by the addition of an arbitrary constant to $\Phi - \psi$, we may without loss assume that $\Phi - \psi$ satisfies the condition

$$\int_R (\Phi - \psi) \, dx = 0. \qquad (4.4)$$

But Bramble and Payne [2] have shown that under condition (4.4) explicit constants K_1 and K_2 can be determined such that

$$\oint_{\partial R} (\Phi - \psi)^2 \, ds \leq K_1 \int_R \frac{\partial}{\partial x_i}[\Phi - \psi]\frac{\partial}{\partial x_i}[\Phi - \psi] \, dx$$

$$\int_R (\Phi - \psi)^2 \, dx \leq K_2 \int_R \frac{\partial}{\partial x_i}[\Phi - \psi]\frac{\partial}{\partial x_i}[\Phi - \psi] \, dx. \quad (4.5)$$

The insertion of (4.5) into (4.3) and the result back into (4.1) leads to the desired bound

$$\left\{ \int_R \frac{\partial}{\partial x_i}[\Phi - \psi]\frac{\partial}{\partial x_i}[\Phi - \psi] \, dx \right\}^{1/2}$$

$$\leq [(1-\alpha)\rho(0)]^{-1}\left[\left\{ K_1 \oint \left[g - \rho(\xi^2)\frac{\partial\psi}{\partial n} \right]^2 ds \right\}^{1/2} \right.$$

$$\left. + \left\{ K_2 \int_R \left(\frac{\partial}{\partial x_i}\left[\rho(\xi^2)\frac{\partial\psi}{\partial x_i} \right] \right)^2 dx \right\}^{1/2} \right]. \quad (4.6)$$

Thus if ψ can be chosen to closely approximate the data in mean square, the right-hand side can be made small. The triangle inequality

$$\left\{ \int_R \frac{\partial\psi}{\partial x_i}\frac{\partial\psi}{\partial x_i} \, dx \right\}^{1/2} - \left\{ \int_R \frac{\partial}{\partial x_i}[\Phi - \psi]\frac{\partial}{\partial x_i}[\Phi - \psi] \, dx \right\}^{1/2}$$

$$\leq \left\{ \int_R \frac{\partial\Phi}{\partial x_i}\frac{\partial\Phi}{\partial x_i} \, dx \right\}^{1/2}$$

$$\leq \left\{ \int_R \frac{\partial\psi}{\partial x_i}\frac{\partial\psi}{\partial x_i} \, dx \right\}^{1/2} + \left\{ \int_R \frac{\partial}{\partial x_i}(\Phi - \psi)\frac{\partial}{\partial x_i}(\Phi - \psi) \, dx \right\}^{1/2} \quad (4.7)$$

would then yield close bounds for the Dirichlet integral of Φ, the integral over R of the square of the velocity.

We have been concerned with the case in which the flow domain R is bounded. If instead we wish to consider the problem of compressible flow in the domain outside the surface ∂R, the procedure just discussed must be varied only slightly. Let R^* denote the region exterior to ∂R. We seek bounds in the following problem:

$$\frac{\partial}{\partial x_i}\left(\rho\frac{\partial\Phi}{\partial x_i} \right) = 0 \quad \text{in} \quad R^*$$

$$\rho\frac{\partial\Phi}{\partial n} = g \quad \text{on} \quad \partial R \quad (4.8)$$

$$\Phi = O(1/r) \quad \text{as} \quad r \to \infty$$

where r is the distance measured from an origin inside ∂R. Inequality (4.1) as well as Eq. (4.2) remain valid. However, instead of (4.3) we obtain

$$I(\Phi, \psi) \leq \left\{ \oint_{\partial R} \tilde{G}(\Phi - \psi)^2 \, ds + \int_{R^*} G(\Phi - \psi)^2 \, dx \right\}^{1/2}$$

$$\times \left\{ \int_{\partial R} \tilde{G}^{-1} \left[g - \rho(\xi^2) \frac{\partial \psi}{\partial n} \right]^2 ds + \int_{R^*} G^{-1} \left(\frac{\partial}{\partial x_i} \left[\rho(\xi^2) \frac{\partial \psi}{\partial x_i} \right] \right)^2 dx \right\}^{1/2}$$

$$(4.9)$$

where $\tilde{G}$ and G are defined in terms of a vector field $g_i(x)$ piecewise continuous in R^* and satisfying (see [8, pp. 565–566])

$$G = \partial g_i / \partial x_i - g_i g_i > 0 \qquad \text{in} \quad R^*$$
$$\tilde{G} = -g_i n_i > 0 \qquad \text{on} \quad \partial R.$$

$$(4.10)$$

In addition g_i is to satisfy

$$g_i = O(1/r), \qquad r \to \infty$$
$$\partial g_i / \partial x_i = O(1/r^2), \qquad r \to \infty.$$

$$(4.11)$$

If ∂R is star-shaped with respect to the origin, we may choose

$$g_i = \beta x_i r^{-2}, \qquad 0 < \beta < 1.$$

$$(4.12)$$

It follows from an application of the arithmetic–geometric mean inequality to the identity

$$\int_{R^*} \frac{\partial g_i}{\partial x_i} (\Phi - \psi)^2 \, dx - \int_{\partial R} g_i n_i (\Phi - \psi)^2 \, ds = -2 \int_{R^*} g_i (\Phi - \psi) \frac{\partial}{\partial x_i} (\Phi - \psi) \, dx$$

$$(4.13)$$

that

$$\int_{\partial R} \tilde{G}(\Phi - \psi)^2 \, ds + \int_{R^*} G(\Phi - \psi)^2 \, ds \leq \int_{R^*} \frac{\partial}{\partial x_i} (\Phi - \psi) \frac{\partial}{\partial x_i} (\Phi - \psi) \, dx.$$

$$(4.14)$$

The insertion of (4.14) back into (4.9) and the result into (4.1) leads after simplification to

$$\int_{R^*} \frac{\partial}{\partial x_i} [\Phi - \psi] \frac{\partial}{\partial x_i} [\Phi - \psi] \, dx \leq [(1 - \alpha)\rho(0)]^{-2} \left\{ \oint_R \tilde{G}^{-2} \left[g - \rho(\xi^2) \frac{\partial \psi}{\partial n} \right]^2 ds \right.$$

$$\left. + \int_{R^*} G^{-1} \left(\frac{\partial}{\partial x_i} \left[\rho(\xi^2) \frac{\partial \psi}{\partial x_i} \right] \right)^2 dx \right\}. \quad (4.15)$$

Inequality (4.14) then leads to L_2 bounds for Φ.

Finally let us consider the problem of uniform flow from infinity past a fixed body, i.e.

$$\frac{\partial}{\partial x_i} \rho \left[\frac{\partial \Phi}{\partial x_i} \right] = 0 \qquad \text{in} \quad R^*$$

$$\Phi = Ux - \varphi, \qquad \varphi = 0(1/r), \quad r \to \infty \qquad (4.16)$$

$$\frac{\partial \Phi}{\partial n} = 0 \qquad \text{on} \quad \partial R.$$

Then if we choose $\psi = Ux - \chi$ as an approximating function, we find

$$\int_{R^*} \frac{\partial}{\partial x_i} [\Phi - \psi] \frac{\partial}{\partial x_i} [\Phi - \psi] \, dx \leq [(1 - \alpha)\rho(0)]^{-2} \left\{ \oint_{\partial R} \tilde{G}^{-1} \left[\rho(\xi^2) \frac{\partial \psi}{\partial n} \right]^2 ds \right.$$

$$\left. + \int_{R^*} G^{-1} \left(\frac{\partial}{\partial x_i} \left[\rho(\xi^2) \frac{\partial \psi}{\partial x_i} \right] \right)^2 dx \right\}. \quad (4.17)$$

5. The Dirichlet Problem

For mathematical completeness rather than physical interest, we indicate in this section a method for obtaining bounds in the Dirichlet problem for the potential flow equation, i.e. the problem

$$\frac{\partial}{\partial x_i} \left(\rho \frac{\partial \Phi}{\partial x_i} \right) = 0 \qquad \text{in} \quad R$$

$$\Phi = f \qquad \text{on} \quad \partial R. \qquad (5.1)$$

We make use of (4.1) where Φ now is the solution of (5.1) and ψ is an approximating function. We require then an upper bound for $I(\Phi, \psi)$ in terms of the "data" of $\Phi - \psi$.

To this end let us decompose $\Phi - \psi$ as follows:

$$\Phi - \psi = h + \chi \qquad (5.2)$$

where

$$\Delta h = 0 \qquad \text{in} \quad R$$

$$h = \Phi - \psi \qquad \text{on} \quad \partial R. \qquad (5.2a)$$

This implies

$$\chi = 0 \qquad \text{on} \quad \partial R. \qquad (5.3)$$

Since Φ and ψ are assumed smooth and the boundary ∂R sufficiently smooth, the existence of h is assured. We shall not be required to exhibit h explicitly.

Now

$$I(\Phi, \psi) = \int_R \left[\rho(q^2) \frac{\partial \Phi}{\partial x_i} - \rho(\xi^2) \frac{\partial \psi}{\partial x_i} \right] \frac{\partial h}{\partial x_i} \, dx$$

$$+ \int_R \left[\rho(q^2) \frac{\partial \Phi}{\partial x_i} - \rho(\xi^2) \frac{\partial \psi}{\partial x_i} \right] \frac{\partial \chi}{\partial x_i} \, dx$$

$$= I_1 + I_2. \tag{5.4}$$

We consider first the term I_1. Clearly from (3.6) and (3.7) we have

$$I_1 = \frac{1}{2} \int_R A_{ij} \left[\frac{\partial}{\partial x_i} (\Phi - \psi) \right] \frac{\partial h}{\partial x_i} \, dx. \tag{5.5}$$

By Schwarz's inequality and (3.8) we obtain

$$I_1 \leq \frac{\lambda_1}{2} \left\{ \int_R \frac{\partial}{\partial x_i} (\Phi - \psi) \frac{\partial}{\partial x_i} (\Phi - \psi) \, dx \right\}^{1/2} \left\{ \int_R \frac{\partial h}{\partial x_i} \frac{\partial h}{\partial x_i} \, dx \right\}^{1/2} \tag{5.6}$$

where

$$\lambda_1 = \tfrac{1}{2} [\rho(q^2) + \rho(\xi^2)] \leq \rho^2(0). \tag{5.7}$$

We turn now to the term I_2. An integration by parts and use of (5.3) yields

$$I_2 = \int_R \chi \frac{\partial}{\partial x_i} \left(\rho(\xi^2) \frac{\partial \psi}{\partial x_i} \right) dx$$

$$\leq \left\{ \int_R \chi^2 \, dx \right\}^{1/2} \left\{ \int_R \left[\frac{\partial}{\partial x_i} \left(\rho(\xi^2) \frac{\partial \psi}{\partial x_i} \right) \right]^2 ds \right\}^{1/2}. \tag{5.8}$$

Since χ vanishes on ∂R we have

$$\int_R \chi^2 \, dx \leq \frac{1}{\Lambda_1} \int_R \frac{\partial \chi}{\partial x_i} \frac{\partial \chi}{\partial x_i} \, dx \tag{5.9}$$

where Λ_1 is the first eigenvalue in the fixed membrane problem for R. Lower bounds for Λ_1 are easily computed from the Faber–Krahn inequality, monotony principles, etc. (see e.g. [3, 8]).

Because of the orthogonality of h and χ in Dirichlet norm we may write

$$\int_R \frac{\partial \chi}{\partial x_i} \frac{\partial \chi}{\partial x_i} \, dx = \int_R \frac{\partial}{\partial x_i} (\Phi - \psi) \frac{\partial}{\partial x_i} (\Phi - \psi) \, dx - \int_R \frac{\partial h}{\partial x_i} \frac{\partial h}{\partial x_i} \, dx. \tag{5.10}$$

Inserting (5.10) into (5.9) and the result into (5.8) we obtain

$$I_2 \leq \left\{ \frac{1}{\Lambda_1} \left(\int_R \frac{\partial}{\partial x_i} (\Phi - \psi) \frac{\partial}{\partial x_i} (\Phi - \psi) \, dx - \int_R \frac{\partial h}{\partial x_i} \frac{\partial h}{\partial x_i} \, dx \right) \right\}^{1/2}$$

$$\times \left\{ \int_R \left[\frac{\partial}{\partial x_i} \left(\rho \frac{\partial \psi}{\partial x_i} \right) \right]^2 dx \right\}^{1/2}. \tag{5.11}$$

We now insert (5.6), (5.7), and (5.11) into (4.1). This yields

$$X^2 \leq 2k_1 XY + 2k_2 Z(X - Y) \tag{5.12}$$

where

$$X^2 = \int_R \frac{\partial}{\partial x_i}(\Phi - \psi)\frac{\partial}{\partial x_i}(\Phi - \psi)\, dx$$

$$Y^2 = \int_R \frac{\partial h}{\partial x_i}\frac{\partial h}{\partial x_i}\, dx \tag{5.13}$$

$$Z^2 = \int_R \left[\frac{\partial}{\partial x_i}\left(\rho\frac{\partial \psi}{\partial x_i}\right)\right]^2 ds$$

and

$$k_1 = \tfrac{1}{4}\rho(0)(1 - \alpha)^{-1}$$
$$k_2 = \tfrac{1}{2}[\Lambda_1]^{-1/2}[(1 - \alpha)\rho(0)]^{-1}. \tag{5.14}$$

The solution of (5.12) is

$$X \leq k_1 Y + k_2 Z + [(k_1 Y + k_2 Z)^2 - 2k_2 YZ]^{1/2}. \tag{5.15}$$

Ignoring the $-2k_2 YZ$ term we obtain the simple result

$$X \leq 2(k_1 Y + k_2 Z). \tag{5.16}$$

We need now merely a bound for Y in terms of the data of h. But such a priori inequalities have been given in [3, 8], i.e. an explicit inequality of the following form is determined:

$$\int_R \frac{\partial h}{\partial x_i}\frac{\partial h}{\partial x_i}\, dx \leq \hat{k}_1 \oint_{\partial R} h^2\, ds + \hat{k}_2 \oint_{\partial R} |\mathrm{grad}_s\, h|^2\, ds$$

$$= \hat{k}_1 \oint_{\partial R} [f - \psi]^2\, ds + \hat{k}_2 \oint_{\partial R} [\mathrm{grad}_s(f - \psi)]^2\, ds. \tag{5.17}$$

Here grad_s denotes the tangential projection of the surface gradient on ∂R. Inserting (5.17) for Y^2 on the right of (5.16), we obtain the desired explicit a priori inequality for X in terms of its "data."

A priori L_2 bounds then follow easily (see e.g. [3, 8]) from the Dirichlet integral bounds. We note finally the following analog of Theorem 1.

Theorem 2. *Let the tangential components of velocity vanish with their tangential derivatives at a point P of ∂R, and let Φ have continuous second derivatives and satisfy the differential equation in the intersection of $\bar{R}$ and a spherical neighborhood of P; then if the flow is subsonic and nonconstant, the maximum velocity can occur at P only if the average curvature of ∂R is negative at P.*

Proof.   Again by the strong form of the maximum principle we know that if q is nonconstant and the maximum value of q occurs at P, then $\partial q/\partial n > 0$ at P, i.e. (3.25) is satisfied at P. Since the flow is assumed subsonic at P it follows that

$$1 - \frac{q^2}{C^2} = 1 + \frac{2\rho'}{\rho} q^2 = 1 + \frac{2\rho'}{\rho} \left(\frac{\partial \Phi}{\partial n} \right)^2 > 0 \qquad (5.18)$$

at P. Thus at P

$$\left[1 + \frac{2\rho'}{\rho} \left(\frac{\partial \Phi}{\partial n} \right)^2 \right] \frac{\partial \Phi}{\partial x_i} \frac{\partial^2 \Phi}{\partial x_i \, \partial x_j} n_j > 0. \qquad (5.19)$$

From the differential equation we have

$$\Delta \Phi = - \frac{2\rho'}{\rho} \frac{\partial \Phi}{\partial x_i} \frac{\partial \Phi}{\partial x_j} \frac{\partial^2 \Phi}{\partial x_i \, \partial x_j} = - \frac{2\rho'}{\rho} \frac{\partial \Phi}{\partial n} \frac{\partial \Phi}{\partial x_i} \frac{\partial^2 \Phi}{\partial x_i \, \partial x_j} n_j. \qquad (5.20)$$

Here Δ denotes the Laplace operator. Thus combining (5.19) and (5.20) we have

$$\frac{\partial \Phi}{\partial x_i} \frac{\partial^2 \Phi}{\partial x_i \, \partial x_j} n_j - \frac{\partial \Phi}{\partial x_i} \Delta \Phi \, n_i > 0 \qquad (5.21)$$

at P. This may be written as

$$n_i \frac{\partial \Phi}{\partial n} \left(n_k \frac{\partial}{\partial x_i} - n_i \frac{\partial}{\partial x_k} \right) \frac{\partial \Phi}{\partial x_k} > 0. \qquad (5.22)$$

Since the first and second tangential derivatives of Φ vanish at P, it follows that at P

$$- \frac{\partial n_k}{\partial x_k} \left(\frac{\partial \Phi}{\partial n} \right)^2 > 0. \qquad (5.23)$$

But (see Weatherburn [10])

$$\frac{\partial n_k}{\partial x_k} = J = R_1^{-1} + R_2^{-1} \qquad (5.24)$$

where the R_i are the principal radii of curvature at the point P. Thus if the average curvature $\frac{1}{2} J$ is nonnegative at P, we are led to a contradiction, and hence conclude that the maximum velocity cannot occur at P. This establishes the theorem.*

---

* Professors G. Pólya and J. B. Diaz have pointed out to the author that results for harmonic functions similar to those contained in our theorems can be found in the literature [see e.g. G. Pólya, Liegt die Stelle der grossten Beanspruchung an der Oberfläche?, Z. Angew. Math. Mech. 10, 353 (1930)].

REFERENCES

[1] Bers, L., "Mathematical Aspects of Subsonic and Transonic Gas Dynamics." Wiley, New York, 1958.

[2] Bramble, J. H., and Payne, L. E., Bounds in the Neumann problem for second-order uniformly elliptic operators, *Pacific J. Math.* **12,** 823 (1962).

[3] Bramble, J. H., and Payne, L. E., Bounds for solutions of second-order elliptic partial differential equations, *Contrib. Diff. Eqs.* **1,** 95 (1963).

[4] Finn, R., and Gilbarg, D., Three dimensional subsonic flows and asymptotic estimates for elliptic partial differential equations, *Acta Math.* **98,** 265 (1957).

[5] Hopf, E., Elemantare Betrachtungen über die Lösungen partieller Differentialgleichungen zweiter Ordnung von elliptischen Typus, *Sitz. Preuss. Akad. Wiss. Physik-math.* **19,** 147 (1927); see also: A remark on linear elliptic differential equations of second order, *Proc. Amer. Math. Soc.* **3,** 791 (1952).

[6] Levin, S., Uniqueness and nonlinearity, Ph.D. dissertation, Univ. of Maryland (1964).

[7] von Mises, R., Geiringer, H., and Ludford, G. S. S., "Mathematical Theory of Compressible Fluid Flow." Academic Press, New York, 1958.

[8] Payne, L. E., and Weinberger, H. F., New bounds for second-order elliptic partial differential equations, *Pacific J. Math.* **8,** 551 (1958).

[9] Schiffer, M. M., Analytical theory of subsonic and supersonic flows. In "*Handbuch der Physik*," Vol. 9 III, pp. 1–161, Springer, Berlin, 1960.

[10] Weatherburn, C. E., "Differential Geometry in Three Dimensions," Vol. 2. Cambridge Univ. Press, London and New York, 1930.

On Spline Functions*†

I. J. SCHOENBERG

Mathematics Research Center, U.S. Army
University of Wisconsin
Madison, Wisconsin

Introduction

In a recent paper [1] the authors discuss the role of spline functions of one or several variables in the broad realm of the numerical analysis of engineering and mathematical physics. Here we consider only spline functions of one real variable and discuss their role in the narrow field of elementary numerical analysis. This is done in Part I which is entirely expository and might serve as an introduction to some of the recent results in this field. We describe and motivate spline interpolation as a direct generalization of Lagrange's interpolation formula

$$f(x) = \sum_{1}^{n} f(x_i) L_i(x) + R, \tag{1}$$

where $L_i(x)$ are the polynomials of degree $n - 1$ such that $L_i(x_j) = \delta_{ij}$. Our main point is to show that the fundamental role played by polynomial interpolation in elementary numerical analysis is taken over by spline interpolation, provided we pass from the classical (Newtonian) approximation formulas for quadratures, derivatives, and like functionals, to the wider field of best approximation formulas in the sense of Sard [9]. This explains the heading of Part I.

Part II is likewise expository in the sense that hardly any proofs are given. The subject, however, is new and a full account will appear elsewhere. This time we are concerned with the Bernstein polynomials

$$B_n(x; f) = \sum_{0}^{n} f\left(\frac{i}{n}\right) \binom{n}{i} x^i (1 - x)^{n-i}. \tag{2}$$

These have been generalized by several authors in various directions. Here we stress the *variation diminishing* property of the Bernstein polynomials.

* Sponsored by the Mathematics Research Center, United States Army, Madison, Wisconsin, under Contract No. DA-11-022-ORD-2059.
† With a Supplement by T. N. E. Greville.

Using this fundamental property as a guide, we develop new generalizations of (2) in terms of spline functions. The approximations so obtained will no doubt show, compared with (2), the usual advantages for numerical applications which we have recently come to expect when passing from polynomials to spline functions. Our error estimates (Theorems 10 and 11) show an improvement in the rate of convergence.† Our formulas (15.17) and (15.18) of quadratic and cubic spline approximations will probably be of interest to statisticians because these formulas, like the Bernstein polynomials, preserve the positivity and monotonicity of the data (see [16] where the Bernstein polynomials are applied to statistical data).

The essential new insight on which the developments of Part II are based may be briefly described as follows: It was shown in [3] that spline functions in an interval (a, b), finite or infinite, with prescribed knots, admit a unique representation in terms of the so-called fundamental spline functions, which we now call B-splines. *This representation enjoys the variation diminishing property* (Theorem 5 is an example). The Descartes rule of signs is a special limit case of this. Another example is the sum (2) defining the Bernstein polynomials. The only thing left to do to obtain a variation diminishing *approximation* method is to make sure that *linear functions are preserved.* This requirement uniquely determines the coefficients and the *nodes,* i.e. the points where the values of the function to be approximated enter into the process.

It is worth mentioning that both our formulas (3.13) which generalize (1), as well as (12.14) which generalize (2), reduce to linear interpolation between successive ordinates for the lowest values of the parameter m ($m = 1$ and $m = 2$, respectively). This shows that the lowly procedure of linear interpolation appears to have all the virtues, being a link between very diverse methods of spline approximation.

I. THE ROLE OF SPLINE FUNCTIONS IN ELEMENTARY NUMERICAL ANALYSIS

1. Peano's Theorem

Our entire discussion being based on this theorem, we begin by recalling its statement. Following Davis' book [4] we state it for functionals of the form

$$Rf = \int_a^b \left[\sum_0^{m-1} a_i(x) f^{(i)}(x) \right] dx + \sum_{j=0}^{m-1} \sum_{i=1}^{n_j} b_{ij} f^{(j)}(x_{ij}). \tag{1.1}$$

---

† See [4, p. 116] where Davis deplores the slow convergence of the Bernstein polynomials. Our estimates (16.2) and (16.6), if compared with (16.3) and (16.5), respectively, seem encouraging.

Here $I = [a, b]$ is a finite interval, m a natural number, $a_i(x)$ are piecewise continuous in I, b_{ij} are real constants, and $x_{ij} \in I$. Thus Rf is a linear functional whose domain contains the class $C^{(m-1)}[a, b]$.

The assumption of the theorem is that

$$Rf = 0 \qquad \text{if} \quad f \in \pi_{m-1}, \tag{1.2}$$

where here and below we denote by π_k the class of real polynomials of degree at most k. The conclusion is that if

$$f(x) \in C^{(m)}[a, b], \tag{1.3}$$

then

$$Rf = \frac{1}{m!} \int_I K(x) f^{(m)}(x) \, dx \tag{1.4}$$

with a kernel $K(x)$ which is independent of $f(x)$. Moreover, $K(x)$ may be represented in the form

$$K(x) = R_t m(t - x)_+^{m-1} \tag{1.5}$$

where the subscript t indicates that the operator R operates on the variable t, while the truncated power function is defined by

$$u_+ = \begin{cases} u & \text{if} \quad u \geq 0 \\ 0 & \text{if} \quad u < 0. \end{cases} \tag{1.6}$$

It is readily seen that $K(x)$, defined by (1.5), is a piecewise continuous function of $x \in I$, the points of discontinuity being $x_{i, m-1}$ $(i = 1, \ldots, n_{m-1})$.

Let us now apply Peano's theorem to the mth-order divided difference operator

$$Rf = f(x_0, x_1, \ldots, x_m) = \sum_0^m \frac{f(x_i)}{\omega'(x_i)}, \tag{1.7}$$

where the x_i are $m + 1$ distinct points in increasing order in I, and where, as usual, we write $\omega(x) = (x - x_0) \cdots (x - x_m)$. Since Rf satisfies the fundamental condition (1.2), we obtain by (1.4) and (1.5) the representation

$$f(x_0, x_1, \ldots, x_m) = \frac{1}{m!} \int_I K(x) f^{(m)}(x) dx \tag{1.8}$$

where

$$K(x) = \sum_0^m \frac{m(x_i - x)_+^{m-1}}{\omega'(x_i)}.$$

I wish to draw attention to this remarkable function. It depends on the parameters $x_0, x_1, \ldots, x_m$ and we shall denote it by the symbol $M(x; x_0, \ldots, x_m)$, occasionally shortened to $M(x)$. This notation becomes entirely consistent with Steffensen's notation for divided differences if we think of $M(x; x_0, \ldots, x_m)$ as the divided difference of the function

$$M(x; t) = m(t - x)_+^{m-1} \tag{1.9}$$

based on the points $t = x_0, \ldots, x_m$. Thus

$$M(x; x_0, \ldots, x_m) = \sum_0^m \frac{m(x_i - x)_+^{m-1}}{\omega'(x_i)} \tag{1.10}$$

and the integral representation (1.8) becomes

$$f(x_0, x_1, \ldots, x_m) = \frac{1}{m!} \int_I M(x; x_0, \ldots, x_m) f^{(m)}(x) \, dx. \tag{1.11}$$

From (1.10) it is easily apparent that $M(x) \in \pi_{m-1}$ in each of the intervals (x_{i-1}, x_i) $(i = 1, \ldots, m)$, while $M(x) = 0$ if $x < x_0$ or $x > x_m$; also that $M(x) \in C^{(m-2)}(-\infty, \infty)$. If $f(x) = x^m$ in (1.11), we obtain

$$\int_{-\infty}^{\infty} M(x; x_0, \ldots, x_m) = 1. \tag{1.12}$$

We add that $M(x) > 0$ in (x_0, x_m), so that we may think of $M(x)$ as a frequency function (see [3]).

The following independent geometric description of $M(x)$, although not used below, is of interest.

Theorem 1.   *The function $M(x; x_0, \ldots, x_m)$ is the linear density function obtained if we project orthogonally on the x-axis the volume of an m-dimensional simplex of volume 1 which is such that its m + 1 vertices project orthogonally in the points $x_0, \ldots, x_m$, respectively.*

Equivalently we may say that the m-fold integral representing the volume of the simplex reduces, by repeated integrations, to the simple integral (1.12) if we integrate first with respect to the other $m - 1$ variables of integration. The simplex being a convex body, Brunn's theorem easily implies that log $M(x)$ is a concave function in the interval (x_0, x_m) (see [3]).

2. Spline Functions

The above function $M(x)$ is a special instance of a spline function. The general definition is as follows: Let

$$\cdots < x_{-2} < x_{-1} < x_0 < x_1 < x_2 < \cdots \tag{2.1}$$

be a sequence of reals, infinite in number in both directions and such that

$$\lim_{n \to -\infty} x_n = \alpha \geqq -\infty, \qquad \lim_{n \to \infty} x_n = \beta \leqq +\infty. \tag{2.2}$$

A function $S(x) = S_m(x)$ is called a *spline function* of order m, or of degree $m - 1$, provided that it satisfies the following conditions:

$$S(x) \in C^{m-2}(\alpha, \beta), \tag{2.3}$$

$$S(x) \in \pi_{m-1} \quad \text{in each interval} \quad (x_i, x_{i+1}) \quad (-\infty < i < \infty). \tag{2.4}$$

We denote by

$$\mathscr{S}_m = \mathscr{S}_m(x_i) \tag{2.5}$$

the entire collection of such functions. The points (2.1) are called the *knots* of $S(x)$. Observe that they may be, but need not be, discontinuities for $S^{(m-1)}(x)$. Thus $\pi_{m-1} \subset \mathscr{S}_m$.

There are several different ways of representing spline functions. One way is to start from an arbitrary step function $S^{(m-1)}(x)$ with jumps at the points (2.1), and obtain $S(x)$ by integrating it $m - 1$ times. Another representation of spline functions is described by the following theorem.

Theorem 2. *Given the knots* (2.1) *we consider the sequence of spline functions*

$$M_j(x) = M(x; x_j, x_{j+1}, \ldots, x_{j+m}) \quad (-\infty < j < \infty). \tag{2.6}$$

Every $S(x) \in \mathscr{S}_m(x_i)$ *may be uniquely represented in the form*

$$S(x) = \sum_{-\infty}^{\infty} c_j M_j(x), \tag{2.7}$$

with constant c_j. *Conversely, every series* (2.7) *with arbitrary constant* c_j *defines an element of* $\mathscr{S}_m(x_i)$.

Because they provide a basis for the linear class $\mathscr{S}_m$, functions of the form (1.10) or (2.6) will be called *B-splines*, where the letter B stands for "basis."

Frequently it is of interest to consider spline functions $S(x)$ having their support within an interval (x_1, x_n), where $x_n \leq +\infty$. If $S(x)$ has this property and

$$n < m + 1, \tag{2.8}$$

then it can be shown that

$$S(x) = 0 \quad \text{for all} \quad x. \tag{2.9}$$

However if $n \geq m + 1$, then

$$S(x) = \sum_{1}^{n-m} c_j M_j(x). \tag{2.10}$$

For these properties including Theorem 2 we refer to [3].

All these results are familiar in the special case when $m = 2$, as they reduce to the well-known representation of continuous broken linear functions as linear combinations of the so-called "roof functions."

3. Spline Interpolation

Let $I = [a, b]$ be a finite interval and

$$(x_i, y_i) \qquad (i = 1, \ldots, n; \quad a \leq x_1 < x_2 < \cdots < x_n \leq b), \qquad (3.1)$$

be n given points. These can be interpolated uniquely by Lagrange's formula (1) resulting in an interpolating polynomial $\pi_{n-1}(x)$.

Let us, however, assume that we have plotted the n points (x_i, y_i) and that an inspection of the graph suggests that we should be able to interpolate these points by a polynomial $\pi_{m-1}(x)$, of degree $m - 1$, where m is an integer such that

$$1 \leq m < n. \qquad (3.2)$$

In general, of course, this is impossible. However, we now try to do the next best thing by proceeding as follows: *Among all functions $f(x)$ having a square-integrable mth derivative we seek to determine one such that*

$$f(x_i) = y_i \qquad (i = 1, \ldots, n), \qquad (3.3)$$

$$\int_I [f^{(m)}(x)]^2 \, dx = \text{minimum}, \qquad (3.4)$$

the reason being that the condition (3.4) should produce a function $f(x)$ which is as close to being an element of π_{m-1} as the interpolation conditions (3.3) will allow.

In order to describe the solution of this problem, we first define a certain subclass of the class $\mathscr{S}_{2m}(x_i)$ as follows: We say that $S(x) = S_{2m}(x)$ is a *natural* spline function of degree $2m - 1$, provided that

$$S(x) \in \mathscr{S}_{2m}(x_1, \ldots, x_n), \qquad (3.5)$$

$$S(x) \in \pi_{m-1} \quad \text{in} \quad (-\infty, x_1) \quad \text{and also in} \quad (x_n, +\infty). \qquad (3.6)$$

Let us denote by

$$\mathscr{S}_{2m}^* = \mathscr{S}_{2m}^*(x_1, \ldots, x_n)$$

the class of such natural spline functions. We may now describe the solution of the minimum-interpolation problem (3.4), (3.3), as follows.†

---

† Theorem 3 is the result of the joint efforts of several people. See [15], [2], and [12].

Theorem 3.   *The solution of the minimum-interpolation problem* (3.4), (3.3) *is unique and is the restriction to* $I = [a, b]$ *of the function* $S(x)$ *which is uniquely defined by the two conditions*

$$S(x) \in \mathscr{S}^*_{2m}(x_1, \ldots, x_n), \tag{3.7}$$

$$S(x_i) = y_i \qquad (i = 1, \ldots, n). \tag{3.8}$$

There are here two theorems stated simultaneously. Indeed, Theorem 3 asserts on the one hand the existence and uniqueness of $S(x)$ satisfying (3.7), (3.8). This property may also be expressed by saying that $\mathscr{S}^*_{2m}$ is an interpolation family for the abscissas $x_1, \ldots, x_n$. On the other hand it asserts that $S(x)$ solves the problem (3.4), (3.3): If $f(x)$ satisfies (3.3) and $f^{(m)}(x)$ is square-integrable, then

$$\int_I [f^{(m)}(x)]^2 \, dx > \int_I [S^{(m)}(x)]^2 \, dx, \tag{3.9}$$

unless $f(x) = S(x)$ in I.

Further comments and special cases.

1.   If $m = 1$, then the elements of $\mathscr{S}_2{}^*$ are continuous broken linear functions with vertices at $x = x_1, \ldots, x_n$, which are *constant* in $(-\infty, x_1)$ and also in (x_n, ∞). Here the unique interpolation property is obvious, while the minimum property (3.9) is easily established by Schwarz's inequality.

2.   If $m = 2$, then $\mathscr{S}_4{}^* \subset C''(-\infty, \infty)$ and its elements are composed of cubics in $(x_1, x_2), \ldots, (x_{n-1}, x_n)$, while being *linear* in $(-\infty, x_1)$ and also in (x_n, ∞). Such is also (approximately) the nature of the curve drawn by means of the "mechanical spline" used by draftsmen, at least if the points (x_i, y_i) are approximately on a straight line (see [*10*, p. 67]). The mechanical spline is a slender straight elastic rod which is made to pass through the points (x_i, y_i) by being held there by n heavy, specially designed objects. Observe that the two free ends of the mechanical spline are straight, suggesting the "natural" spline functions. This instrument gave its name to the entire class of functions here discussed.

3.   We have assumed above that (3.2) holds, hence $m < n$. However, the case $m = n$ is also acceptable. The main point to observe now is that if

$$m = n, \tag{3.10}$$

then

$$\mathscr{S}^*_{2n} = \pi_{n-1}. \tag{3.11}$$

Thus in this case the interpolating natural spline function $S(x)$, solution of (3.8), is identical with the Lagrange interpolation polynomial. This is easily seen from a previous result: Observe that (3.6) implies that $S^{(m)}(x)$ is a spline function of degree $m-1$ with its support in (x_1, x_n). If we assume (3.10), then (2.8) holds and now (2.9) shows that $S^{(m)}(x) = 0$, for all x, whence $S(x) \in \pi_{n-1}$. This establishes (3.11).

4. We finally wish to recast Theorem 3 in the convenient Lagrange form. If $L_i(x)$ satisfies

$$L_i(x) \in \mathscr{S}_{2m}^*, \qquad L_i(x_j) = \delta_{ij}, \tag{3.12}$$

then the solution of (3.8) may be expressed in the form

$$S(x) = \sum_1^n y_i L_i(x).$$

If $f(x)$ is an arbitrary function defined in $I = \lceil a, b \rceil$, we may write

$$f(x) = \sum_1^n f(x_i) L_i(x) + R, \tag{3.13}$$

where the sum represents the natural spline function which interpolates $f(x)$. We call (3.13) *the spline interpolation formula of order m*. Observe that it is exact, i.e. its remainder vanishes, whenever $f(x) \in \mathscr{S}_{2m}^*$, and in particular if $f(x) \in \pi_{m-1}$.

A last remark: The spline interpolation formula (3.13) reduces to Lagrange's formula (1) if $m = n$.

4. The Best Approximation of Linear Functionals

We now turn to some of the fundamental problems of elementary numerical analysis. Let $I = [a, b]$ be a finite interval and let $f(x)$ be real-valued and defined in I. Finally, let $\mathscr{L}f$ be an operator (functional) of the same form (1.1) as Rf. Important examples of such operators are

$$f(\xi), f'(\xi), \ldots \qquad (\xi \text{ fixed in } I), \tag{4.1}$$

$$\int_I f(x)\, dx, \qquad \int_a^\beta f(x)\, dx, \ldots, \qquad [\alpha, \beta] \subset I. \tag{4.2}$$

We are now concerned with the following

Problem. *Given the n abscissas*

$$a \le x_1 < x_2 < \cdots < x_n \le b \tag{4.3}$$

and the corresponding values $f(x_1), \ldots, f(x_n)$, find an approximation formula

$$\mathscr{L}f = \sum_1^n B_i f(x_i) + Rf, \tag{4.4}$$

that is, determine the constants B_i such that the sum should approximate $\mathscr{L}f$ best in a certain sense.

There are, of course, numerous ways to interpret the requirement that the approximation be "best." The following section describes the classical interpretation.

5. The Newton–Cotes Procedure

The Newton–Cotes procedure requires that formula (4.4) be exact (i.e. $Rf = 0$) for polynomials of as high a degree as possible. As we have n parameters B_i at our disposal, we may require that

$$Rf = 0 \quad \text{if} \quad f \in \pi_{n-1}. \tag{5.1}$$

This requirement leads to the equivalent system of equations

$$\mathscr{L}x^r = \sum_{i=1}^{n} B_i x_i^r \quad (r = 0, \ldots, n-1). \tag{5.2}$$

The uniquely determined B_i are now substituted into (4.4) and furnish the desired best approximation. This is the classical procedure of numerical analysis. If applied to the operators (4.1), it leads to Lagrange's interpolation formula (1), to Newton's approximate differentiation formula, etc. If applied to the operators (4.2), it gives the Newton–Cotes mechanical quadrature formulas.

6. Sard's Procedure

There is more than one way of going beyond the Newton–Cotes point of view. Gauss showed that we may obtain exactness for all $f \in \pi_{2m-1}$ in the case of the first operator (4.2) if we place the points x_i at the roots of the Legendre polynomial of the interval I. However, we wish to assume that the x_i are given and *fixed*, a requirement which bars this avenue of refinement.

In 1949, Sard generalized the Newton–Cotes approach by means of the following effective and simple idea: Select a number m such that

$$1 \leq m < n \tag{6.1}$$

and require that

$$Rf = 0 \quad \text{if} \quad f \in \pi_{m-1}. \tag{6.2}$$

Equivalently, we require that

$$\mathscr{L}x^r = \sum_{i=1}^{n} B_i x_i^r \quad (r = 0, \ldots, m-1). \tag{6.3}$$

Since $m < n$, we see that the constraints (6.3) will leave $n - m$ of the B_i free to vary. Sard disposes of and determines these $n - m$ degrees of freedom in the following way: He observes that

$$Rf = \mathscr{L}f - \sum_{1}^{n} B_i f(x_i)$$

is a linear functional, also of the form (1.1), satisfying Peano's condition (6.2) which is identical with (1.2). By Peano's theorem (1.4) we can express our functional in the form

$$Rf = \frac{1}{m!} \int_I K(x) f^{(m)}(x)\, dx \tag{6.4}$$

where

$$K(x) = R_t m (t - x)_+^{m-1} \tag{6.5}$$

is independent of $f(x)$. However, $K(x)$ still depends on the $n - m$ free parameters. Sard determines these by requiring that

$$\int_I [K(x)]^2\, dx = \text{minimum}. \tag{6.6}$$

It turns out that the B_i are thereby uniquely determined. Substituting the values of the B_i so determined into (4.4), Sard obtains a formula which he calls the *best approximation of $\mathscr{L}f$ for the nodes* $x_1, \ldots, x_n$ *and the order m*.

We notice that if $m = n$, then the minimum problem (6.6) is trivially solved, there being no variables, so that we again have the Newton–Cotes procedure.

One way to interpret and justify Sard's procedure is as follows: (6.4) shows that

$$(m!\, Rf)^2 \le \int_I [K(x)]^2\, dx \cdot \int_I [f^{(m)}(x)]^2\, dx.$$

If we denote by J the value of the minimum (6.6) and if we restrict ourselves to the class of functions such that

$$\int_I [f^{(m)}(x)]^2\, dx \le M, \tag{6.7}$$

then the remainder of Sard's best formula satisfies the inequality

$$(Rf)^2 \le \frac{1}{(m!)^2} J \cdot M. \tag{6.8}$$

Within the class of functions subject to (6.7), J is the least possible constant in (6.8), and among all possible approximation formulas satisfying (6.2), the inequality (6.8) is valid only for Sard's best formula.

Sard made numerous applications of his procedure (see [9], for further references) and derived explicitly the best approximations for the operators (4.1), (4.2), in many cases of equidistant abscissas. The connection of these problems with spline interpolation is very close and perhaps also dramatic, as is shown in the next section.

7. The Role of Spline Interpolation†

The reader may have observed that in both Secs. 3 and 6 we deal with an interval $I = [a, b]$ and n given abscissas x_i [see (3.1) and (4.3)]; also with an integer m such that $1 \leq m < n$ [see (3.2) and (6.1)]. We now identify the similarly named quantities in both places. In particular, we return to the spline interpolation formula (3.13), where we recall that the sum on the right side represents the natural spline function of degree $2m - 1$ which interpolates $f(x)$ at the points x_i.

Its connection with Sard's problem is described by the following theorem.

Theorem 4. *The best approximation of order* m

$$\sum_1^n B_i f(x_i) \tag{7.1}$$

to a linear operator $\mathscr{L}f$ *is obtained by operating with* $\mathscr{L}$ *on the spline function*

$$S(x) = \sum_1^n f(x_i) L_i(x) \tag{7.2}$$

which interpolates $f(x)$ *for the same order* m. *This means that*

$$\mathscr{L} \sum_1^n f(x_i) L_i(x) = \sum_1^n f(x_i) \mathscr{L} L_i(x) = \sum_1^n f(x_i) B_i,$$

or, finally, that

$$B_i = \mathscr{L} L_i(x) \qquad (i = 1, \ldots, n). \tag{7.3}$$

Examples. To obtain a best-quadrature formula

$$\int_a^\beta f(x) dx = \sum_1^n B_i f(x_i) + R$$

† See [13]. For a direct and lucid description and derivation of the results of our Part I see Greville's paper [6].

exact for the degree $m - 1$, we must choose

$$B_i = \int_a^\beta L_i(x)\, dx \qquad (i = 1, \dots, n).$$

Similarly

$$f'(\xi) = \sum_1^n f(x_i) L_i'(\xi) + R$$

gives, for a fixed $\xi \in I$, the best approximate differentiation formula exact for the degree $m - 1$.

Perhaps the most interesting application of Theorem 4 is obtained if we apply it to the interpolation operator $\mathscr{L}f = f(\xi)$. Now we obtain

$$\mathscr{L}L_i(x) = L_i(\xi),$$

the resulting best interpolation formula being

$$f(\xi) = \sum_1^n f(x_i) L_i(\xi) + R. \tag{7.4}$$

This, however, being visibly identical with the formula (3.13), we obtain the following corollary.

Corollary 1. *The spline interpolation formula* (3.13) *is the best interpolation formula of order m in the sense of Sard.*

Theorem 4 calls for the following remarks. It shows that the best approximations for various operators $\mathscr{L}f$, for the same order m, are automatically obtained once we are in possession of the best interpolation formula (7.4) for the order m. This may be interpreted as a kind of (internal) consistency of Sard's approximations in the following sense: The operations of calculus, such as differentiation and integration, are performed on the approximating spline functions and lead to (best) approximations of the results of the same operations performed on the function $f(x)$ itself. This kind of consistency was evidently enjoyed by the Newton–Cotes approximations. We may therefore say that Theorem 4 once again places interpolation in the central position it occupied in the case $m = n$ of the classical approximations.

We add that all results concerning spline interpolation and best approximation remain valid in the case of *multiple nodes*.† For a discussion of such cases we refer to [*14, 14a*].

Our discussion has pretty much covered the field of elementary numerical analysis. A detailed account would seem to call for a textbook along the lines which were here only sketched.

---

† For a thorough discussion of *multiple knots* for generalized spline functions see the work of Karlin and Ziegler [7].

II. SPLINE FUNCTIONS AND VARIATION DIMINISHING APPROXIMATION METHODS

8. The Bernstein Polynomials

We know now what spline functions are and we knew right along what approximations were, but what on earth are variation diminishing approximation methods? Rather than give a general definition, we prefer to discuss the example of the Bernstein polynomials (2).

It was pointed out by Pólya and Schoenberg [8] that the relation (2) implies the inequality

$$\underset{0 < x < 1}{Z} (B_n) \leq v(f), \tag{8.1}$$

where on the left we have the number of zeros of $B_n(x)$ in $(0, 1)$, and on the right the number of variations of sign of $f(x)$ in $[0, 1]$. The proof of this fact is so short that we reproduce it here: Writing $z = x/(1 - x)$ we have $B_n(x)/(1 - x)^n = \sum_0^n f(i/n)\binom{n}{i}z^i$ and therefore

$$\underset{0 < x < 1}{Z} (B_n) = \underset{0 < z < \infty}{Z} \left[\sum_0^n f\left(\frac{i}{n}\right)\binom{n}{i}z^i \right] \leq v\left[f\left(\frac{i}{n}\right)\binom{n}{i} \right]$$

$$= v\left[f\left(\frac{i}{n}\right) \right] \leq v(f),$$

the first inequality following from Descartes' rule of signs. This establishes (8.1) and therefore also the weaker inequality

$$v(B_n) \leq v(f). \tag{8.2}$$

Now (8.2) can easily be refined in a significant way: It is well known that

$$B_n(x; a + bx) = a + bx, \tag{8.3}$$

which expresses the fact that the Bernstein polynomial of a linear function coincides with the function. From (2) and (8.3) we conclude that

$$B_n(x; f(x) - a - bx) = B_n(x) - a - bx.$$

Applying (8.2) to the difference $f(x) - a - bx$ we obtain the inequality

$$v[B_n(x) - a - bx] \leq v[f(x) - a - bx]. \tag{8.4}$$

The relations (8.3) and (8.2), whence (8.4) follows, describe the *variation diminishing property* of the Bernstein polynomials. We shall apply the same term to *any* linear approximation method which preserves linear functions [property (8.3)] and gives an approximation $S(x)$ which, like (8.2), has the property $v(S) \leq v(f)$.

Returning to the Bernstein polynomials we observe that (8.4) has a simple and remarkable geometric interpretation: (8.4) shows that the graph of $y = B_n(x)$ *never* crosses a line $y = a + bx$ more often than the graph of $y = f(x)$ does. A further remark is this: (8.4) implies in particular that

$$v[B_n(x) - t] \leq v[f(x) - t] \qquad \text{for all real } t. \tag{8.5}$$

Recalling that

$$\int_{-\infty}^{\infty} v[f(x) - t] \, dt = T(f)$$

is the total variation of $f(x)$, finite or infinite (see [*11*]), we obtain by integrating both sides of (8.5) the inequality

$$T(B_n) \leq T(f) \tag{8.6}$$

which is a known theorem due to Popoviciu. In his lectures [*5*, pp. 236–237] Golomb refers to (8.6) as the variation diminishing property of the $B_n(x)$. We prefer to reserve this name for the more fundamental property (8.2), from which (8.6) follows easily, as just shown. For all I know, the two definitions might be equivalent, but this has not been shown.†

A final remark is that the Bernstein construction does *not* preserve quadratic polynomials. We refer to [*11*] for the simple proof of the fact that *a linear approximation method which is variation diminishing* (and therefore preserves linear functions) *can not possibly preserve quadratic functions, unless it is the identity transformation.*

9. The Variation Diminishing Properties of Spline Functions

We again consider the knots (2.1) and the corresponding sequence of B-splines (2.6). By Theorem 2 we know that every spline function

$$S(x) \in \mathscr{S}_m(x_i) \tag{9.1}$$

admits the unique representation

$$S(x) = \sum_{-\infty}^{\infty} c_j M_j(x) \tag{9.2}$$

in terms of the B-splines. Our further progress is based on the following theorem.

---

† Paul Donis, a graduate student at the University of Wisconsin, pointed out to me that the property (8.6) is a consequence of the *positivity* of the Bernstein operator, while (8.2) follows from its *total positivity*. Therefore the two definitions are not equivalent. (*Added in proof.*)

Theorem 5.   *The basis representation* (9.2) *has the property*

$$v[S(x)] \leq v(c_j). \tag{9.3}$$

Here the left side of (9.3) represents the number of variations of sign of $S(x)$ in the interval (α, β) which is the least open interval containing the knots (2.1). A proof of Theorem 5, to be given elsewhere, requires, on the one hand, upper estimates for the zeros of spline functions, and on the other, theorems of Fekete and Gantmacher–Krein on variation diminishing linear transformations.

We recognize in (9.3) *one* of the properties required of a variation diminishing approximation method, being the analogue of (8.2) for Bernstein polynomials. *The other property, still missing, is the preservation of linear functions.* This second property can now be achieved by an appropriate construction which is possible again because of Theorem 2 and the fact that

$$\pi_{m-1} \subset \mathscr{S}_m(x_i).$$

By Theorem 2 we conclude the existence and uniqueness of the following m expansions:

$$
\begin{aligned}
1 &= \sum a_j M_j(x), \\
x &= \sum a_j' M_j(x), \\
&\;\;\vdots \\
x^{m-1} &= \sum a_j^{(m-1)} M_j(x),
\end{aligned}
\tag{9.4}
$$

with constant coefficients. Here we have assumed that

$$m \geq 2 \tag{9.5}$$

in order to be sure that the expansion of x is present in (9.4).

The coefficients of the expansions (9.4) possess a remarkable property expressed by the following theorem.

Theorem 6.   *The matrix*

$$
A = \left\|
\begin{array}{ccccc}
\cdots & a_{-1} & a_0 & a_1 & \cdots \\
\cdots & a'_{-1} & a_0' & a_1' & \cdots \\
& \vdots & \vdots & \vdots & \\
\cdots & a_{-1}^{(m-1)} & a_0^{(m-1)} & a_1^{(m-1)} & \cdots
\end{array}
\right\|
\tag{9.6}
$$

of the coefficients of the expansions (9.4) *has the property that all its kth-order minors formed from its first k rows* ($k = 1, 2, \ldots, m$) *are positive. In particular*

$$a_j > 0 \quad and \quad a_j'/a_j < a_{j+1}'/a_{j+1} \quad for\ all\ j. \tag{9.7}$$

We now renormalize our B-splines by defining the new functions

$$N_j(x) = a_j M_j(x). \tag{9.8}$$

In terms of the new quantities

$$\xi_j = a_j'/a_j, \tag{9.9}$$

we may rewrite the first two expansions (9.4) in the form

$$1 = \sum N_j(x), \qquad x = \sum \xi_j N_j(x), \tag{9.10}$$

It is clear from (9.7) that the ξ_j form a strictly *increasing* sequence. We add the further information that all ξ_j are in the interval (α, β) and that no subinterval of (α, β) will contain them all.

10. A General Variation Diminishing Approximation Formula

Given a function $f(x)$ defined in the interval $\alpha < x < \beta$, we introduce the spline function

$$S(x) = \sum_{-\infty}^{\infty} f(\xi_j) N_j(x). \tag{10.1}$$

It is well defined because of the properties of the sequence $\{\xi_j\}$ stated at the end of Sec. 9. The spline function (10.1) gives rise to the approximation formula

$$f(x) = \sum_{-\infty}^{\infty} f(\xi_j) N_j(x) + R \qquad (\alpha < x < \beta). \tag{10.2}$$

The $N_j(x)$ are the *fundamental functions* of the formula, while the ξ_j are called its *nodes*.

Theorem 7.   *The approximation formula* (10.2) *preserves linear functions, and beyond this it has in the interval* (α, β) *the variation diminishing property*

$$v(S) \le v(f). \tag{10.3}$$

Indeed, if $f(x) = 1$ or if $f(x) = x$, then (10.2), with $R = 0$, reduces to the expansions (9.10). Moreover, (10.1) and Theorem 5 imply that

$$v(S) \le v[f(\xi_j)].$$

On the other hand, the monotonicity of the ξ_j shows that $v[f(\xi_j)] \le v(f)$ and (10.3) is thereby established.

11. The Entire Real Line with All Integers as Knots

We consider now and describe explicitly the general approximation formula (10.2) for the case when the knots (2.1) are the set of consecutive integers

$$x_i = i \qquad (-\infty < i < \infty). \tag{11.1}$$

This we assume throughout this section. The problem is to determine the functions $N_j(x)$ and the nodes ξ_j by means of the relations (9.4), (9.8), and (9.9).

By (2.6) and (11.1) we have

$$M_j(x) = M(x; j, j+1, \ldots, j+m). \tag{11.2}$$

It is clear from the geometry of the situation that these are translates of one and the same function $Q_m(x)$ which can be expressed in several equivalent ways in view of (1.10):

$$Q_m(x) = M_0(x) \tag{11.3}$$

$$Q_m(x) = \frac{1}{(m-1)!} \sum_0^m (-1)^{m-i} \binom{m}{i} (i-x)_+^{m-1} \tag{11.4}$$

$$Q_m(x) = \frac{1}{(m-1)!} \sum_0^m (-1)^i \binom{m}{i} (x-i)_+^{m-1} \tag{11.5}$$

Thus

$$M_j(x) = Q_m(x-j), \qquad \text{for all } j. \tag{11.6}$$

We begin by establishing the first two identities (9.4) which in the present case turn out to be

$$\sum_{-\infty}^{\infty} Q_m(x-j) = 1 \tag{11.7}$$

and

$$\sum_{-\infty}^{\infty} (j+m/2) Q_m(x-j) = x \qquad (m \geq 2). \tag{11.8}$$

Proof. Observe, to begin with, that our functions $Q_m(x)$ may be successively determined by means of the relation

$$Q_{m+1}(x) = \int_{x-1}^{x} Q_m(x) \, dx, \tag{11.9}$$

which is easily verified by using (11.5). Notice furthermore, that both (11.7) and (11.8) are certainly true if $m = 2$. Indeed, $Q_2(x-j)$ is the roof function with the peak of its roof at the point $x = j + 1$. Since linear interpolation preserves linear functions, the two identities result. From these identities for $m = 2$ we now obtain them by induction for all m by successively performing on both sides of these relations the operation

$$\int_{x-1}^{x} (\cdots)\, dx.$$

By (11.6), the relations (11.7), (11.8) become

$$\sum M_j(x) = 1, \qquad \sum_j (j + \tfrac{1}{2}m)M_j(x) = x. \tag{11.10}$$

These, then, must be the first two of the uniquely defined relations (9.4). By (9.8) and (9.9) we therefore obtain

$$N_j(x) = Q_m(x - j), \tag{11.11}$$

$$\xi_j = j + \tfrac{1}{2}m. \tag{11.12}$$

For the knots (11.1) we thus obtain the variation diminishing approximation formula

$$f(x) = \sum_{-\infty}^{\infty} f(j + \tfrac{1}{2}m)Q_m(x - j) + R. \tag{11.13}$$

This formula is essentially identical with the smoothing formula of Theorem 4 of my old paper [10, p. 72] which was here derived independently of this source. The fact that (11.13) is variation diminishing is, of course, new.

12. The Finite Interval with Finitely Many Knots

In Sec. 10 we established the approximation formula (10.2) and showed in Sec. 11 that it assumes a simple and explicit form (11.13) for the case (11.1) of knots at all the integers. Now we wish to derive similar approximation methods for a finite interval $I = [a, b]$, for functions defined in I. True, the knots (2.1) may be such that the interval (α, β), defined by (2.2), is finite. However, the corresponding formula (10.2) still involves infinitely many nodes ξ_j. We wish to have in I only *finitely* many knots as well as nodes.

This objective can be nicely achieved by an appropriate use of *multiple* knots. It was shown in [12, 3] and extensively used in [14], that a knot of a spline function of degree $m - 1$ may appear with a multiplicity r, where r is any number such that $0 \le r \le m$. That x_j is a knot of multiplicity r merely means that in a sufficiently small neighborhood of x_j, the spline function is only required to be of the continuity class C^{m-1-r}. Thus $r = 0$ means that x_j is really not a knot. At the other extreme, $r = m$ means that there are no continuity requirements between the two components of the spline function, below and above x_j.

$I = [a, b]$ being finite, and m and n being natural numbers such that

$$m \geq 2, \qquad n \geq 1, \tag{12.1}$$

we wish to discuss the family of spline functions $\mathscr{S}_m(x_1, \ldots, x_{n-1})$ of degree $m - 1$, defined in I and having in I the knots $x_1, \ldots, x_{n-1}$ such that

$$a < x_1 < x_2 < \cdots < x_{n-1} < b. \tag{12.2}$$

To be sure, these knots are to be simple knots and

$$\mathscr{S}_m(x_1, \ldots, x_{n-1}) \subset C^{m-2}[a, b]. \tag{12.3}$$

The problem is to find an appropriate basis for this family. This problem is easily solved if we introduce two more knots

$$x_0 = a, \qquad x_n = b, \qquad \textit{both of multiplicity } m. \tag{12.4}$$

In terms of our previous notations we really have now $2m + n - 1$ knots, a fact which we indicate by writing out the knots as follows:

$$\overbrace{x_0, x_0, \ldots, x_0}^{m}, \quad x_1, x_2, \ldots, x_{n-1}, \quad \overbrace{x_n, x_n, \ldots, x_n}^{m}. \tag{12.5}$$

A basis for the family $\mathscr{S}_m(x_1, \ldots, x_{n-1})$ in $I = [a, b]$ is now formed by the following $m + n - 1$ B-splines (see [3, Sec. 4, Theorem 5])

$$M_0(x) = M(x; \overbrace{x_0, \ldots, x_0}^{m}, x_1),$$

$$M_1(x) = M(x; \overbrace{x_0, \ldots, x_0}^{m-1}, x_1, x_2),$$

$$\vdots \tag{12.6}$$

$$M_l(x) = M(x; x_{n-1}, \overbrace{x_n, \ldots, x_n}^{m}),$$

where we set

$$l = m + n - 2. \tag{12.7}$$

In (12.6) we are, of course, using our notation of Sec. 1. Observe, however, that the formula (1.10) is no longer valid for multiple knots and must be replaced by the appropriate expressions for confluent divided differences.

All our results of Secs. 2 and 9 remain valid for the present finite case. To begin with, every $S(x) \in \mathscr{S}_m(x_1, \ldots, x_{n-1})$ has a unique representation

$$S(x) = \sum_{0}^{l} c_j M_j(x) \qquad (x \in I). \tag{12.8}$$

In particular, we have unique expansions

$$1 = \sum_0^l a_j M_j(x), \qquad x = \sum_0^l a_j' M_j(x) \tag{12.9}$$

which are the analogues of the first two expansions (9.4). Similar expansions hold for x^r $(r = 2, \ldots, m-1)$ and Theorem 6 is again valid for the corresponding finite matrix. The last-mentioned property implies the following: If we set

$$\xi_j = a_j'/a_j \qquad (j = 0, \ldots, l), \tag{12.10}$$

then

$$a = \xi_0 < \xi_1 < \cdots < \xi_{l-1} < \xi_l = b. \tag{12.11}$$

Again, setting

$$N_j(x) = a_j M_j(x) \qquad (j = 0, \ldots, l), \tag{12.12}$$

we obtain the expansions

$$1 = \sum_0^l N_j(x), \qquad x = \sum_0^l \xi_j N_j(x) \qquad (a \le x \le b). \tag{12.13}$$

In terms of these quantities and functions we may state the following theorem.

Theorem 8. *The approximation formula*

$$f(x) = \sum_0^l f(\xi_j) N_j(x) + R \qquad (a \le x \le b), \tag{12.14}$$

is exact for linear functions and is variation diminishing. This means that the right-hand-side sum is a spline function having no more variations of sign in $[a, b]$ than $f(x)$ has.

13. Special Cases

1. *Linear interpolation.* If $m = 2$, then (12.7) shows that $l = n$. Moreover, (12.6) and (12.12) show that the $N_j(x)$ are the familiar roof functions. In particular, due to the *double* knots x_0 and x_n, the extreme functions $N_0(x)$ and $N_n(x)$ show only one half of the roof. Also

$$\xi_j = x_j \qquad (j = 0, \ldots, n). \tag{13.1}$$

so that knots and nodes coincide. In short: *If $m = 2$, then the formula (12.14) reduces to the formula of linear interpolation between each pair of neighbors among the ordinates $f(a), f(x_1), \ldots, f(x_{n-1}), f(b)$.*

In this case the variation diminishing properties of (12.14) are self-evident and require no proof.

2. *The Bernstein polynomials.* We now pass to the other extreme case: *We leave m its general value, but set* $n = 1$. At the same time we normalize I by setting

$$a = x_0 = 0, \qquad b = x_1 = 1. \tag{13.2}$$

Now (12.7) shows that $l = m - 1$, while the approximating spline function

$$S(x) = \sum_0^{m-1} f(\xi_j) N_j(x) \tag{13.3}$$

is a polynomial of degree $m - 1$, there being no knots between $x_0 = 0$ and $x_1 = 1$.

There remains to determine the fundamental functions $N_j(x)$ and the nodes ξ_j. We begin by observing that (12.6) and (12.12) define our $N_j(x)$ for all real x, in fact $N_j(x) = 0$ outside the interval (x_0, x_n). In our present case, the representation

$$N_0(x) = a_0 M(x; \overbrace{0, 0, \ldots, 0}^{m}, 1)$$

shows that $x = 1$ is a simple knot of $N_0(x)$, so that from the continuity requirement we conclude that $x = 1$ is a zero of the polynomial $N_0(x)$ of multiplicity $m - 1$, *at least.* Since $N_0(x) \in \pi_{m-1}$ we must have

$$N_0(x) = c_0(1 - x)^{m-1}.$$

Likewise

$$N_1(x) = a_1 M(x; \overbrace{0, \ldots, 0}^{m-1}, 1, 1)$$

shows that $x = 0$ must be a simple zero, *at least,* of the polynomial $N_1(x)$, while $x = 1$ is a zero of multiplicity $m - 2$, *at least.* Again, since $N_1(x) \in \pi_{m-1}$, we must have

$$N_1(x) = c_1 x(1 - x)^{m-2}.$$

Proceeding in this way we see that

$$N_j(x) = c_j x^j (1 - x)^{m-1-j} \qquad (j = 0, \ldots, m-1). \tag{13.4}$$

At this point we recall the identity

$$1 = \sum_0^{m-1} \binom{m-1}{j} x^j (1 - x)^{m-1-j}. \tag{13.5}$$

In view of (13.4) we see that (13.5) must be identical with the first of the identities (12.13), which are unique. But then

$$N_j(x) = \binom{m-1}{j} x^j (1 - x)^{m-1-j} \qquad (j = 0, \ldots, m-1.) \tag{13.6}$$

Finally, the equally familiar identity

$$x = \sum_0^{m-1} \frac{j}{m-1} \binom{m-1}{j} x^j (1-x)^{m-1-j},$$

which now must be the second identity (12.13) for our case, shows that

$$\xi_j = j/(m-1) \qquad (j=0,\ldots,m-1). \tag{13.7}$$

Now it is clear that $S(x)$, *defined by* (13.3), *is identical with the Bernstein polynomial* $B_{m-1}(x)$.

We have just seen that the approximation formula (12.14) of Theorem 8 generalizes the Bernstein polynomials by introducing a new parameter n which counts the number of knots of the approximating spline function. However, the formula requires a preliminary determination of the functions $N_j(x)$ and nodes ξ_j. In one case, however, these difficulties will fortunately disappear: *the case when the $n+1$ points* (12.2) *are equidistant*. This case will furnish our applicable generalizations of the Bernstein polynomials (Sec. 15).

In order to arrive at these useful results we must first discuss the following analogue of the results of Sec. 11: the case of spline functions defined on the half-line $0 \le x < \infty$, having knots at all positive integers. This case is the subject of the next section.

14. The Half-Line with All Positive Integers as Knots

As just mentioned, we wish to find a basis for the family

$$\mathscr{S}_m = \mathscr{S}_m(1, 2, 3, \ldots) \tag{14.1}$$

of spline functions defined for $x \ge 0$ and having as simple knots the integers

$$x_j = j \qquad (j=1, 2, \ldots). \tag{14.2}$$

The device of an additional m-fold knot works here as well: *We introduce the m-fold knot $x_0 = 0$*.

In view of the similar situation (12.6), it is clear that the basis of $\mathscr{S}_m$ will be furnished by the sequence of B-splines

$$M_0(x) \quad = M(x; \overbrace{0, \ldots, 0}^{m}, 1),$$

$$M_1(x) \quad = M(x; \overbrace{0, \ldots, 0}^{m-1}, 1, 2), \tag{14.3}$$

$$\vdots$$

$$M_{m-2}(x) = M(x; 0, 0, 1, 2, \ldots, m-1),$$

and

$$M_{m-1}(x) = M(x; 0, 1, \ldots, m),$$

$$M_m(x) \quad = M(x; 1, 2, \ldots, m+1), \tag{14.4}$$

$$\vdots$$

We have separated these B-splines into two groups. The functions of the second group are evidently expressible as

$$M_{m-1+j}(x) = M(x; j, \ldots, j+m) = Q_m(x-j) \qquad (j=0, 1, \ldots) \qquad (14.5)$$

where $Q_m(x)$ is the B-spline defined by (11.3)–(11.5).

Our problem is to discuss the functions (14.3) and in particular, to establish *explicitly* the fundamental identities

$$1 = \sum_0^\infty a_j M_j(x), \qquad (14.6)$$

$$x = \sum_0^\infty a_j' M_j(x), \qquad (14.7)$$

which will then furnish

$$N_j(x) = a_j M_j(x), \qquad \xi_j = a_j'/a_j. \qquad (14.8)$$

The final result will be the approximation formula

$$f(x) = \sum_0^\infty f(\xi_j) N_j(x) + R \qquad (0 \le x < \infty), \qquad (14.9)$$

representing an analogue of (11.13) for the *positive* real axis.

1.   The evaluation of the confluent divided differences is well known and presents no difficulties. One way, due to Hermite, is to proceed as follows: Assuming $f(z)$ to be analytic, we represent the divided difference $f(0, \ldots, 0, 1, 2, \ldots, n)$ by a contour integral which is then evaluated by decomposing the integrand into partial fractions. The result is then applied to the function $M(x, t) = m(t-x)_+^{m-1}$ with respect to the variable t, and we obtain the functions (14.3). In this way, or another, we obtain the expressions

$$M_j(x) = \frac{m}{(j+1)!} \sum_{r=1}^{j+1} (-1)^{j-r+1} r^{-m+j+1} \binom{j+1}{r} (r-x)_+^{m-1}$$

$$(x \ge 0) \quad \text{for} \quad j=0, 1, \ldots, m-2. \qquad (14.10)$$

2.   Our next objective is to show that the identities (14.6) and (14.7) assume in the present case the forms

$$\frac{1}{m} M_0(x) + \frac{2}{m} M_1(x) + \cdots + \frac{m-1}{m} M_{m-2}(x)$$

$$+ M_{m-1}(x) + M_m(x) + M_{m+1}(x) + \cdots = 1 \qquad (x \ge 0), \qquad (14.11)$$

and

$$\sum_{j=0}^{m-2} \frac{j(j+1)^2}{2m(m-1)} M_j(x) + \sum_{j=m-1}^\infty \left(j - \frac{m}{2} + 1\right) M_j(x) = x \qquad (x \ge 0), \qquad (14.12)$$

respectively.

In order to prove (14.11), we first note that since $x \geq 0$, it follows from (11.5) that $Q_m(x-j) = 0$ if $j \leq -m$. Therefore (11.7) gives

$$\sum_{j=-m+1}^{\infty} Q_m(x-j) = 1 \tag{14.13}$$

for all $x \geq 0$. Let S_1 denote the left member of (14.11), hence

$$S_1 = \sum_{j=0}^{m-2} \frac{j+1}{m} M_j(x) + \sum_{j=0}^{\infty} M_{m-1+j}(x). \tag{14.14}$$

In view of (14.5), (14.13) and (14.14) give

$$S_1 - 1 = \sum_{j=0}^{m-2} \frac{j+1}{m} M_j(x) - \sum_{j=-m+1}^{-1} Q_m(x-j) \tag{14.15}$$

and we must show that the right member of (14.15) vanishes.

By (11.2) and (11.6)

$$Q_m(x-j) = M(x; j, j+1, \ldots, j+m),$$

and the familiar recurrence relation for divided differences gives

$$Q_m(x-j) = \frac{1}{m} [M(x; j+1, j+2, \ldots, j+m)$$
$$- M(x; j, j+1, \ldots, j+m-1)]. \tag{14.16}$$

Therefore

$$\sum_{j=-m+1}^{-1} Q_m(x-j) = \frac{1}{m} [M(x; 0, 1, \ldots, m-1)$$
$$- M(x; -m+1, -m+2, \ldots, 0)]$$
$$= \frac{1}{m} M(x; 0, 1, \ldots, m-1). \tag{14.17}$$

Similarly, by (14.3)

$$M_j(x) = M(x; \overbrace{0, \ldots, 0}^{m-j}, 1, 2, \ldots, j+1)$$
$$= \frac{1}{j+1} [M(x; \overbrace{0, \ldots, 0}^{m-j-1}, 1, 2, \ldots, j+1)$$
$$- M(x; \overbrace{0, \ldots, 0}^{m-j}, 1, 2, \ldots, j)] \qquad (j = 1, 2, \ldots, m-2) \tag{14.18}$$

and therefore

$$\sum_{j=0}^{m-2} \frac{j+1}{m} M_j(x) = \frac{1}{m} [M(x; 0, 1, \ldots, m-1) - M(x; \overbrace{0, \ldots, 0}^{m})]$$

$$= \frac{1}{m} M(x; 0, 1, \ldots, m-1), \tag{14.19}$$

for, indeed, observe that $(m-1)! M(x; \overbrace{0, \ldots, 0}^{m})$ is the value of

$$D_t^{m-1} m(t-x)_+^{m-1}$$

for $t = 0$ and this vanishes if $x > 0$. Our results (14.17) and (14.19) establish the vanishing of the right side of (14.15).

The proof of (14.12) is similar. From (11.8) we have

$$\sum_{j=-m+1}^{\infty} \left(j + \frac{m}{2}\right) Q_m(x-j) = x. \tag{14.20}$$

If S_2 denotes the left side of (14.12), then (14.5) and (14.20) show that

$$S_2 - x = \sum_{j=0}^{m-2} \frac{j(j+1)^2}{2m(m-1)} M_j(x) - \sum_{j=-m+1}^{-1} \left(j + \frac{m}{2}\right) Q_m(x-j) \tag{14.21}$$

and we must show that the right member of (14.21) vanishes if $x > 0$. Substitution of (14.16) in the last term of (14.21) gives

$$\sum_{-m+1}^{-1} (j + \tfrac{1}{2}m) Q_m(x-j) = \frac{1}{m} \sum_{j=-m+1}^{-1} (j + \tfrac{1}{2}m) \times$$

$$[M(x; j+1, j+2, \ldots, j+m)$$

$$- M(x; j, j+1, \ldots, j+m-1)]$$

$$= \tfrac{1}{2}[M(x; 0, 1, \ldots, m-1)$$

$$+ M(x; -m+1, -m+2, \ldots, 0)]$$

$$- \frac{1}{m} \sum_{j=-m+1}^{0} M(x; j, j+1, \ldots, j+m-1)$$

$$= \tfrac{1}{2} M(x; 0, 1, \ldots, m-1) - \frac{1}{m(m-1)}$$

$$\times \sum_{j=-m+1}^{0} [M(x; j+1, \ldots, j+m-1)$$

$$- M(x; j, \ldots, j+m-2)]$$

or, finally,

$$\sum_{j=-m+1}^{-1} \left(j + \frac{m}{2}\right) Q_m(x-j) = \tfrac{1}{2}M(x; 0, 1, \ldots, m-1)$$
$$- \frac{1}{m(m-1)} M(x; 1, 2, \ldots, m-1).$$

(14.22)

Similarly, using (14.18), we obtain

$$\sum_{j=1}^{m-2} \frac{j(j+1)^2}{2m(m-1)} M_j(x) = \frac{1}{2m(m-1)} \sum_{j=1}^{m-2} j(j+1) \times$$

$$[M(x; \overbrace{0, \ldots, 0}^{m-j-1}, 1, 2, \ldots, j+1)$$

$$- M(x; \overbrace{0, \ldots, 0}^{m-j}, 1, 2, \ldots, j)]$$

$$= \tfrac{1}{2}M(x; 0, 1, \ldots, m-1) - \frac{1}{m(m-1)} \times$$

$$\sum_{j=1}^{m-1} j\, M(x; \overbrace{0, \ldots, 0}^{m-j}, 1, 2, \ldots, j)$$

$$= \tfrac{1}{2}M(x; 0, 1, \ldots, m-1) - \frac{1}{m(m-1)} \times$$

$$\sum_{j=1}^{m-1} [M(x; \overbrace{0, \ldots, 0}^{m-j-1}, 1, 2, \ldots, j)$$

$$- M(x; \overbrace{0, \ldots, 0}^{m-j}, 1, 2, \ldots, j-1)]$$

$$= \tfrac{1}{2}M(x; 0, 1, \ldots, m-1) - \frac{1}{m(m-1)} \times$$

$$M(x; 1, 2, \ldots, m-1),$$

the last term containing $M(x; \overbrace{0, \ldots, 0}^{m-1})$ being equal to zero for reasons already mentioned. The last result agreeing with the right member of (14.22) completes the proof of our identity (14.12).

From (14.6)–(14.8) and our newly established identities (14.11) and (14.12), we conclude that

$$N_j(x) = \frac{j+1}{m} M_j(x) \qquad (j=0, 1, \ldots, m-2) \qquad (14.23)$$

$$N_j(x) = M_j(x) \qquad (j=m-1, m, m+1, \ldots) \qquad (14.24)$$

while the nodes are given by

$$\xi_j = \begin{cases} \dfrac{j(j+1)}{2(m-1)} & (j=0,1,\ldots,m-2) \\ \\ j - \dfrac{m}{2} + 1 & (j=m-1,m,m+1,\ldots). \end{cases} \qquad (14.25)$$

We assemble our results as a theorem.

Theorem 9. *The variation diminishing spline approximation formula for the positive real axis with knots at the positive integers is the following*

$$f(x) = \sum_{j=1}^{m-2} f\left(\frac{j(j+1)}{2(m-1)}\right) N_j(x) + \sum_{j=m-1}^{\infty} f\left(j - \frac{m}{2} + 1\right) N_j(x) + R.$$

$$(14.26)$$

Here, the functions $N_j(x)$ are defined by (14.23) and (14.24) which in turn are described by (14.3) and (14.5). Also notice the explicit expressions (14.10) for the functions (14.3).

It seems worthwhile to single out the few simplest cases.
If $m=2$ then (14.26) evidently becomes the formula

$$f(x) = \sum_{0}^{\infty} f(j) N_j(x) + R$$

of linear interpolation between neighboring ordinates.
For $m=3$ we obtain the formula of *quadratic* spline approximation

$$f(x) = f(0) N_0(x) + f(\tfrac{1}{2}) N_1(x) + f(\tfrac{3}{2}) N_2(x) + \cdots + R, \qquad (14.27)$$

where the general formulas easily furnish the following explicit expressions:

$$\begin{aligned} N_0(x) &= (1-x)_+^2, \\ N_1(x) &= \tfrac{1}{2}(2-x)_+^2 - 2(1-x)_+^2 \qquad (x \geq 0), \qquad (14.28) \\ N_{j+2}(x) &= Q_3(x-j) \qquad (j=0,1,\ldots) \end{aligned}$$

where

$$2! Q_3(x) = (3-x)_+^2 - 3(2-x)_+^2 + 3(1-x)_+^2 - (-x)_+^2$$
$$(-\infty < x < \infty).$$

If $m=4$ we obtain the formula of *cubic* spline approximation

$$f(x) = f(0) N_0(x) + f(\tfrac{1}{3}) N_1(x) + f(1) N_2(x) + f(2) N_3(x) + \cdots + R,$$

$$(14.29)$$

where

$$N_0(x) = (1 - x)_+{}^3$$
$$N_1(x) = \tfrac{1}{4}(2 - x)_+{}^3 - 2(1 - x)_+{}^3$$
$$N_2(x) = \tfrac{1}{6}(3 - x)_+{}^3 - \tfrac{3}{4}(2 - x)_+{}^3 + \tfrac{3}{2}(1 - x)_+{}^3 \qquad (x \geq 0), \qquad (14.30)$$
$$N_{j+3}(x) = Q_4(x - j) \qquad (j = 0, 1, \ldots),$$

where

$$3! Q_4(x) = (4 - x)_+{}^3 - 4(3 - x)_+{}^3 + 6(2 - x)_+{}^3 - 4(1 - x)_+{}^3$$
$$+ (-x)_+{}^3 \qquad (-\infty < x < \infty).$$

15. The Finite Interval with Equidistant Knots

The explicit results of the last section have paved the way to implement the general formula of Theorem 8 in the special case when the $n + 1$ points (12.2) are *equidistant*. Indeed, let us return to Sec. 12, assuming now that

$$a = x_0 = 0, \quad x_1 = 1, \quad x_2 = 2, \ldots, x_n = b = n. \qquad (15.1)$$

For technical reasons we will also assume that

$$m \leq n. \qquad (15.2)$$

This last assumption, not inherent in Theorem 8, will allow us to apply the results of Sec. 14 without the need for additional computations.

It seems fairly clear that the fundamental functions $N_j(x)$ and nodes ξ_j, of Theorem 9, may be used to construct readily the formula (12.14) of Theorem 8 under the assumptions (15.1) and (15.2). The precise connection is described as follows.

Theorem 10. *The spline approximation formula of degree $m - 1$*

$$f(x) = \sum_0^l \tilde{\xi}_j \tilde{N}_j(x) + R \qquad (l = m + n - 2), \qquad (15.3)$$

for the interval $[0, n]$, the knots $1, 2, \ldots, n - 1$, and subject to (15.2), is described in terms of the $N_j(x)$ and ξ_j of Sec. 14 by

$$\tilde{N}_j(x) = N_j(x), \qquad\qquad j = 0, 1, \ldots, n - 1, \qquad (15.4)$$
$$\tilde{N}_j(x) = N_{l-j}(n - x), \qquad\quad j = n, n + 1, \ldots, l, \qquad (15.5)$$
$$\tilde{\xi}_j = \xi_j, \qquad\qquad\qquad j = 0, \ldots, n - 1, \qquad (15.6)$$
$$\tilde{\xi}_j = n - \xi_{l-j}, \qquad\qquad j = n, \ldots, l. \qquad (15.7)$$

Proof. We know that the $\tilde{N}_j(x)$ and $\tilde{\xi}_j$ are uniquely defined by the two relations

$$\sum_0^l \tilde{N}_j(x) = 1, \qquad \sum_0^l \tilde{\xi}_j \tilde{N}_j(x) = x \qquad (0 \le x \le n). \qquad (15.8)$$

Their unicity easily implies the symmetry properties

$$\tilde{N}_j(x) = \tilde{N}_{l-j}(n - x) \qquad (j = 0, \ldots, l), \qquad (15.9)$$

$$\tilde{\xi}_j = n - \tilde{\xi}_{l-j} \qquad (j = 0, \ldots, l), \qquad (15.10)$$

by obvious arguments which we may omit.

We shall now confront (15.8) with the identities

$$\sum_0^\infty N_j(x) = 1, \qquad \sum_0^\infty \xi_j N_j(x) = x \qquad (x \ge 0) \qquad (15.11)$$

of Sec. 14. Observing that

$$N_n(x) = N_{n+1}(x) = \cdots = 0 \qquad \text{if} \quad x < n - m + 1, \qquad (15.12)$$

we conclude from (15.11) that

$$\sum_0^{n-1} N_j(x) = 0, \qquad \sum_0^{n-1} \xi_j N_j(x) = x \qquad \text{if} \quad x < n - m + 1. \quad (15.13)$$

However, for the values of $j = 0, 1, \ldots, n - 1$ we have

$$\tilde{N}_j(x) = c_j N_j(x) \qquad \text{(for appropriate constants } c_j > 0). \qquad (15.14)$$

Therefore (15.14), (15.12), and (15.8) also imply

$$\sum_0^{n-1} \tilde{N}_j(x) = 0, \qquad \sum_0^{n-1} \tilde{\xi}_j \tilde{N}_j(x) = x \qquad \text{if} \quad x < n - m + 1. \quad (15.15)$$

Finally (15.13)–(15.15) show that

$$\sum_{j=0}^{n-1} (1 - c_j) N_j(x) = 0, \qquad \sum_0^{n-1} (\xi_j - \tilde{\xi}_j c_j) N_j(x) = 0 \qquad \text{if} \quad x < n - m + 1.$$

$$(15.16)$$

At this point we appeal to the representation Theorem 2 (Sec. 2) in its general form for the case of multiple knots [3, Sec. 4, Theorem 5]. This theorem implies that all coefficients of the expansions (15.16) must vanish. This means that $c_j = 1$ $(j = 0, \ldots, n - 1)$ and the relations (15.4) and (15.6) are thereby established. The remaining relations (15.5) and (15.7) now follow easily from the symmetry relations (15.9), (15.10). Indeed

$$\tilde{N}_j(x) = \tilde{N}_{l-j}(n - x) = N_{l-j}(n - x) \qquad \text{if} \quad j = n, n + 1, \ldots, l$$

because then $l - j = m - 2, m - 3, \ldots, 0$, remembering that $m \le n$ by (5.2). Likewise by (15.10) and (15.6) we have

$$\tilde{\xi}_j = n - \tilde{\xi}_{l-j} = n - \xi_{l-j} \qquad \text{if } \quad j = n, n+1, \ldots, l.$$

This completes a proof of our theorem.

We write below the formulas for $m = 3$ and for $m = 4$:

1. $m = 3$, hence $l = n + 1$,

$$
\begin{aligned}
f(x) = &f(0)N_0(x) + f(\tfrac{1}{2})N_1(x) + f(\tfrac{3}{2})Q_3(x) + f(\tfrac{5}{2})Q_3(x-1) \\
&+ \cdots + f(n - \tfrac{3}{2})Q_3(x - n + 3) + f(n - \tfrac{1}{2})N_1(n - x) \\
&+ f(n)N_0(n - x) + R.
\end{aligned}
\tag{15.17}
$$

The functions appearing in this formula are described by our formulas (14.28).

2. $m = 4$, hence $l = n + 2$,

$$
\begin{aligned}
f(x) = &f(0)N_0(x) + f(\tfrac{1}{3})N_1(x) + f(1)N_2(x) + f(2)Q_4(x) \\
&+ f(3)Q_4(x - 1) + \cdots + f(n - 2)Q_4(x - n + 4) \\
&+ f(n - 1)N_2(n - x) + f(n - \tfrac{1}{3})N_1(n - x) \\
&+ f(n)N_0(n - x) + R.
\end{aligned}
\tag{15.18}
$$

The functions appearing here are described by our formulas (14.30).

If $f(x)$ is defined in $[0, n]$, we obtain in this way an approximation $S(x)$ which is a spline function with knots at $1, 2, \ldots, n - 1$. Let us now assume that $f(x)$ is defined in the unit interval $0 \le x \le 1$. To obtain an approximation we consider $f(x/n)$ in $[0, n]$, constructing as before the spline approximation $S(x)$. Replacing x by nx we see that $S(nx)$ will approximate to $f(x)$ in $[0, 1]$. We denote this approximation by the symbol

$$S_{m,n}(x) \qquad (0 \le x \le 1), \tag{15.19}$$

and observe that it is a spline function of degree $m - 1$ having the $n - 1$ knots j/n $(j = 1, \ldots, n - 1)$. As an example, assuming that $m = 4$ and $n \ge 4$, we obtain from (15.18) the expression

$$
S_{4,n}(x) = f(0)N_0(nx) + f\left(\frac{1}{3n}\right)N_1(nx) + f\left(\frac{1}{n}\right)N_2(nx) + f\left(\frac{2}{n}\right)Q_4(nx)
$$

$$
+ \cdots + f\left(1 - \frac{2}{n}\right)Q_4(nx - n + 4) + f\left(1 - \frac{1}{n}\right)N_2(n - nx)
$$

$$
+ f\left(1 - \frac{1}{3n}\right)N_1(n - nx) + f(1)N_0(n - nx).
$$

16. Error Estimates

For functions $f(x)$ defined in $[0, 1]$ we have explicitly described the spline approximation formula

$$f(x) = S_{m,n}(x) + R(x) \qquad (n \geq m \geq 2; \quad 0 \leq x \leq 1), \qquad (16.1)$$

for the case of the knots j/n $(j = 1, \ldots, n-1)$.

Concerning the size of the error term $R(x)$ the following theorem holds.

Theorem 10. *If $\omega(\delta)$ is the modulus of continuity of $f(x)$, then*

$$|S_{m,n}(x) - f(x)| \leq [(m/12)^{1/2} + 1]\omega(1/n) \qquad (m \geq 2), \qquad (16.2)$$

throughout $[0, 1]$.

This should be compared with Popoviciu's estimate for $S_{m,1}(x) = B_{m-1}(x)$ which is [5, p. 231]

$$|S_{m,1}(x) - f(x)| \leq \tfrac{3}{2}\omega[(m-1)^{-1/2}]. \qquad (16.3)$$

Evidently, (16.2) gives a favorable estimate for large n and small m. Thus, for cubic spline functions $(m = 4)$ we obtain

$$|S_{4,n}(x) - f(x)| \leq (1 + 3^{-1/2})\omega(1/n). \qquad (16.4)$$

A comparison with (16.3) suggests that it is more advantageous to use cubic spline functions for large n, rather than to approximate by Bernstein polynomials $(n = 1)$ using a large m. If cubic spline functions are not smooth enough, we may increase m beyond 4. However, (16.2) shows that the estimate deteriorates as m increases, for a fixed n. This seems to be a price to be paid for the increased local smoothness of the approximation.

For Bernstein polynomials we also have the following relation due to Woronowskaja [4, p. 117]

$$S_{m,1}(x) - f(x) = \frac{f''(x) \cdot x(1-x)}{2(m-1)} + o\left(\frac{1}{m}\right) \qquad \text{as} \quad m \to \infty, \qquad (16.5)$$

which holds for bounded $f(x)$ for such x where $f''(x)$ exists. The corresponding result for spline functions may be stated as follows:

Theorem 11. *If $f(x) \in C''$, $m > 2$ and x is fixed, $0 < x < 1$, then*

$$S_{m,n}(x) - f(x) = \frac{m}{24n^2} f''(x) + o\left(\frac{m}{n^2}\right) \qquad (16.6)$$

as $m/n^2 \to 0$.

The estimates (16.2) and (16.6) show that $S_{m,n}(x)$ converges to $f(x)$ under fairly general conditions. Thus (16.2) implies uniform convergence if $f(x) \in C[0, 1]$ provided that m remains bounded. On the other hand, assuming $f(x) \in C''[0, 1]$, (16.6) assures pointwise convergence if $m/n^2 \to 0$. Thus also m may grow indefinitely, provided that it does not grow too rapidly compared to n. At the endpoints we have in any case

$$S_{m,n}(0) = f(0), \qquad S_{m,n}(1) = f(1).$$

For $m = 4$, i.e. cubic spline approximation, (16.6) becomes

$$S_{4,n}(x) - f(x) = \frac{1}{6n^2} f''(x) + o\left(\frac{1}{n^2}\right) \qquad \text{as} \quad n \to \infty.$$

All these formulas show again that the approximation is *below* the function where the function is *concave*, and *above* where it is *convex*, a fact which is suggested by the variation diminishing property similar to (8.4).

ACKNOWLEDGMENT

I wish to acknowledge the invaluable help of T. N. E. Greville. While reviewing this paper for the Mathematics Research Center, he found the present proof of the identity (14.11) which now replaces my previous clumsy one. He also noticed that my original version of the identity (14.12) was incorrect, found its present correct form, and devised the present elegant proof of (14.12).

SUPPLEMENT

On the Normalization of the B-Splines and the Location of the Nodes for the Case of Unequally Spaced Knots

T. N. E. GREVILLE†

It follows from Theorem 2 that the coefficients a_j of (9.8) and the nodes ξ_j of (10.1) are uniquely determined by the two identities (9.10). It is the purpose of this supplement to show that these quantities are given by

$$a_j = \frac{1}{m}(x_{j+m} - x_j) \tag{17.1}$$

and

$$\xi_j = \frac{1}{m-1}(x_{j+1} + x_{j+2} + \cdots + x_{j+m-1}). \tag{17.2}$$

These formulas are valid also for the case of a finite interval with finitely many knots considered in Sec. 12, and the results obtained in Secs. 14 and 15 for the special case of equidistant knots can be arrived at merely by substitution in (17.1) and (17.2).

† Mathematics Research Center, U.S. Army, University of Wisconsin, Madison, Wisconsin.

In order to prove (17.1) and (17.2) it is sufficient to show that (17.1) and (17.2) satisfy both identities (9.10). From (2.6) and from the well-known expression for a divided difference in terms of divided differences of the next lower order, we obtain

$$M_j(x) = \frac{1}{x_{j+m} - x_j} [M(x; x_{j+1}, x_{j+2}, \ldots, x_{j+m})$$

$$- M(x; x_j, x_{j+1}, \ldots, x_{j+m-1})]. \tag{17.3}$$

For a given, but arbitrary x in (α, β) let A and B be integers such that

$$x_{A+m} \leq x \leq x_B. \tag{17.4}$$

Then it follows from (1.9) and (2.6) that $M_j(x) = 0$ for $j < A$ and for $j > B$. Substitution of (17.1) and (17.3) therefore gives

$$\sum_{=-\infty}^{\infty} N_j(x) = \sum_{j=A}^{B} a_j M_j(x) = \frac{1}{m} \sum_{j=A}^{B} [M(x; x_{j+1}, x_{j+2}, \ldots, x_{j+m})$$

$$- M(x; x_j, x_{j+1}, \ldots, x_{j+m-1})]$$

$$= \frac{1}{m} [M(x; x_{B+1}, x_{B+2}, \ldots, x_{B+m})$$

$$- M(x; x_A, x_{A+1}, \ldots, x_{A+m-1})]. \tag{17.5}$$

It follows from (1.9) and (17.4) that $M(x; t) = 0$ for $t < x_{A+m}$, while for $t > x_B$, $M(x; t) = m(t - x)^{m-1}$. As a divided difference of order r of a polynomial of degree r is a constant equal to the coefficient of x^r, the expression (17.5) reduces to unity, and the first identity (9.10) is satisfied.

Again making use of (17.1) and (17.3) we obtain

$$\sum_{j=-\infty}^{\infty} \xi_j N_j(x) = \sum_{j=A}^{B} a_j \xi_j M_j(x)$$

$$= \frac{1}{m} \sum_{j=A}^{B} [M(x; x_{j+1}, x_{j+2}, \ldots, x_{j+m})$$

$$- M(x; x_j, x_{j+1}, \ldots, x_{j+m-1})]$$

$$= \frac{1}{m} \xi_B M(x; x_{B+1}, x_{B+2}, \ldots, x_{B+m})$$

$$- \frac{1}{m} \xi_A M(x; x_A, x_{A+1}, \ldots, x_{A+m-1})$$

$$- \frac{1}{m} \sum_{j=A+1}^{B} (\xi_j - \xi_{j-1}) M(x; x_j, x_{j+1}, \ldots, x_{j+m-1}). \tag{17.6}$$

It follows from (17.2) that

$$\xi_j - \xi_{j-1} = \frac{1}{m-1}(x_{j+m-1} - x_j).\tag{17.7}$$

By means of (17.7) and the expression for the divided difference in terms of divided differences of the next lower order, and in view of the remarks made following (17.5), (17.6) reduces to

$$\xi_B - \frac{1}{m(m-1)} \times$$

$$\sum_{j=A+1}^{B}[M(x; x_{j+1}, x_{j+2}, \ldots, x_{j+m-1}) - M(x; x_j, x_{j+1}, \ldots, x_{j+m-2})]$$

$$= \xi_B - \frac{1}{m(m-1)} M(x; x_{B+1}, x_{B+2}, \ldots, x_{B+m-1}),\tag{17.8}$$

where we have again used the fact that $M(x; t) = 0$ for $t < x_{A+m}$. It is shown in [1, p. 8] that for $f(x) \equiv x^r$, r being a positive integer,†

$$f(x_1, x_2, \ldots, x_r) = x_1 + x_2 + \cdots + x_r.\tag{17.9}$$

Since $M(x; t) = m(t-x)^{m-1}$ for $t > x_B$, evaluation of (17.8) by means of (17.9) gives

$$\xi_B - \frac{1}{m-1}\sum_{j=1}^{m-1}(x_{B+j} - x) = x,$$

in view of (17.2). Hence, the second identity (9.10) is satisfied.

It will be noted that if the various divided differences are interpreted, when appropriate, as confluent divided differences, the preceding demonstrations are equally valid for the case of multiple knots, so long as the multiplicity does not exceed m. Moreover, if it does not exceed $m-1$ (with the possible exception of the ends of the sequence of knots in the finite case), (17.7) shows that the nodes ξ_j continue to form a strictly increasing sequence. It is clear also that these results carry over, with only trivial modification, to the case considered in Sec. 12 of a finite interval (a, b) with finitely many knots. In particular, since the end points a and b are m-fold knots, as indicated by (12.5), it follows from (17.2) that these points are always nodes.

† Schoenberg points out that (17.9) is easily established in the following manner. It follows from Newton's divided-difference interpolation formula that $f(x_1, x_2, \ldots, x_r)$ is the coefficient of x^{r-1} in the Lagrange interpolation polynomial for $f(x)$ of degree $r-1$ with the nodes $x_1, x_2, \ldots, x_r$. However, this polynomial is unique, and it is immediately verified that for $f(x) \equiv x^r$, the polynomial $x^n - (x - x_1)(x - x_2) \cdots (x - x_r)$ has the required properties.

Schoenberg has pointed out that upper bounds for the B-splines $M_j(x)$ are easily obtained by a particular application of the identities (12.9). I am indebted to him for the following remarks. Consider approximation over the interval (a, b) where $a = x_j$ and $b = x_{j+m}$, and in setting up the approximation scheme let each of the two knots at a and b have a total multiplicity of m, as in (12.5). In other words, if a is an r-fold knot of the function $M_j(x)$, we take

$$x_{j-m+r} = x_{j-m+r+1} = \cdots = x_{j-1} = a,$$

and similarly for the knot at b. Thus, in view of (12.10), the identities (12.9) become

$$\frac{1}{m} \sum_{k=A}^{B} (x_{k+m} - x_k) M_k(x) = 1, \qquad (17.10)$$

$$\frac{1}{m} \sum_{k=A}^{B} (x_{k+m} - x_k) \xi_k M_k(x) = x, \qquad (17.11)$$

where $j - m + 1 \leq A \leq j$ and $j \leq B \leq j + m - 1$. As every term of the summation in (17.10) is nonnegative, it follows that

$$\frac{1}{m} (b - a) M_j(x) \leq 1,$$

and therefore

$$M_j(x) \leq \frac{m}{b - a}. \qquad (17.12)$$

Making use of both (17.10) and (17.11), we obtain a sharper bound for $M_j(x)$. We have

$$\frac{1}{m} \sum_{x=A}^{B} (x_{m+k} - x_k)(\xi_k - a) M_k(x) = x - a. \qquad (17.13)$$

As each term of the summation in (17.13) is nonnegative,

$$M_j(x) \leq \frac{m(x - a)}{(b - a)(\xi_j - a)}. \qquad (17.14)$$

In a similar manner, we obtain

$$M_j(x) \leq \frac{m(b - x)}{(b - a)(b - \xi_j)}. \qquad (17.15)$$

For $x = \xi_j$, the right members of both (17.14) and (17.15) reduce to $m/(b - a)$. Thus, we have a second proof of (17.12) and have also shown that the graph of $M_j(x)$ is bounded from above by two sides of a triangle of which the base coincides with the support of $M_j(x)$ and a vertex is situated at $[\xi_j, m/(b-a)]$.

It is easily shown that there does not exist a sharper bound of this type (i.e., two sides of a triangle with the vertex depending *only* on a, b, and ξ_j). Consider the case in which $x_{j+1} = x_{j+2} = \cdots = x_{j+m-1} = c$, $a < c < b$. Here $\xi_j = c$, and it is easily verified that

$$
M_j(x) = \begin{cases} \dfrac{m(x-a)^{m-1}}{(b-a)(c-a)^{m-1}} & (a \le x \le c) \\[2ex] \dfrac{m(b-x)^{m-1}}{(b-a)(b-c)^{m-1}} & (c \le x \le b). \end{cases}
$$

We observe that $M_j(c) = m/(b-a)$; the upper bound is actually attained.

SUPPLEMENT REFERENCE

[1] Milne-Thomson, L. M., "The Calculus of Finite Differences." Macmillan, New York, 1933.

REFERENCES

[1] Birkhoff, G., and de Boor, C. R., Piecewise polynomial interpolation and approximation, G. M. Symposium: "Approximation of Functions," (H. L. Garabedian, ed.) pp. 164–190. Elsevier, Amsterdam, 1965.

[2] de Boor, C., Best approximation properties of spline functions of odd degree, *J. Math. Mech.* **12,** 747–749 (1963).

[3] Curry, H. B., and Schoenberg, I. J. On Pólya frequency functions. IV: The fundamental spline functions and their limits, *J. Analyse Math.* **17,** 71–107 (1966).

[4] Davis, P. J., "Interpolation and Approximation." Random House (Blaisdell), New York, 1963.

[5] Golomb, M., "Lectures on Theory of Approximation," Argonne Natl. Lab., Argonne, Illinois, 1962.

[6] Greville, T. N. E., Spline functions, Interpolation and Numerical Quadrature, *in* "Mathematical Methods for Digital Computers" (A. Ralston and H. S. Wilf, eds.), Vol. 2. Wiley, New York, 1967.

[7] Karlin, S., and Ziegler, Z., Chebyshevian spline functions, *J. SIAM Numerical Analysis* **3,** 514–543 (1966).

[8] Pólya, G., and Schoenberg, I. J., Remarks on the de la Vallée-Poussin means and convex conformal maps of the circle, *Pacific J. Math.* **8,** 295–334 (1958).

[9] Sard, A., "Linear Approximation" (Math. Surveys No. 9). Amer. Math. Soc., Providence, Rhode Island, 1963.

[10] Schoenberg, I. J., Contributions to the problem of approximation of equidistant data by analytic functions, *Quart. Appl. Math.* **4,** 45–99 and 112–141, 1946.

[11] Schoenberg, I. J., On variation diminishing approximation methods, *in* "On Numerical Approximation" (MRC Symp.) (R. E. Langer, ed.), pp. 249–274. Univ. of Wisconsin Press, Madison, Wisconsin, 1959.

[12] Schoenberg, I. J., On interpolation by spline functions and its minimal properties, *in* "On Approximation Theory" (Oberwolfach Symp.) (P. L. Butzer, ed.), *Internat. Ser. Numerical Math.* **5,** 109–129 (1964).

[13] Schoenberg, I. J., On best approximation of linear operators, *Indag. Math.* **26,** 155–163 (1964).

[14] Schoenberg, I. J., On monosplines of least deviation and best quadrature formulae, *J. SIAM Numerical Analysis, Ser. B* **2,** 144–170 (1965).

[14a] Schoenberg, I. J., On monosplines of least square deviation and best quadrature formulae II, *J. SIAM Numerical Analysis* **3,** 321–328 (1966).

[15] Walsh, J. L., Ahlberg, J. H., and Nilson, E. N., Best approximation properties of the spline fit, *J. Math. Mech.* **11,** 225–234 (1962).

[16] Wegmüller, W., Ausgleichung durch Bernstein-Polynome, *Mitt. Verein. Schweiz. Versich-Math.* **36,** 15–59 (1938).

Bounds on Differences of Means

O. SHISHA and B. MOND
Aerospace Research Laboratories
Wright-Patterson Air Force Base
Dayton, Ohio

1

Let $q_1, q_2, \ldots, q_n$ be positive numbers with $\sum_{k=1}^{n} q_k = 1$. For every sequence $(x_1, \ldots, x_n)$ with all $x_k > 0$ and for every real r, consider the *mean of order r*, $M_r(x_1, x_2, \ldots, x_n)$, defined as $(\sum_{k=1}^{n} q_k x_k^r)^{1/r}$ if $r \neq 0$, and as $\prod_{k=1}^{n} x_k^{q_k}$ if $r = 0$. For given positive $x_1, x_2, \ldots, x_n$, it is known (see, e.g. [3, p. 17], or [11, p. 26]) that $M_r(x_1, x_2, \ldots, x_n)$ is strictly increasing with r (except when $x_1 = x_2 = \cdots = x_n$). Thus, if r and s are given reals, $r < s$, then for every sequence $(x_1, \ldots, x_n)$ of positive numbers,

$$1 \leq M_s(x, \ldots, x_n)/M_r(x_1, \ldots, x_n), \tag{1}$$

$$0 \leq M_s(x_1, \ldots, x_n) - M_r(x_1, \ldots, x_n). \tag{2}$$

2

A natural question to ask is whether one can give *upper bounds* for the right-hand sides of (1) and (2), under, say, the hypothesis that each x_j satisfies $A \leq x_j \leq B$, where A, B are constants with $0 < A < B$. Such an upper bound for the ratio in (1) was given by Cargo and Shisha [4] in a paper which served as a motivation and starting point for a considerable amount of further work by various authors.

3

The main purpose of the present paper is to give an upper bound for the difference in (2) under the restriction on the x_j as stated above. As applications, we shall obtain a number of inequalities, including "complements" to the classical inequalities of Cauchy and Hölder. Also, the determination of an upper bound for the difference in (2) yields a matrix interpretation (Theorem 3). We derive, finally, a number of matrix inequalities.

4

In this section $q_1, q_2, \ldots, q_n$ $(n \geq 1)$ are fixed positive numbers with $\sum_{k=1}^{n} q_k = 1$, and for every sequence $(x_1, \ldots, x_n)$ with all $x_k > 0$ and every real r, $M_r(x_1, x_2, \ldots, x_n)$ is as in Sec. 1.

Theorem 1. *Let r, s, A, B be given reals $(0 < A < B, r < s)$, and let I denote the n-dimensional cube $\{(x_1, \ldots, x_n) : A \leq x_k \leq B, k = 1, 2, \ldots, n\}$. Then throughout I,*

$$M_s(x_1, x_2, \ldots, x_n) - M_r(x_1, x_2, \ldots, x_n) \leq \Delta, \tag{3}$$

where Δ is

$$
\begin{array}{ll}
[\theta B^s + (1-\theta)A^s]^{1/s} - [\theta B^r + (1-\theta)A^r]^{1/r} & \text{if } rs \neq 0, \qquad (4) \\
[\theta B^s + (1-\theta)A^s]^{1/s} - B^\theta A^{1-\theta} & \text{if } r = 0,
\end{array}
$$

and

$$
B^\theta A^{1-\theta} - [\theta B^r + (1-\theta)A^r]^{1/r} \qquad\qquad \text{if } s = 0.
$$

θ is defined as follows. Let

$$h(x) \equiv x^{1/s} - (ax + b)^{1/r}$$

with

$$
a = \frac{B^r - A^r}{B^s - A^s}, \qquad b = \frac{B^s A^r - B^r A^s}{B^s - A^s}, \qquad \text{if } rs \neq 0,
$$

$$
h(x) \equiv x^{1/s} - A(B/A)^{(x - A^s)/(B^s - A^s)}, \qquad \text{if } r = 0,
$$

and

$$
h(x) \equiv -x^{1/r} + A(B/A)^{(x - A^r)/(B^r - A^r)}, \qquad \text{if } s = 0.
$$

Let J denote the open interval joining A^s to B^s if $s \neq 0$, and let $J = (B^r, A^r)$ if $s = 0$. Let $\bar{J}$ be the closure of J. Then there is a unique $x^* \in \bar{J}$ where $h(x)$ attains its maximum in $\bar{J}$. (Observe, that if $rs \neq 0$, then $ax + b > 0$ at the end points of $\bar{J}$ and, therefore, throughout $\bar{J}$.) This x^* lies in J. We set

$$\theta = (x^* - A^s)/(B^s - A^s) \qquad \text{if } s \neq 0, \tag{5}$$

and

$$\theta = (x^* - A^r)/(B^r - A^r) \qquad \text{if } s = 0.$$

Equality in (3) for a point $(x_1, \ldots, x_n) \in I$ holds if and only if there exists a subsequence $(k_1, k_2, \ldots, k_p)$ of $(1, 2, \ldots, n)$ such that $\sum_{m=1}^{p} q_{k_m} = \theta$, $x_{k_m} = B$ $(m = 1, 2, \ldots, p)$, and $x_k = A$ for every k distinct from all k_m. Finally, if $s \geq 1$, then x^* is the unique solution of $h'(x) = 0$ in J.

We shall use (cf. [12]) two lemmas due to Marshall and Olkin, which, for the sake of completeness, are reproduced here with their proofs.

Lemma 1. *Let $0 < A < B$, $r < s$, $rs \neq 0$,*

$$a = (B^r - A^r)/(B^s - A^s), \qquad b = (B^s A^r - B^r A^s)/(B^s - A^s).$$

Then throughout (A, B),

$$f(x) \equiv r[x^r - ax^s - b] > 0.$$

Proof of Lemma 1. For $0 < x < \infty, f'(x) = rx^{r-1}(r - asx^{s-r})$. So f' has a unique zero in $(0, \infty)$. Since $f(A) = f(B) = 0$, $f(x)$ is either positive throughout (A, B), or negative throughout (A, B). Suppose the latter. If $r > 0$, then $f(0) = -rb < 0$. If $r < 0$, then

$$\lim_{x \to 0+0} f(x) = \lim_{x \to 0+0} [rx^r(1 - ax^{s-r}) - rb] = -\infty.$$

In any case, there exists a C, $0 < C < A$, such that $f(C) < 0$. Let D $(A < D < B)$ be such that $f(D) = \min\{f(x) : A \leq x \leq B\}$. Then $f'(D) = 0$. Let E $(C < E < D)$ be such that $f(E) = \max\{f(x) : C \leq x \leq D\}$. Then $f'(E) = 0$. We have reached a contradiction with the second sentence of the present proof.

Lemma 2. *Assume the hypotheses and notations of Lemma 1. Let $A \leq x_k \leq B$ $(k = 1, 2, \ldots, n)$. Then*

$$r\left(\left(\sum_{k=1}^{n} q_k x_k^r\right) - a\left(\sum_{k=1}^{n} q_k x_k^s\right) - b\right) \geq 0, \tag{6}$$

equality holding if and only if each x_k is A or B.

Proof of Lemma 2. For $k = 1, 2, \ldots, n$,

$$r(q_k x_k^r - aq_k x_k^s - bq_k) \geq 0, \tag{7}$$

from which (6) follows. Equality holds in (6) if and only if it holds in (7) for $k = 1, 2, \ldots, n$, which is true if and only if each x_k is A or B.

Proof of Theorem 1. (a) *Assume that $rs \neq 0$.* For every $(x_1, x_2, \ldots, x_n) \in I$ we have, by Lemma 2,

$$M_s(x_1, x_2, \ldots, x_n) - M_r(x_1, x_2, \ldots, x_n) \leq \left[\sum_{k=1}^{n} q_k x_k^s\right]^{1/s}$$

$$- \left[a\left(\sum_{k=1}^{n} q_k x_k^s\right) + b\right]^{1/r}$$

$$= h\left(\sum_{k=1}^{n} q_k x_k^s\right),$$

equality holding if and only if each x_k is A or B. Let x^* be such that

$$x^* \in \bar{J}, \qquad h(x^*) = \max\{h(x) : x \in \bar{J}\}.$$

With θ given by (5), we have throughout I,

$$M_s(x_1, x_2, \ldots, x_n) - M_r(x_1, x_2, \ldots, x_n) \leq h(x^*)$$
$$= h[\theta B^s + (1 - \theta)A^s]$$
$$= [\theta B^s + (1 - \theta)A^s]^{1/s} - \{a[\theta B^s + (1 - \theta)A^s] + b\}^{1/r}$$
$$= [\theta B^s + (1 - \theta)A^s]^{1/s} - [\theta(aB^s + b) + (1 - \theta)(aA^s + b)]^{1/r}$$
$$= [\theta B^s + (1 - \theta)A^s]^{1/s} - [\theta B^r + (1 - \theta)A^r]^{1/r}.$$

Let us prove now the uniqueness of x^*. For every $x \in J$, we have $h(x) > 0$, whereas $h(A^s) = h(B^s) = 0$. So $x^* \in J$, and $h'(x^*) = 0$. Suppose x_1^* and x_2^* ($> x_1^*$) were such that

$$x_j^* \in \bar{J}, \qquad h(x_j^*) = \max\{h(x) : x \in \bar{J}\}, \qquad j = 1, 2.$$

Then $h'(x_j^*) = 0$, $x_j^* \in J$, $j = 1, 2$. Now, throughout J,

$$h'(x) = s^{-1}x^{(1/s)-1} - ar^{-1}(ax + b)^{(1/r)-1},$$
$$h''(x) = s^{-1}(s^{-1} - 1)x^{(1/s)-2} - a^2r^{-1}(r^{-1} - 1)(ax + b)^{(1/r)-2}.$$

So at every point of J where $h'(x) = 0$, we have

$$h''(x) = s^{-1}x^{(1/s)-2}[(s^{-1} - 1) - a(r^{-1} - 1)(ax + b)^{-1}x]$$
$$= s^{-1}x^{(1/s)-2}(ax + b)^{-1}[(s^{-1} - 1)(ax + b) - a(r^{-1} - 1)x]$$
$$= s^{-1}x^{(1/s)-2}(ax + b)^{-1}[a(s^{-1} - r^{-1})x + b(s^{-1} - 1)].$$

Now the expression in the last square brackets times s^{-1} is ≤ 0 at x_1^* and at x_2^*. Consequently $h''(x) < 0$ at every point x of (x_1^*, x_2^*) where $h'(x) = 0$.

Let x^{**} be a point in $[x_1^*, x_2^*]$ where $h(x)$ attains its minimum in $[x_1^*, x_2^*]$. Then $x_1^* < x^{**} < x_2^*$, $h'(x^{**}) = 0$, $h''(x^{**}) \geq 0$, contradicting the statement just made.

Suppose that equality holds in (3) for some $(x_1, x_2, \ldots, x_n) \in I$. Then first of all, each x_k must be A or B. Secondly, we must have $h(\sum_{k=1}^n q_k x_k^s) = h(x^*)$, and consequently $\sum_{k=1}^n q_k x_k^s = x^*$. Let $k_1, k_2, \ldots, k_p$ ($k_1 < k_2 \cdots < k_p$) be those elements k of $\{1, 2, \ldots, n\}$ for which $x_k = B$. Then $x^* = (\sum_{m=1}^p q_{k_m})B^s + (1 - \sum_{m=1}^p q_{k_m})A^s$, and consequently, $\sum_{m=1}^p q_{k_m} = \theta$.

Conversely, suppose that $(x_1, x_2, \ldots, x_n) \in I$ is such that there exists a subsequence $(k_1, k_2, \ldots, k_p)$ of $(1, 2, \ldots, n)$ such that $\sum_{m=1}^p q_{k_m} = \theta$, $x_{k_m} = B$ ($m = 1, 2, \ldots, p$), and $x_k = A$ for every k distinct from all k_m. Then $x^* = \sum_{k=1}^n q_k x_k^s$, and consequently

$$M_s(x_1, x_2, \ldots, x_n) - M_r(x_1, x_2, \ldots, x_n) = h\left(\sum_{k=1}^n q_k x_k^s\right) = h(x^*)$$
$$= [\theta B^s + (1 - \theta)A^s]^{1/s}$$
$$- [\theta B^r + (1 - \theta)A^r]^{1/r}.$$

Assume now that $s \geq 1$. We shall prove that x^* is the unique point of J where $h'(x)$ vanishes. Suppose y^* was another such point. Now $a(s^{-1} - r^{-1}) < 0$ and $b(s^{-1} - 1) \leq 0$. Therefore $h''(x) < 0$ at every point of K where $h'(x) = 0$. Here K denotes the open interval joining x^* to y^*, and $\bar{K}$ the closure of K. In particular, x^* and y^* are local maxima of $h(x)$. Let z^* be a point of $\bar{K}$ where $h(x)$ attains its minimum in $\bar{K}$. Then $z^* \in K$, and consequently $h'(z^*) = 0$, $h''(z^*) \geq 0$, contradicting a statement just made.

(b) *Assume that* $r = 0$. If $A < x < B$, and $q > 0$, then

$$x^q = \left[\frac{x^s - A^s}{B^s - A^s} B^s + \frac{B^s - x^s}{B^s - A^s} A^s \right]^{q/s} > B^{q(x^s - A^s)/(B^s - A^s)} A^{q(B^s - x^s)/(B^s - A^s)}.$$

$$(8)$$

If $x = A$ or $x = B$, then (8) holds with $>$ replaced by $=$. Thus, for every $(x_1, x_2, \ldots, x_n) \in I$,

$$\prod_{k=1}^{n} x_k^{q_k} \geq B^{[(\sum_{k=1}^{n} q_k x_k^s) - A^s]/(B^s - A^s)} A^{(B^s - \sum_{k=1}^{n} q_k x_k^s)/(B^s - A^s)},$$

equality holding if and only if each x_k is A or B. So for every $(x_1, \ldots, x_n) \in I$,

$$M_s(x_1, x_2, \ldots, x_n) - M_0(x_1, x_2, \ldots, x_n) = \left(\sum_{k=1}^{n} q_k x_k^s \right)^{1/s} - \prod_{k=1}^{n} x_k^{q_k}$$

$$\leq \left(\sum_{k=1}^{n} q_k x_k^s \right)^{1/s} - B^{[(\sum_{k=1}^{n} q_k x_k^s) - A^s]/(B^s - A^s)} A^{(B^s - \sum_{k=1}^{n} q_k x_k^s)/(B^s - A^s)}$$

$$= h\left(\sum_{k=1}^{n} q_k x_k^s \right),$$

equality holding if and only if each x_k is A or B. Let x^* be such that

$$x^* \in \bar{J}, \qquad h(x^*) = \max\{h(x) : x \in \bar{J}\}.$$

With θ given by (5), we have, throughout I,

$$M_s(x_1, x_2, \ldots, x_n) - M_0(x_1, x_2, \ldots, x_n)$$
$$\leq h(x^*) = h(\theta B^s + (1 - \theta)A^s) = [\theta B^s + (1 - \theta)A^s]^{1/s} - B^\theta A^{1-\theta}.$$

We prove now the uniqueness of x^*. If $A^s < x < B^s$, then

$$x = \frac{x - A^s}{B^s - A^s} B^s + \frac{B^s - x}{B^s - A^s} A^s > B^{s(x - A^s)/(B^s - A^s)} A^{s(B^s - x)/(B^s - A^s)}$$

$$= A^s (B/A)^{s(x - A^s)/(B^s - A^s)},$$

and so $h(x) > 0$. Also $h(A^s) = h(B^s) = 0$. So $A^s < x^* < B^s$, and $h'(x^*) = 0$.

Suppose x_1* and x_2* ($>x_1*$) were such that

$$x_j* \in \bar{J}, \qquad h(x_j*) = \max\{h(x) : x \in \bar{J}\}, \quad j = 1, 2.$$

Then $h'(x_j*) = 0$, $x_j* \in J$, $j = 1, 2$. One easily finds that at every point of J where $h'(x) = 0$ we have

$$h''(x) = s^{-1}x^{(1/s)-2}\left[(s^{-1} - 1) - x\,\frac{\log(B/A)}{B^s - A^s}\right].$$

Now the expression in the square brackets is ≤ 0 at x_1* and at x_2*. Consequently, $h''(x) < 0$ at every point x of (x_1*, x_2*) where $h'(x) = 0$. We reach from here a contradiction as in part (a).

Also, the necessary and sufficient condition for equality in (3) for a point of I is proved as in part (a).

Suppose that $s \geq 1$. Suppose that some $y*$ ($\in J$, $\neq x*$) was, like $x*$, a zero of h'. Then for some $x** \in (x*, y*)$ we would have $h''(x**) = 0$. This is, however, impossible, since $h''(x) < 0$ throughout the positive x-axis.

(c) *Assume, finally, that* $s = 0$. The proof is analogous to that in case (b).

We give now another proof of Theorem 1, under the additional assumption $s \geq 1$. We shall assume also in the proof that $n > 1$.

For every $(x_1, x_2, \ldots, x_n) \in I$, let

$$F(x_1, x_2, \ldots, x_n) = M_s(x_1, x_2, \ldots, x_n) - M_r(x_1, x_2, \ldots, x_n).$$

(A) *Assume that* $r \neq 0$. Let $X* = (x_1*, x_2*, \ldots, x_n*) \in I$ be such that $F(X*) = \max\{F(X) : X \in I\}$. We shall show that $X*$ is a vertex of I. Indeed, suppose this is not the case, and let j be such that $A < x_j* < B$.

For every $x \in [A, B]$, let

$$f(x) = F(x_1*, x_2*, \ldots, x_{j-1}^*, x, x_{j+1}^*, \ldots, x_n*).$$

Then

$$f(x_j*) = \max\{f(x) : A \leq x \leq B\}, \tag{9}$$

and therefore $f'(x_j*) = 0$. Now, throughout (A, B),

$$f'(x) = q_j x^{s-1}\left[q_j x^s + \sum_{\substack{k=1 \\ k \neq j}}^{n} q_k x_k^{*s}\right]^{(1/s)-1} - q_j x^{r-1}\left[q_j x^r + \sum_{\substack{k=1 \\ k \neq j}}^{n} q_k x_k^{*r}\right]^{(1/r)-1}.$$

So

$$x_j^{*r-1}\left[\sum_{k=1}^{n} q_k x_k^{*r}\right]^{(1/r)-1} = x_j^{*s-1}\left[\sum_{k=1}^{n} q_k x_k^{*s}\right]^{(1/s)-1}. \tag{10}$$

Throughout (A, B),

$$f''(x) = (1-s)q_j x^{s-2} \left[q_j x^s + \sum_{\substack{k=1 \\ k \neq j}}^{n} q_k x_k^{*s} \right]^{(1/s)-1} \left[\frac{q_j x^s}{q_j x^s + \sum_{\substack{k=1 \\ k \neq j}}^{n} q_k x_k^{*s}} - 1 \right]$$

$$- (1-r)q_j x^{r-2} \left[q_j x^r + \sum_{\substack{k=1 \\ k \neq j}}^{n} q_k x_k^{*r} \right]^{(1/r)-1} \left[\frac{q_j x^r}{q_j x^r + \sum_{\substack{k=1 \\ k \neq j}}^{n} q_k x_k^{*r}} - 1 \right].$$

In particular, by virtue of (10),

$$f''(x_j^*) = q_j x_j^{*s-2} \left[\sum_{k=1}^{n} q_k x_k^{*s} \right]^{(1/s)-1}$$

$$\times \left\{ (1-s) \left[\frac{q_j x_j^{*s}}{\sum_{k=1}^{n} q_k x_k^{*s}} - 1 \right] - (1-r) \left[\frac{q_j x_j^{*r}}{\sum_{k=1}^{n} q_k x_k^{*r}} - 1 \right] \right\}$$

$$= q_j x_j^{*s-2} \left\{ \sum_{k=1}^{n} q_k x_k^{*s} \right\}^{(1/s)-1} \left\{ s - r + \frac{(1-s)q_j x_j^{*s}}{\sum_{k=1}^{n} q_k x_k^{*s}} - \frac{(1-r)q_j x_j^{*r}}{\sum_{k=1}^{n} q_k x_k^{*r}} \right\}.$$

$$(11)$$

From (10) and

$$\left(\sum_{k=1}^{n} q_k x_k^{*r} \right)^{-1/r} \geq \left(\sum_{k=1}^{n} q_k x_k^{*s} \right)^{-1/s},$$

we get

$$\frac{x_j^{*r}}{\sum_{k=1}^{n} q_k x_k^{*r}} \geq \frac{x_j^{*s}}{\sum_{k=1}^{n} q_k x_k^{*s}}.$$

Thus, from (11) we obtain

$$f''(x_j^*) \geq q_j x_j^{*s-2} \left[\sum_{k=1}^{n} q_k x_k^{*s} \right]^{(1/s)-1} \left\{ s - r + [(1-s)-(1-r)] \frac{q_j x_j^{*r}}{\sum_{k=1}^{n} q_k x_k^{*r}} \right\} > 0.$$

Consequently, $f(x)$ has at x_j^* a local minimum, contradicting (9).

For every $x \in [0, 1]$, let

$$G(x) = [xB^s + (1-x)A^s]^{1/s} - [xB^r + (1-x)A^r]^{1/r}.$$

Since X^* is a vertex of I, $F(X^*) = G(u^*)$ for some $u^* \in [0, 1]$. Thus, for every $X \in I$, $F(X) \leq G(u^*)$; and for every point X of I which is not a vertex, $F(X) < G(u^*)$.

Since $G(0) = G(1) = 0$, there must be in $(0, 1)$ a zero of

$$G'(x) \equiv A\left\{\frac{\gamma^s - 1}{s}[x(\gamma^s - 1) + 1]^{(1/s)-1} - \frac{\gamma^r - 1}{r}[x(\gamma^r - 1) + 1]^{(1/r)-1}\right\},$$

where $\gamma = B/A$.

Throughout $(0, 1)$ we have

$$G''(x)/A = s^{-1}(s^{-1} - 1)(\gamma^s - 1)^2[x(\gamma^s - 1) + 1]^{(1/s)-2}$$
$$- r^{-1}(r^{-1} - 1)(\gamma^r - 1)^2[x(\gamma^r - 1) + 1]^{(1/r)-2}.$$

Suppose that $0 < x_0 < 1$ and $G'(x_0) = 0$. Then

$$G''(x_0)/A = (\gamma^s - 1)s^{-1}[x_0(\gamma^s - 1) + 1]^{(1/s)-1}\{(1 - s)s^{-1}(\gamma^s - 1)[x_0(\gamma^s - 1)$$
$$+ 1]^{-1} - (1 - r)r^{-1}(\gamma^r - 1)[x_0(\gamma^r - 1) + 1]^{-1}\}. \qquad (12)$$

From $G'(x_0) = 0$ and $[x_0\gamma^s + (1 - x_0)]^{-1/s} < [x_0\gamma^r + (1 - x_0)]^{-1/r}$, one obtains

$$s^{-1}(\gamma^s - 1)[x_0(\gamma^s - 1) + 1]^{-1} < r^{-1}(\gamma^r - 1)[x_0(\gamma^r - 1) + 1]^{-1}.$$

Consequently, if $r \leq 1$, we have by (12),

$$\frac{G''(x_0)}{A} \leq \frac{s^{-1}(\gamma^s - 1)[x_0(\gamma^s - 1) + 1]^{(1/s)-1}[1 - s - (1 - r)]s^{-1}(\gamma^s - 1)}{x_0(\gamma^s - 1) + 1} < 0.$$

Also, if $r > 1$, then since the function $x/(x + 1)$ is strictly increasing for $x > 0$, we have, again by (12),

$$G''(x_0)/A < s^{-1}(\gamma^s - 1)[x_0(\gamma^s - 1) + 1]^{s-1}\{(1 - s)s^{-1}(\gamma^s - 1)[x_0(\gamma^s - 1)$$
$$+ 1]^{-1} - r^{-1}(1 - r)(\gamma^s - 1)[x_0(\gamma^s - 1) + 1]^{-1}\} < 0.$$

Thus, invariably $G''(x_0) < 0$.

Suppose there exist α, β with $0 < \alpha < \beta < 1$, $G'(\alpha) = G'(\beta) = 0$. Let δ be such that $\alpha \leq \delta \leq \beta$, $G(\delta) = \min\{G(u) : \alpha \leq u \leq \beta\}$. Since $G''(\alpha) < 0$, $G''(\beta) < 0$, we must have $\alpha < \delta < \beta$. Consequently $G'(\delta) = 0$. But this implies $G''(\delta) < 0$, which is incompatible with the definition of δ. Consequently there exists a unique solution θ of $G'(x) = 0$ in $(0, 1)$, and $G(x) < G(\theta)$ for every $x \in [0, 1]$ distinct from θ. Now, for every $x \in J$, $h(x) = G((x - A^s)/(B^s - A^s))$. Consequently there is a unique point x^* in $\bar{J}$ where $h(x)$ attains its maximum in $\bar{J}$, and $\theta = (x^* - A^s)/(B^s - A^s)$. Since $\Delta = G(\theta)$, (3) follows, as well as the necessary and sufficient condition for equality in (3), given in Theorem 1. Finally, x^* is clearly the unique solution of $h'(x) = 0$ in J.

(B) *Assume that* $r = 0$. The proof is analogous to that in case (A), with $G(x)$ being now, for $0 \leq x \leq 1$, $[xB^s + (1 - x)A^s]^{1/s} - B^xA^{1-x}$.

Remark. We repeat here explicitly, for subsequent use, that if $r \neq 0$, $s \geq 1$, then θ of Theorem 1 is the unique solution in $(0, 1)$ of

$$[(\gamma^s - 1)/s][x(\gamma^s - 1) + 1]^{(1/s)-1} - [(\gamma^r - 1)/r][x(\gamma^r - 1) + 1]^{(1/r)-1} = 0$$

with $\gamma = B/A$. Similarly, if $r = 0$, $s \geq 1$, then θ of Theorem 1 is the unique solution in $(0, 1)$ of

$$[(\gamma^s - 1)/s][x(\gamma^s - 1) + 1]^{(1/s)-1} - \gamma^x \log \gamma = 0.$$

Example 1. Let $0 < A < B$, set $\gamma = B/A$, and let I denote as before the n-dimensional cube $\{(x_1, x_2, \ldots, x_n) : A \leq x_k \leq B, k = 1, 2, \ldots, n\}$. Then by Theorem 1, and by the preceding Remark, we have, throughout I,

$$\sum_{j=1}^{n} q_j x_j - \left(\sum_{j=1}^{n} \frac{q_j}{x_j} \right)^{-1} \leq \theta B + (1 - \theta)A - \left[\frac{\theta}{B} + \frac{1-\theta}{A} \right]^{-1},$$

where θ is the unique solution in $(0, 1)$ of

$$\gamma - 1 + (\gamma^{-1} - 1)[x(\gamma^{-1} - 1) + 1]^{-2} = 0.$$

Solving for θ and substituting in the last inequality, one gets, with a little computing, that throughout I,

$$\sum_{j=1}^{n} q_j x_j - \left(\sum_{j=1}^{n} \frac{q_j}{x_j} \right)^{-1} \leq (B^{1/2} - A^{1/2})^2. \tag{13}$$

Equality holds in (13) for a point $(x_1, x_2, \ldots, x_n) \in I$ if and only if there exists a subsequence $(k_1, k_2, \ldots, k_p)$ of $(1, 2, \ldots, n)$ such that

$$\sum_{m=1}^{p} q_{k_m} = (1 + \gamma^{-1/2})^{-1} (= \theta),$$

$x_{k_m} = B \ (m = 1, 2, \ldots, p)$, and $x_k = A$ for every k distinct from all k_m.

Example 2. A, B, γ, and I being as in Example 1, we have throughout I,

$$\left(\sum_{j=1}^{n} q_j x_j^2 \right)^{1/2} - \sum_{j=1}^{n} q_j x_j \leq [\theta B^2 + (1 - \theta)A^2]^{1/2} - [\theta B + (1 - \theta)A],$$

where θ is the unique solution in $(0, 1)$ of

$$\tfrac{1}{2}(\gamma^2 - 1)[x(\gamma^2 - 1) + 1]^{-1/2} - (\gamma - 1) = 0.$$

A short calculation yields that, throughout I,

$$\left(\sum_{j=1}^{n} q_j x_j^2 \right)^{1/2} - \sum_{j=1}^{n} q_j x_j \leq \frac{(B - A)^2}{4(B + A)}. \tag{14}$$

Equality holds in (14) for a point $(x_1, x_2, \ldots, x_n) \in I$ if and only if there exists a subsequence $(k_1, k_2, \ldots, k_p)$ of $(1, 2, \ldots, n)$ such that

$$\sum_{m=1}^{p} q_{km} = \frac{B + 3A}{4(B + A)} \, (=\theta),$$

$x_{k_m} = B \, (m = 1, 2, \ldots, p)$, and $x_k = A$ for every k distinct from all k_m.

5

Let $0 < m_1 \le a_j \le M_1$, $0 < m_2 \le b_j \le M_2$, $j = 1, 2, \ldots, n$, $n \ge 1$, $m_1 m_2 < M_1 M_2$, and let $\xi_1, \xi_2, \ldots, \xi_n$ be real numbers $\ne 0$. Set $q_j = a_j b_j \xi_j^2 / \sum_{k=1}^{n} a_k b_k \xi_k^2$, $x_j = a_j/b_j \, (j = 1, 2, \ldots, n)$. Observe that

$$0 < \frac{m_1}{M_2} \le x_j \le \frac{M_1}{m_2} \qquad (j = 1, 2, \ldots, n).$$

By (13),

$$\frac{\sum_{j=1}^{n} a_j^2 \xi_j^2}{\sum_{j=1}^{n} a_j b_j \xi_j^2} \frac{\sum_{j=1}^{n} a_j b_j \xi_j^2}{\sum_{j=1}^{n} b_j^2 \xi_j^2} \le \left[\left(\frac{M_1}{m_2} \right)^{1/2} - \left(\frac{m_1}{M_2} \right)^{1/2} \right]^2. \tag{15}$$

Equality holds in (15) if and only if there exists a subsequence $(k_1, k_2, \ldots, k_p)$ of $(1, 2, \ldots, n)$ such that

$$\sum_{\mu=1}^{p} a_{k_\mu} b_{k_\mu} \xi_{k_\mu}^2 = \left[1 + \left(\frac{m_1 m_2}{M_1 M_2} \right)^{1/2} \right]^{-1} \sum_{j=1}^{n} a_j b_j \xi_j^2, \tag{*}$$

$a_{k_\mu} = M_1$, $b_{k_\mu} = m_2 \, (\mu = 1, 2, \ldots, p)$, and $a_k = m_1$, $b_k = M_2$

for every k distinct from all k_μ.

The system of conditions (*) is easily seen to be equivalent to

$$\sum_{\mu=1}^{p} \xi_{k_\mu}^2 = \left[1 + \left(\frac{M_1}{m_1} \right)^{1/2} \left(\frac{m_2}{M_2} \right)^{3/2} \right]^{-1} \sum_{j=1}^{n} \xi_j^2, \tag{**}$$

$a_{k_\mu} = M_1$, $b_{k_\mu} = m_2 \, (\mu = 1, 2, \ldots, p)$, and $a_k = m_1$, $b_k = M_2$

for every k distinct from all k_μ.

Since the left-hand side of (15) is ≥ 0 by Cauchy's inequality, (15) may be considered a "complementary" inequality to Cauchy's. (The term "complementary inequality" is due to Diaz and Metcalf; we use it in a slightly more general sense.)

Taking $\xi_1 = \xi_2 = \cdots = \xi_n = 1$, we obtain

$$\frac{\sum\limits_{j=1}^{n} a_j^2}{\sum\limits_{j=1}^{n} a_j b_j} - \frac{\sum\limits_{j=1}^{n} a_j b_j}{\sum\limits_{j=1}^{n} b_j^2} \le \left[\left(\frac{M_1}{m_2} \right)^{1/2} - \left(\frac{m_1}{M_2} \right)^{1/2} \right]^2,$$

equality holding if and only if there exists a subsequence $(k_1, k_2, \ldots, k_p)$ of $(1, 2, \ldots, n)$ such that $n/p = 1 + (M_1/m_1)^{1/2}(m_2/M_2)^{3/2}$, $a_{k_\mu} = M_1$, $b_{k_\mu} = m_2$ $(\mu = 1, 2, \ldots, p)$, and $a_k = m_1$, $b_k = M_2$ for every k distinct from all k_μ.

6

We give now a complement to Hölder's inequality.

Theorem 2. *Let $p > 1$, $(1/p) + (1/q) = 1$, $0 < A < B$, and let $a_1, a_2, \ldots, a_n$, $b_1, b_2, \ldots, b_n$ $(n \ge 1)$ be positive numbers with $A \le a_j^{1/q}/b_j^{1/p} \le B$ $(j = 1, 2, \ldots, n)$. Set $\gamma = B/A$. Then*

$$0 \le \left[\left(\sum_{j=1}^{n} a_j{}^p \right) \Big/ \sum_{j=1}^{n} a_j b_j \right]^{1/p} - \left[\left(\sum_{j=1}^{n} a_j b_j \right) \Big/ \sum_{j=1}^{n} b_j{}^q \right]^{1/q}$$

$$\le [\theta B^p + (1 - \theta)A^p]^{1/p} - [\theta B^{-q} + (1 - \theta)A^{-q}]^{-1/q}, \qquad (16)$$

where θ is the unique solution in $(0, 1)$ of

$$q(\gamma^p - 1)[x(\gamma^p - 1) + 1]^{-1/q} + p(\gamma^{-q} - 1)[x(\gamma^{-q} - 1) + 1]^{-(1/q)-1} = 0.$$

Equality on the right in (16) holds if and only if there exists a subsequence $(k_1, k_2, \ldots, k_t)$ of $(1, 2, \ldots, n)$ such that $\left(\sum_{m=1}^{t} a_{k_m} b_{k_m} \right) / \sum_{j=1}^{n} a_j b_j = \theta$, $a_{k_m}^{1/q}/b_{k_m}^{1/p} = B$ $(m = 1, 2, \ldots, t)$, and $a_k^{1/q}/b_k^{1/p} = A$ for every k distinct from all k_m. Equality on the left in (16) holds if and only if all the ratios $a_j^{1/q}/b_j^{1/p}$ are equal.

Proof. In Theorem 1 set $r = -q$, $s = p$, $q_j = a_j b_j / \sum_{k=1}^{n} a_k b_k$. Then for $x_j = a_j^{1/q}/b_j^{1/p}$ $(j = 1, 2, \ldots, n)$ we have by (3)

$$0 \le M_p(x_1, x_2, \ldots, x_n) - M_{-q}(x_1, x_2, \ldots, x_n) \le \Delta. \qquad (17)$$

Equality on the left holds if and only if all the x_j are equal. The difference in (17) equals the middle member of (16). The number Δ, by (4) and by the Remark in Sec. 4, is the right-hand member of (16). The necessary and sufficient condition in Theorem 2 for equality on the right in (16) follows, too, from Theorem 1. The inequality on the left in (16) is, of course, just the Hölder inequality, and the condition given for equality there is just the familiar condition for equality in the Hölder inequality.

7

Let N denote an arbitrary positive integer which will be held fixed. Let P_N denote the set of all $N \times N$ matrices over the field of complex numbers which are Hermitian and positive-definite. The term "vector" will refer to a column vector

$$\begin{pmatrix} x_1 \\ x_2 \\ \vdots \\ x_N \end{pmatrix}$$

over the field of complex numbers. If X and Y are vectors, (X, Y) will denote their inner product.

Let $A \in P_N$, and let X be a vector of length 1. For every eigenvalue λ of A, let $\sum_\lambda$ consist of the null vector and of all eigenvectors of A corresponding to λ. Let $\lambda_1, \lambda_2, \ldots, \lambda_n$ be all the distinct eigenvalues λ of A for which $\bar{X}$, the conjugate of X, is not orthogonal to $\sum_\lambda$. For $j = 1, 2, \ldots, n$, let η_j be the norm of the projection of $\bar{X}$ on $\sum_{\lambda_j}$. Then each η_j is positive and $\sum_{j=1}^n \eta_j^2 = 1$. Furthermore, for every real $r \neq 0$, we have

$$(A^r X, X) = \sum_{j=1}^n \eta_j^2 \lambda_j^r, \tag{18}$$

so that $(A^r X, X)^{1/r}$ is $(\sum_{j=1}^n \eta_j^2 \lambda_j^r)^{1/r}$, a mean of order r.

Since

$$\lim_{r \to 0} \left(\sum_{j=1}^n \eta_j^2 \lambda_j^r \right)^{1/r} = \prod_{j=1}^n \lambda_j^{\eta_j^2},$$

we define

$$(A^0 X, X)^{1/0} = \prod_{j=1}^n \lambda_j^{\eta_j^2}. \tag{19}$$

8

We can now give matrix interpretations to our preceding results.

Theorem 3. *Let A be a matrix of P_N, let X be a vector of length 1, and let $\lambda_1, \lambda_2, \ldots, \lambda_n, \eta_1, \eta_2, \ldots, \eta_n$ be as in Sec. 7. Let r, s, α, β be given reals $(0 < \alpha < \beta, r < s)$ and suppose $\alpha \leq \lambda_j \leq \beta, j = 1, 2, \ldots, n$. Then*

$$0 \leq (A^s X, X)^{1/s} - (A^r X, X)^{1/r} \leq \Delta \tag{20}$$

where Δ is

$$[\theta\beta^s + (1-\theta)\alpha^s]^{1/s} - [\theta\beta^r + (1-\theta)\alpha^r]^{1/r} \qquad if \quad rs \neq 0,$$

$$[\theta\beta^s + (1-\theta)\alpha^s]^{1/s} - \beta^\theta\alpha^{1-\theta} \qquad if \quad r = 0,$$

and

$$\beta^\theta\alpha^{1-\theta} - [\theta\beta^r + (1-\theta)\alpha^r]^{1/r} \qquad if \quad s = 0.$$

θ is defined as follows. Let (x denoting a real variable)

$$h(x) \equiv x^{1/s} - (ax + b)^{1/r}$$

with

$$a = \frac{\beta^r - \alpha^r}{\beta^s - \alpha^s}, \qquad b = \frac{\beta^s \alpha^r - \beta^r \alpha^s}{\beta^s - \alpha^s}, \qquad \text{if} \quad rs \neq 0,$$

$$h(x) \equiv x^{1/s} - \alpha(\beta/\alpha)^{(x-\alpha^s)/(\beta^s-\alpha^s)} \qquad , \qquad \text{if} \quad r = 0,$$

and

$$h(x) \equiv -x^{1/r} + \alpha(\beta/\alpha)^{(x-\alpha^r)/(\beta^r-\alpha^r)} \qquad , \qquad \text{if} \quad s = 0.$$

Let J denote the open interval joining α^s to β^s if $s \neq 0$, and let J be the open interval (β^r, α^r) if $s = 0$. Let $\bar{J}$ be the closure of J. Then there is a unique $x^* \in \bar{J}$ where $h(x)$ attains its maximum in $\bar{J}$. This x^* lies in J. We set

$$\theta = \frac{x^* - \alpha^s}{\beta^s - \alpha^s} \qquad \text{if} \quad s \neq 0,$$

and

$$\theta = \frac{x^* - \alpha^r}{\beta^r - \alpha^r} \qquad \text{if} \quad s = 0.$$

Equality on the left in (20) holds if and only if all λ_k are equal. Equality on the right in (20) holds if and only if there exists a subsequence $(k_1, k_2, \ldots, k_p)$ of $(1, 2, \ldots, n)$ such that $\sum_{m=1}^{p} \eta_{k_m}^2 = \theta$, $\lambda_{k_m} = \beta$ ($m = 1, 2, \ldots, p$), and $\lambda_k = \alpha$ for every k distinct from all k_m. If $s \geq 1$, then (i) x^* is the unique solution of $h'(x) = 0$ in J, (ii) θ is the unique solution in $(0, 1)$ of

$$\frac{\gamma^s - 1}{s} [x(\gamma^s - 1) + 1]^{(1/s)-1} - \frac{\gamma^r - 1}{r} [x(\gamma^r - 1) + 1]^{(1/r)-1} = 0$$

if $r \neq 0$, (iii) θ is the unique solution in $(0, 1)$ of

$$\frac{\gamma^s - 1}{s} [x(\gamma^s - 1) + 1]^{(1/s)-1} - \gamma^x \log \gamma = 0$$

if $r = 0$. (Here $\gamma = \beta/\alpha$).

Theorem 3 follows immediately from Sec. 1, from Theorem 1, and from the Remark in Sec. 4, by virtue of (18) and (19).

In particular, from Example 1 we obtain:

Example 3. Let A be a matrix of P_N, let X be a vector of length 1, let $\lambda_1, \lambda_2, \ldots, \lambda_n, \eta_1, \eta_2, \ldots, \eta_n$ be as in Sec. 7, and suppose $\alpha \leq \lambda_j \leq \beta$, $j = 1, 2, \ldots, n$, where $0 < \alpha < \beta$. Then

$$(AX, X) - (A^{-1}X, X)^{-1} \leq (\beta^{1/2} - \alpha^{1/2})^2.$$

Equality holds if and only if there exists a subsequence $(k_1, k_2, \ldots, k_p)$ of $(1, 2, \ldots, n)$ such that $\sum_{m=1}^{p} \eta_{k_m}^2 = (1 + \gamma^{-1/2})^{-1}$, $\lambda_{k_m} = \beta$ $(m = 1, 2, \ldots, p)$, and $\lambda_k = \alpha$ for every k distinct from all k_m. (Again, $\gamma = \beta/\alpha$).

Similarly one gets at once a matrix version of Example 2.

As an application of Example 3 we have the following result which was motivated by Theorem 2 of [10].

Theorem 4. *Let A and B be commuting matrices of P_N. Let $\lambda_1, \lambda_2,$ $\ldots, \lambda_N$ $(\lambda_1 \geq \lambda_2 \geq \cdots \geq \lambda_N)$ be the eigenvalues of A (each appearing as many times as its multiplicity), and similarly let $\mu_1, \mu_2, \ldots, \mu_N$ $(\mu_1 \geq \mu_2 \geq \cdots \geq \mu_N)$ be the eigenvalues of B. Let X be an arbitrary nonnull vector. Then*

$$\frac{(AX, AX)}{(AX, BX)} - \frac{(AX, BX)}{(BX, BX)} \leq \left[\left(\frac{\lambda_1}{\mu_N} \right)^{1/2} - \left(\frac{\lambda_N}{\mu_1} \right)^{1/2} \right]^2. \tag{21}$$

Observe that the left-hand side of (21) is ≥ 0 by the Cauchy–Schwarz inequality.

Proof of Theorem 4. We may suppose $\lambda_N \mu_N < \lambda_1 \mu_1$, for otherwise, $\lambda_1 = \lambda_N$, $\mu_1 = \mu_N$, $A = \lambda_1 I$, $B = \mu_1 I$ (I being the unit $N \times N$ matrix), and (21) trivially holds.

Consider the vector $Y = \|(AB)^{1/2}X\|^{-1} (AB)^{1/2}X$. Since the eigenvalues λ of AB^{-1} satisfy

$$\lambda_N/\mu_1 \leq \lambda \leq \lambda_1/\mu_N,$$

we have by Example 3,

$$(AB^{-1}Y, Y) - ((AB^{-1})^{-1}Y, Y)^{-1} \leq \left[\left(\frac{\lambda_1}{\mu_N} \right)^{1/2} - \left(\frac{\lambda_N}{\mu_1} \right)^{1/2} \right]^2.$$

Substituting for Y its explicit form, one obtains (21).

Theorem 5. *Assume the hypotheses of Theorem 4, and suppose $\lambda_1 \mu_1 > \lambda_N \mu_N$. Let p (>1) and q be reals with $(1/p) + (1/q) = 1$. Set $\gamma = (\lambda_1/\lambda_N)^{1/q} \times (\mu_1/\mu_N)^{1/p}$. Then*

$$0 \leq [(A^p X, X)/(AX, BX)]^{1/p} - [(AX, BX)/(B^q X, X)]^{1/q}$$
$$\leq [\theta \lambda_1^{p/q} \mu_N^{-1} + (1 - \theta)\lambda_N^{p/q} \mu_1^{-1}]^{1/p} - [\theta \lambda_1^{-1} \mu_N^{q/p} + (1 - \theta)\lambda_N^{-1} \mu_1^{q/p}]^{-1/q}, \tag{22}$$

where θ is the unique solution in $(0, 1)$ of

$$q(\gamma^p - 1)[x(\gamma^p - 1) + 1]^{-1/q} + p(\gamma^{-q} - 1)[x(\gamma^{-q} - 1) + 1]^{(-1/q)-1} = 0.$$

Proof. Set $s = p$, $r = -q$. Note that all eigenvalues λ of $C = A^{1/q}B^{-1/p}$ satisfy

$$\lambda_N^{1/q}\mu_1^{-1/p} \leq \lambda \leq \lambda_1^{1/q}\mu_N^{-1/p}.$$

With Y as in the last proof, we have

$$(C^sY, Y)^{1/s} - (C^rY, Y)^{1/r} = \left(\frac{(A^pX, X)}{(AX, BX)}\right)^{1/p} - \left(\frac{(AX, BX)}{(B^qX, X)}\right)^{1/q}.$$

Applying Theorem 3 to C and to Y, we obtain (22). Theorem 5 can be proved also by reducing (22) to (16).

If in the hypotheses of Theorem 5, instead of $\lambda_1\mu_1 > \lambda_N\mu_N$ one has $\lambda_1\mu_1 = \lambda_N\mu_N$, then as one easily sees, the left-hand inequality in (22) can be replaced by an equality.

The left-hand inequality in (22) can also be written

$$(AX, BX) \leq (A^pX, X)^{1/p}(B^qX, X)^{1/q}$$

and may be considered as a matrix version of Hölder's inequality.

REFERENCES

[1] Beckenbach, E. F., On the inequality of Kantorovich, *Amer. Math. Monthly* **71**, 606–619 (1964).

[2] Beckenbach, E. F., A "workshop" on Minkowski's inequality, these Proceedings.

[3] Beckenbach, E. F., and Bellman, R., "Inequalities," 2nd revised printing. Springer, New York, 1965.

[4] Cargo, G. T., and Shisha, O., Bounds on ratios of means, *J. Res. Nat. Bur. Standards* **66B**, 169–170 (1962).

[5] Diaz, J. B., Goldman, A. J., and Metcalf, F. T., Equivalence of certain inequalities complementing those of Cauchy–Schwarz and Hölder, *J. Res. Nat. Bur. Standards* **68B**, 147–149 (1964).

[6] Diaz, J. B., and Metcalf, F. T., Stronger forms of a class of inequalities of G. Pólya–G. Szegö, and L. V. Kantorovich, *Bull. Amer. Math. Soc.* **69**, 415–418 (1963).

[7] Diaz, J. B., and Metcalf, F. T., Complementary inequalities I: Inequalities complementary to Cauchy's inequality for sums of real numbers, *J. Math. Anal. Appl.* **9**, 59–74 (1964).

[8] Diaz, J. B., and Metcalf, F. T., Inequalities complementary to Cauchy's inequality for sums of real numbers, these Proceedings.

[9] Goldman, A. J., A generalization of Rennie's inequality, *J. Res. Nat. Bur. Standards* **68B**, 59–63 (1964).

[10] Greub, W., and Rheinboldt, W., On a generalization of an inequality of L. V. Kantorovich, *Proc. Amer. Math. Soc.* **10**, 407–415 (1959).

[11] Hardy, G. H., Littlewood, J. E., and Pólya, G., "Inequalities," 2nd ed. Cambridge Univ. Press, London and New York, 1952.

[12] Marshall, A. W., and Olkin, I., Reversal of the Lyapunov, Hölder, and Minkowski inequalities and other extensions of the Kantorovich inequality, *J. Math. Anal. Appl.* **8**, 503–514 (1964).

[13] Mond, B., A matrix inequality including that of Kantorovich, *J. Math. Anal. Appl.* **13**, 49–52 (1966).

[14] Mond, B., An inequality for operators in a Hilbert space, *Pacific J. Math.* **18**, 161–163 (1966).

[15] Mond, B., and Shisha, O., A difference inequality for operators in Hilbert space, *in* "Blanch Anniversary Volume" (B. Mond, ed.). Aerospace Research Laboratories, Wright-Patterson Air Force Base, Ohio, 1967.

[16] Mond, B., and Shisha, O., Ratios of means and applications, these Proceedings.

[17] Pólya, G., and Szegö, G., "Aufgaben und Lehrsätze aus der Analysis," Vol. 1, pp. 57, 213–214. Springer, Berlin, 1925.

[18] Rennie, B. C., On a class of inequalities, *J. Austral. Math. Soc.* **3**, 442–448 (1963).

[19] Shisha, O., and Cargo, G. T., On comparable means, *Pacific J. Math.* **14**, 1053–1058 (1964).

[20] Shisha, O., and Mond, B., Differences of means, *Bull. Amer. Math. Soc.* **73**, 328–333 (1967).

Positive-Definite Matrices*

OLGA TAUSSKY
Department of Mathematics
California Institute of Technology
Pasadena, California

Inequalities between numbers start with $a > 0$. If we study inequalities between $n \times n$ matrices A, we can start by defining when is $A > 0$, where 0 now stands for the zero matrix. Two definitions come to one's mind:

(i) all elements in the matrix are > 0,
(ii) the matrix is hermitian and positive-definite.

In this lecture the second aspect will be followed and a positive-definite matrix so defined will be denoted by p.d.m.

However, this attitude does not ignore the first aspect completely. For some time already I have pointed to a number of facts in common to these two classes of matrices and I suggested that a unified treatment be sought. Actually some results are known showing that the operator defined by a nonnegative matrix and the operator defined by $F(X) = CXC^*$ can sometimes be given a unified treatment.

The best known p.d.m. is the unit matrix. Many interesting and attractive theorems and theories can be developed by replacing the unit matrix by a certain fixed p.d.m. This is done, e.g., in number theory, in differential geometry, or in the theory of partial differential equations. This immediately encourages a further step, namely the step to general symmetric matrices, e.g., the orthogonal transformations leave $\sum x_i^2$ unchanged, from this it is only one step to transformations which leave a p.d. form unchanged, and the next step is to take transformations which leave a general quadratic form invariant, like the Lorentz transformations which leave $x_1^2 + x_2^2 + x_3^2 - x_4^2$ invariant. But this is not the end of the road. Why stop at general symmetric matrices, why not take general matrices, particularly since every matrix is the sum of a symmetric and a skew-symmetric matrix? Correspondingly, e.g., the quadratic forms $x'Ax$, $A = A'$ have been extended to $x'Ax$ (or x^*Ax) which define the "field of values" of a matrix.

*This work was supported (in part) by the National Science Foundation Grant GP 3909 at the California Institute of Technology, and by the Fulbright Commission at the University of Vienna.

Every real p.d.m. is of the form XX' which means that the corresponding quadratic form is a sum of squares of linear forms. The study of p.d.m. comes therefore under the heading "sum of squares." It is known that this concept is of great importance, for instance in connection with the abstract concept of "ordering" in abstract fields, in connection with the study of spheres, with the Laplace operator, or with the norm definition in algebras, as with the complex numbers, quaternions, and Cayley numbers.

Great progress was made recently in the study of expressing 0 as a sum of squares in fields (see papers by Pfister).

In number theory sums of squares have been appreciated for a long time. It is well known that every positive rational integer is a sum of 4 squares and special facts hold for integers which are sums of 3, 2 or 1 squares. Similar problems arise in algebraic number fields. Quadratic residues and sums of squares mod p come under this heading too.

On the other hand, the number of theoretical problems which arise for p.d. integral matrices are truly enormous. There are the problems in the geometry of numbers when the defining region is given by a p.d. quadratic form. Even if a general convex domain is used instead, by a theorem of F. John, it has a unique inscribed and circumscribed ellipsoid of maximal, resp. minimal volume. Next we have the famous result of Minkowski that every p.d. unimodular matrix A of dimension ≤ 7 is of the form $A = XX'$ with X an integral $n \times n$ matrix. What happens for higher dimensions was investigated by Korkine and Zolotareff, Mordell, Chao Ko, and Kneser. If A is also a group matrix corresponding to the finite group G and $A = XX'$, X integral and $n \times n$, then it was shown that X itself is a group matrix for G (Taussky, Taussky and M. Newman, R. C. Thompson, M. Kneser.

If an $n \times n$ integral p.d.m. is not of the form XX' with X a square matrix, it may still be expressible in this form with X a rectangular integral matrix, say $n \times m$. More generally, the problem of expressing a matrix A in the form XBX' has been studied in full generality by Siegel where now A and B do not need to have the same dimension. This even includes the case where A is a number, i.e., a 1×1 matrix. The last problem, namely the "representation" of a positive number by a given p.d. quadratic form and the further problem of finding the number of all representations has led to an enormous literature. H. Braun evaluated Siegel's results for the case $n = 2$, $m \leq 8$, $A = I$. Mordell showed that every positive-definite $n \times n$ integral matrix is expressible as XX' with X an integral $n \times (n + 3)$ matrix, provided $n < 6$. For $n \geq 6$ there exist cases which cannot be expressed in the form XX' at all. Mordell's result concerning positive-definite binary forms which are of the form XX' with X a 2×4 integral matrix was reproved by Pall and Taussky who found all such representations. The number of these representations is a factorable function of the divisor of the form.

Special interest concerns p.d. integral forms which represent all positive integers, thus generalizing the result concerning the representation by four squares. Special results by Kloosterman, Linnik, Pall, Ramanujan could be cited here.

An application of unimodular integral p.d.m. was noticed independently by Faddeev and Taussky. It concerns the existence of integral symmetric $n \times n$ matrices with a given integral irreducible characteristic polynomial $f(x)$ of degree n. It can be shown that with every such matrix a p.d. integral unimodular matrix can be associated which is of the form TT', T integral and $n \times n$. Faddeev obtains this directly while Taussky studies all integral matrix roots of $f(x) = 0$. If A is one such root, then $S^{-1}AS$ is another one, if S is unimodular integral. The set of all $S^{-1}AS$ is called a class of matrices. Although A' is another root of $f(x) = 0$, it is not always in the same class. If, however, A' is in the same class (and only in this case), this class can contain a symmetric matrix. The necessary and sufficient condition for the class to contain a symmetric matrix is, then, that the unimodular matrix S for which $A' = S^{-1}AS$ can be chosen as $S = TT'$, T integral and $n \times n$. This S can be shown to be identical with Faddeev's.

In group theory there is Auerbach's theorem that a bounded matrix group leaves a p.d. form invariant. But also in the chapters of group theory dealing with characters, sums of squares and hence p.d.m. play a big role.

A great number of so-far isolated results concerning p.d.m. turn up in the literature frequently, some fairly recently. Just a few of them will be mentioned briefly in this introduction (with apologies concerning others not mentioned).[*]

(1) The classical determinantal inequality of Hadamard has been generalized in two ways, on one hand to block matrices, on the other hand to a more general concept of determinants introduced by Schur involving characters of groups as coefficients, instead of ± 1. The permanent then becomes a special case of this general concept. Further results on the Schur and Hadamard inequalities were obtained by M. Marcus recently. In particular, Marcus proved a "Hadamard" inequality for permanents.

Also the Minkowski inequality (and its "Hölderized" version) between the determinant of the sum of two p.d.m. and the sum of their determinants was generalized.

Both in the case of the Hadamard and in the case of the Minkowski inequality, generalizations were obtained in the following way: the characteristic roots of the matrices are ordered according to size and the

---

[*] See also T. S. Motzkin, Signs of minors, these Proceedings.

inequalities are studied for the products of the first k factors ($k = 1, \ldots,$ $n-1$) instead of for $k = n$ (see Fan, Oppenheim).

(2) Work on copositive forms has been continued: these are quadratic forms which assume positive values for positive vectors (see M. Hall and M. Newman, Baumert, T. S. Motzkin).

(3) Fiedler obtained results concerning the Schur product $A \circ A^{-1}$ when A is p.d. and concerning the elements in A^{-1} for A p.d.

(4) The Robertson inequality concerns the decomposition of a p.d. hermitian $H = A + iB$, when A, B are real. H. P. Robertson proved that $\det A > \det B$. Taussky showed $\det H \leq \det A$. Further, if α_i are the characteristic roots of A and β_i those of iB, both in nondecreasing order, then $\alpha_i > \beta_i$. Marcus again generalized to products of the first k characteristic roots.

(5) R. C. Thompson generalized an inequality of Everitt concerning the determinant of a p.d. block matrix H, with each block H_{ij} of the same dimension. Then $H \leq \det(\det H_{ij})$ with equality if and only if all $H_{ij} = 0$, $i \neq j$. Subsequently, Marcus and Gordon found a stronger inequality which contains Thompson's. The technique of proof used by Marcus and Gordon has been applied by Marcus in a number of different situations.

(6) L. Foster studied the characteristic roots of certain 2×2 matrices of the form XX' where X is an integral matrix.

The book on inequalities by Hardy, Littlewood, and Pólya [1], has a brief discussion of p.d.m., but avoids algebraic and arithmetic issues; however, Beckenbach and Bellman [2] devote a large chapter to it. The present lecture tries to mention further material. It is not a survey lecture, it tries to discuss new results and problems linked with the author's research; no aim at completeness is made. In spite of its great importance the positive-semidefinite case is not discussed. It is usually a good deal more complicated.

The following two areas will be studied:

1. Pencils of real symmetric matrices which contain a p.d.m.
2. The theorem of Lyapunov.

Unless stated otherwise every square matrix is assumed $n \times n$.

1. Pencils of Real Symmetric Matrices

Not every pencil of real symmetric matrices contains a p.d.m. Let A, B be two generators of the pencil. Then the pencil consists of the matrices $\lambda A + \mu B$ where λ, μ run through all real numbers. Let $\lambda_0 A + \mu_0 B$ be p.d. for some real values of λ_0, μ_0. It is then clear that for every real vector x,

$$x'Ax = x'Bx = 0 \Rightarrow x = 0. \tag{1}$$

It was shown by Calabi [3] that for $n > 2$, this condition is also sufficient for the existence of a p.d.m. in the pencil.

The following classical theorem is well known: any real symmetric matrix A can be transformed to diagonal form by a congruence transformation XAX' where at the same time X also transforms a given positive-definite matrix P into diagonal form (the case $P = I$ simply means that X can be chosen orthogonal). (This goes back to Cauchy, Sylvester, Kronecker, and Weierstrass.)

It therefore follows for $n > 2$ that a pencil $\lambda A + \mu B$ for which (1) holds can be transformed to diagonal form and that this fact is a generalization of the classical theorem about a pair A, B with one of them p.d.

On the other hand, without using the existence of a p.d. $\lambda A + \mu B$, it was shown earlier by Greub and Milnor [4] that, for $n > 2$, under the same conditions (1), A and B can be transformed to diagonal form simultaneously [of course, here (1) is only sufficient].

It will now be shown that Calabi's theorem follows from the theorem of Greub and Milnor.

For this purpose we use the following theorem of Stiemke.

Stiemke's Theorem. *Let $S = (s_{ik})$ be a real $m \times n$ matrix. Then either*

$$Sv = 0$$

for some n-vector $v \geq 0$, $v \neq 0$, or

$$S'u > 0$$

for some m-vector u.

Let (1) be satisfied. Then by the theorem of Greub and Milnor we may assume $A = \text{diag}(a_1, \ldots, a_n)$, $B = \text{diag}(b_1, \ldots, b_n)$. Form the $2 \times n$ matrix

$$S = \begin{pmatrix} a_1 \cdots a_n \\ b_1 \cdots b_n \end{pmatrix}.$$

Then $S'u > 0$ for some real 2-vector $u = (\lambda, \mu)$ means that

$$\lambda a_1 + \mu b_1 > 0$$
$$\vdots$$
$$\lambda a_n + \mu b_n > 0.$$

This is equivalent with $\lambda A + \mu B$ p.d. By Stiemke's theorem this is implied if

$$Sv = 0 \quad \text{impossible for} \quad v \geq 0, \qquad v \neq 0.$$

This means in our case that

$$\sum a_i x_i = \sum b_i x_i = 0 \quad \text{for} \quad x = (x_1, \ldots, x_n) \geq 0 \Rightarrow x = 0.$$

Write $x_i = y_i{}^2$, y_i real, $i = 1, \ldots, n$; then we have

$$\sum a_i y_i{}^2 = \sum b_i y_i{}^2 = 0 \Rightarrow y_i = 0, \qquad i = 1, \ldots, n$$

which is exactly (1).

Of course, only a minor application of Stiemke's theorem was made. But the application suggested to me the following idea:

Given a system of linear inequalities

$$\sum_{k=1}^{n} a_{ik} x_k \geq 0, \qquad i = 1, \ldots, m$$

with matrix $A = (a_{ik})$. If these inequalities are to be solved for values $x_k \geq 0$, then we can replace the x_k by $y_k{}^2$ and study the system

$$\sum_{k=1}^{n} a_{ik} y_k{}^2 \geq 0.$$

These are now quadratic inequalities and once we have them in this form we can also apply a simultaneous nonsingular transformation to the quadratic forms

$$y' \begin{pmatrix} a_{i1} \\ & \ddots \\ & & a_{in} \end{pmatrix} y$$

and obtain a set of more general quadratic forms $z' B_i z$ for which the inequalities

$$z' B_i z \geq 0$$

are to be studied.

I am now returning to the theorems of Calabi and Greub–Milnor. Both these theorems are valid for $n > 2$ only. An easy example showing that they break down for $n = 2$ is

$$A = \begin{pmatrix} 1 & 0 \\ 0 & -1 \end{pmatrix}, \qquad B = \begin{pmatrix} 0 & 1 \\ 1 & 0 \end{pmatrix}.$$

A related theorem, also valid only for $n > 2$, is by Brickman [6].

Brickman's Theorem. *Let A, B be real symmetric matrices, v a real n-vector. Consider all pairs*

$$v' A v, \quad v' B v$$

for all v's with $v'v = 1$. Interpreted as points in the complex plane, these pairs form a convex region.

Assume now that A, B satisfy condition (1) and use the fact that owing to the convexity of the region there exists a straight line in the plane separating $(0, 0)$ from the region. From this follows the existence of a positive-definite matrix in the pencil.

The theorem fails if more than two matrices are considered.

A deeper understanding of Calabi's theorem was obtained by Bohnenblust [7] by imbedding the problem in a more general setup. A set $A_1, \ldots, A_p$ of real symmetric matrices is called jointly definite of degree r if the p equations $\sum_{i=1}^{r} x_i' A_k x_i = 0$, $k = 1, \ldots, p$, imply $x_i = 0$ for each i [For $r = 1$, $p = 2$ this condition expresses Eqs. (1).] Let $f(r) = \frac{1}{2}(r + 1)(r + 2)$. At least one linear combination of the matrices $A_1, \ldots, A_p$ is positive-definite if $A_1, \ldots, A_p$ are jointly definite of degree r and if

$$1 \leq r \leq n - 1, \qquad p \leq f(r) - \delta_{n,r+1} - 1.$$

The presence of the Kronecker delta $\delta_{n,r+1}$ exhibits the special role played by $n = 2$ in the case $r = 1$ investigated by Calabi. This result is best possible: given r, there exist $f(r) - \delta_{n,r+1}$ matrices jointly definite of degree r which admit no definite linear combination.

The results are valid for hermitian matrices if $f(r)$ is interpreted as $(r + 1)^2$. For three hermitian matrices Wielandt [8] has obtained a related result.

Pairs of hermitian matrices one of which is p.d. play an important role in another connection. A matrix A is called symmetrizable if a p.d. H exists such that $AH = K$ is hermitian. The matrix A can then be expressed as the product of two hermitian matrices one of which is p.d. Such matrices have real characteristic roots and linear elementary divisors. They are actually similar to hermitian matrices. In general AH is not hermitian for any p.d. H. In this case the expression $AH + HA^*$ can be studied and, in fact, has been studied and leads to very interesting problems. This will be discussed in Sec. 2.

2. Lyapunov's Theorem

The most important fact concerned with the expression

$$AG + GA^*, \qquad G > 0, \tag{2}$$

is the famed theorem of Lyapunov. It concerns stable matrices, i.e. matrices with characteristic roots which all have negative real parts. Such matrices can be characterized by the fact that the above expression can be made negative-definite and in fact equal to $-I$ for a suitable p.d. G (see, e.g., Gantmacher [9]).

Equivalent to this theorem is the characterization of matrices C with $C^n \to 0$ by P. Stein.

Stein's Theorem. *Let C be a matrix. Then $C^n \to 0$ if and only if there exists a p.d. G such that*

$$G - CGC^*$$

is p.d.

That the theorems are equivalent can be shown by applying the Cayley transformation $C = (I - A)^{-1}(I + A)$ (see Taussky [11]).

The case in which for a stable A the matrix G can even be chosen as I itself has been studied for some time. The matrix $-A$ can then be called dissipative as a special case of a dissipative operator. Various properties of such matrices are known, in particular the fact that all principal minors of $-A$ are positive (see, e.g., Fiedler and Pták [12]). If the matrix $-A$ is not dissipative, then the possible p.d. G's for which (2) is negative-definite must have a maximum number ($<n$) of equal characteristic roots. The meaning of this number is not yet known; one could call it the index of dissipation (problem).

Further, if A is not stable, it can still be the case that the number of positive characteristic roots of $A + A^*$ coincides with the number of positive (negative) real parts of the characteristic roots of $-A$. This would then lead to a generalization of dissipative matrices (problem). Altogether, the set of p.d. G's for which (2) is negative-definite for a stable matrix deserves to be studied (problem). These G's form a cone, i.e. with G every rG ($r > 0$) belongs to the set and further with any G_1, G_2 in the set, $G_1 + G_2$ is also in the set.

Another set of questions arises when we study the range of (2). The following question seems worthwhile: For a stable A, what is the range of (2) if G runs through all p.d.m.? (Problem). This question was communicated to P. Stein [13] and he found an answer for an easier question:

If A runs through all stable matrices and G through all p.d.m., then (2) runs through all matrices which have at least one negative characteristic root.

Up to now I discussed the influence of changes in G on (2). Let me now treat the dual question. Given a p.d. G, what are the solutions A of

$$AG + GA^* = -I? \tag{3}$$

1. All solutions A have only characteristic roots with real parts $\neq 0$.

Proof. Suppose $i\rho$, ρ real, is a characteristic root of A. Let U be a unitary matrix for which $U^{-1}AU$ is upper triangular and let $i\rho$ be in the bottom right corner. We then have

$$U^{-1}AU \cdot U^{-1}GU + U^{-1}GU \cdot (U^{-1}AU)^* = -I.$$

The matrix $U^{-1}GU$ is also hermitian; let it have the elements h_{ik}. The element in the bottom right corner of the left-hand side is

$$i\rho h_{nn} - i\rho h_{nn} = 0$$

which is a contradiction.

2. Two solutions $X = A$, B of (3) differ by SG^{-1}, where S is skew-hermitian and arbitrary.

Proof. Let

$$AG + GA^* = -I$$
$$BG + GB^* = -I.$$

Subtracting, we obtain

$$(A - B)G + G(A^* - B^*) = 0$$

or

$$(A - B)G = G(B^* - A^*).$$

Put $(A - B)G = S$, then

$$S^* = -S,$$

hence

$$A - B = SG^{-1}, \qquad \text{or} \qquad A = B + SG^{-1}.$$

Conversely, let B be a solution and S arbitrary skew-hermitian. Form $A = B + SG^{-1}$. Then

$$AG + GA^* = BG + GB^* + SG^{-1}G + GG^{-1}S^* = BG + GB^* = -I.$$

3. All solutions A of (3) have the same number of characteristic roots with positive real parts.

Proof. Let

$$U^{-1}GU = \begin{pmatrix} g_1 & & 0 \\ & \ddots & \\ 0 & & g_n \end{pmatrix},$$

with U unitary. Then

$$X = \left(-\frac{1}{2}\right)\begin{pmatrix} 1/g_1 & & \\ & \ddots & \\ & & 1/g_n \end{pmatrix}$$

is a solution of

$$X \cdot U^{-1}GU + U^{-1}GU \cdot X^* = -I.$$

This solution has the same number of characteristic roots with negative real parts as G and the same is, of course, true for

$$U \cdot \left(-\frac{1}{2}\right) \begin{pmatrix} 1/g_1 & & \\ & \ddots & \\ & & 1/g_n \end{pmatrix} \cdot U^{-1}$$

which is a solution of

$$XG + GX^* = -I.$$

Hence the assertion is true for this particular solution. Let A be any other solution. Because of 2., there is a continuous transition between any two solutions. In virtue of 1., at no intermediate state will a solution have a purely imaginary characteristic root, hence A has as many positive real parts for its characteristic roots as the particular solution above. This proves 3.

If A is also hermitian then the expression (2) for all hermitian G's is called the Jordan product of A and G. All $n \times n$ hermitian matrices form a Jordan algebra, a concept originating from quantum theory. The results implied by Lyapunov's theorem and the further problems suggested by it indicate that the algebraic properties of the composition

$$AB + B^*A^*$$

for arbitrary $n \times n$ complex matrices should be worthy of study (problem). Further, Koecher [14] has studied "domains of positivity" and in collaboration with Artin and H. Braun set up a correspondence between them and Jordan algebras. Taussky noticed that some of these results go over to these "generalized" Jordan products.

Wigner and Yanase [15] used the special case of Lyapunov's theorem where A is itself hermitian to obtain a much more complicated result:

Let S be p.d., N be hermitian, T the unique p.d. solution of

$$ST + TS = N^2;$$

then

$$S \otimes \bar{T} + T \otimes \bar{S} - N \otimes \bar{N}$$

is positive-semidefinite (bar denotes complex conjugate). It may be possible to generalize this to the case where S is not hermitian (problem).

ACKNOWLEDGMENT

The author acknowledges the helpful discussions with M. Kneser, G. Pall, and H. Zassenhaus.

SELECTED REFERENCES

[1] Hardy, G. H., Littlewood, J. E., and Pólya, G., "Inequalities," 2nd ed. Cambridge Univ. Press, London and New York, 1952.

[2] Beckenbach, E. F., and Bellman, R., "Inequalities," 2nd revised printing. Springer, New York, 1965.

[3] Calabi, E., Linear systems of real quadratic forms, Proc. Amer. Math. Soc. 15, 844–846 (1964).

[4] Milnor, J., in Greub, W. H., "Linear Algebra," 2nd ed. Academic Press, New York, 1965.

[5] Stiemke, E., Über positive Lösungen homogener linearer Gleichungen, Math. Ann. 76, 340–342 (1915).

[6] Brickman, L., On the field of values of a matrix, Proc. Amer. Math. Soc. 12, 61–66 (1961).

[7] Bohnenblust, H. F., unpublished.

[8] Wielandt, H., unpublished.

[9] Gantmacher, F. R. "The Theory of Matrices." Chelsea, New York, 1959.

[10] Stein, P., Some general theorems on iterants, J. Res. Natl. Bur. Std. 48B, 82–83 (1952).

[11] Taussky, O., Matrices C with $C^n \to 0$, J. Algebra 1, 5–10 (1964).

[12] Fiedler, M., and Pták, V., On matrices with non-positive off-diagonal elements and positive principal minors, Czech. Math. J. 12, 382–400 (1962).

[13] Stein, P., On the ranges of two functions of positive definite matrices, J. Algebra 2, 350–353 (1965).

[14] Koecher, M., Positivitätsbereiche im R^n, Amer. J. Math. 53, 575–596 (1957).

[15] Wigner, E., and Yanase, M. M., On the positive semidefinite nature of a certain matrix expression, Canad. J. Math. 16, 397–406 (1964).

[16] Redheffer, R., Remark on a paper of Taussky, J. Algebra 2, 42–47 (1965).

[17] Taussky, O., Stable matrices, in Proc. Colloq. Intern. du CNRS Besancon, September 1966, "Programmation en Analyse Numérique," to appear.

[18] Wonenburger, M., Simultaneous diagonalization of symmetric bilinear forms, J. Math. Mech. 15, 617–622 (1966).

[19] Stein, P., and Pfeffer, A. M., On the ranges of two functions of positive definite matrices II. To be published in Bull. ICC, Rome.

[20] Weilandt, H., On the Eigenvalues of $A + B$ and AB. Natl. Bur. Std. Rept., 1951.

Inequalities of Chebyshev, Zolotareff, Cauer, and W. B. Jordan*

JOHN TODD
Department of Mathematics
California Institute of Technology
Pasadena, California 91109

1

A classical result of Chebyshev is the following:

Theorem 1.   *If $p_m(x) \equiv x^m + a_1 x^{m-1} + \cdots + a_{m-1} + a_m$, where the a_i are real, and if $\mu_m = \max\limits_{-1 \leq x \leq 1} |p_m(x)|$ then*

$$\mu_m \geq 2^{1-m}.$$

There is equality if and only if

$$p_m(x) \equiv \tilde{T}_m(x) = 2^{1-m} \cos(m \arccos x),$$

and then the extreme values are attained with sign $(-1)^j$ at

$$x_j = \cos j\pi/m, \qquad j = 0, 1, 2, \ldots, m.$$

For proofs of this see, e.g. Todd [*10*, pp. 24, and 30]. This result clearly includes the following theorem. In it, and in Theorem 5, we assume that $r_1 \geq r_2 \geq \cdots \geq r_m$; similarly for the a_j's in Theorems 3, 4.

Theorem 2.   *For any real $r_1, r_2, \ldots, r_m$ we have*

$$\max_{-1 \leq x \leq 1} \prod_{j=1}^{m} |x - r_j| \geq 2^{1-m}.$$

There is equality if and only if

$$r_j = \cos[(2j-1)\pi/2m)], \qquad j = 1, 2, \ldots, m,$$

and then the extreme values are attained with sign $(-1)^j$ at

$$x_j = \cos j\pi/m, \qquad j = 0, 1, 2, \ldots, m.$$

* The preparation of this paper was supported in part by the National Science Foundation.

In 1933 Cauer (cf. [2]), in aid of a problem in the design of electrical filter circuits, established the following results.

Theorem 3.   *If k, $0 \leq k \leq 1$, and an integer m are given, and $a_1, a_2, \ldots$, a_m are real, then*

$$\max_{0 \leq x \leq k^{1/2}} \prod_{j=1}^{m} \left| \frac{a_j^2 - x^2}{1 - a_j^2 x^2} \right| \geq (k_{2m})^{1/2} = \left(\frac{1 - k_m'}{1 + k_m'} \right)^{1/2}.$$

There is equality if and only if

$$a_j = \sqrt{k} \, \mathrm{sn}[(2j - 1)K/2m, \, k], \qquad j = 1, 2, \ldots, m,$$

and then the extreme values are attained with sign $(-1)^j$ at

$$x_j = \sqrt{k} \, \mathrm{sn}(jK/2m, \, k), \qquad j = 0, 1, 2, \ldots, m.$$

(Here, and elsewhere, in the usual notation of elliptic functions, k_m corresponds to $m\tau$, where τ corresponds to k.)

Theorem 4.   *If k, $0 \leq k \leq 1$, and an integer m are given, and $a_1, a_2, \ldots$, a_m are real, then*

$$\max_{0 \leq x \leq k^{1/2}} x \prod_{j=1}^{m} \left| \frac{a_j^2 - x^2}{1 - a_j^2 x^2} \right| \geq (k_{2m})^{1/2} = \left(\frac{1 - k_m'}{1 + k_m'} \right)^{1/2}.$$

There is equality if and only if

$$a_j = \sqrt{k} \, \mathrm{sn}[2jK/(2m + 1), \, k], \qquad j = 0, 1, 2, \ldots, m,$$

and then the extreme values are attained with sign $(-1)^j$ at

$$x_j = \sqrt{k} \, \mathrm{sn}[(2j + 1)K/(2m + 1), \, k], \qquad j = 0, 1, 2, \ldots, m.$$

For a proof of Theorem 3 see Oberhettinger and Magnus [9]. The results were actually established by Zolotareff in 1877 and, in part, independently, by Chebyshev in 1894—for an account of the history see Cauer [1].

In 1964 W. B. Jordan (see Wachspress [13]), in support of the design of optimal ADI-algorithms, established the following theorem.

Theorem 5.   *If k', $0 \leq k' \leq 1$, and an integer m are given, and $r_1, r_2, \ldots$, r_m are real, then*

$$\max_{k' \leq x \leq 1} \left| \prod_{j=1}^{m} \frac{x - r_j}{x + r_j} \right| \geq (k_{4m})^{1/2} = \frac{1 - (k_m')^{1/2}}{1 + (k_m')^{1/2}}.$$

There is equality if and only if

$$r_j = \mathrm{dn}[(2j-1)K/2m, \; k], \qquad j = 1, 2, \ldots, m,$$

and then the extreme values are attained with sign $(-1)^j$ at

$$x_j = \mathrm{dn}(jK/m, \; k), \qquad j = 0, 1, 2, \ldots, m.$$

For an alternate, more motivated proof, see Todd [11].

We note that the distribution of the parameters, as a function of k, is easy to visualize from Fig. 1 (Jahnke *et al.* [8]). In realistic circumstances

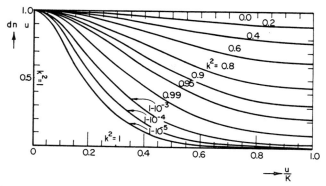

FIG. 1. $\mathrm{dn}\,u$ as function of u/K. (From E. Jahnke, F. Emde, and F. Lösch, "Tables of Higher Functions," 6th ed., p. 77. McGraw-Hill, New York, 1960).

we have k about $1 - \frac{1}{3} \times 10^{-7}$ so that the appropriate graph is well below those given and about half the parameters are concentrated near zero.

In this paper we discuss mainly the Jordan result further, in the context of its original application. Before turning to this we note that it may be presumed that there are results corresponding to Theorems 3–5 in the same way as Theorem 1 corresponds to Theorem 2. It is doubtful whether these results are of physical or computational significance, but we note that Young has discussed successive over-relaxation with complex parameters.

2

It has been shown (e.g., Todd [11]) that the effective spectral radius for the optimal m-parameter ADI method for the solution of the "model problem" is

$$\eta_m = \left[\frac{1 - (k_m')^{1/2}}{1 + (k_m')^{1/2}} \right]^{1/m}$$

where $k' \doteq \pi^2/4n^2$, the linear mesh length being $(n+1)^{-1}$. It is with the behavior of the sequence $\{\eta_m\}$ that we shall be concerned.

We begin with the following result stated as an exercise in Varga [12].

Theorem 6. *The subsequence $\{\eta_{2m}\}$ is steadily decreasing.*

Proof. It will be sufficient to show that $\eta_2 < \eta_1$. We use a standard result about the Landen transformation $\tau \to 2\tau$:

$$k_2 = \frac{1-k'}{1+k'}, \qquad k_2' = \frac{2(k')^{1/2}}{1+k'}.$$

We have to show

$$\left[\frac{1-(k_2')^{1/2}}{1+(k_2')^{1/2}}\right] < \left[\frac{1-(k')^{1/2}}{1+(k')^{1/2}}\right]^2.$$

This comes by elementary algebra on substituting for k_2' in terms of k'.

3

It is plausible to conjecture that the sequence $\{\eta_m\}$ itself is actually monotone. So far* we have only been able to determine $\lim \eta_m$; this is accomplished in Sec. 4. At present we give some indications that the problem of monotony may be rather difficult.

We begin by noting that

$$\eta_m = \left[\frac{\vartheta_2(0, q^{4m})}{\vartheta_3(0, q^{4m})}\right]^{1/m}.$$

(See, e.g. Whittaker and Watson [14, p. 486].) The Jacobi imaginary transformation gives

$$\frac{\vartheta_2(0, q')}{\vartheta_3(0, q')} = \frac{\vartheta_4(0, q)}{\vartheta_3(0, q)}$$

where

$$\ln q' \ln q = \pi^2.$$

Hence

$$\eta_m = \left[\prod_{n=1}^{\infty}\left(\frac{1-(q_{4m}')^{2n-1}}{1+(q_{4m}')^{2n-1}}\right)\right]^{1/m}.$$

* *Note added in proof:* In the meantime D. Gaier and the author have established first the ultimate monotony of $\{\eta_m\}$ and then its actual monotony. The detailed proofs will appear in *Numer. Math.*

It is tempting to try to prove that each factor in this infinite product is monotone. However, it is easy to verify that if

$$\lambda_m = \lambda_m(x) = \left[\frac{1 - x^{1/m}}{1 + x^{1/m}}\right]^{1/m},$$

then $\lambda_1 > \lambda_2$ for x near zero, but $\lambda_2 > \lambda_1$ for x near 1. What this implies is the following: we have

$$(q'_{4m})^{2n-1} = \left[\exp\left(\frac{\pi^2}{4m \ln q}\right)\right]^{2n-1} = \left\{\exp\left[\frac{(2n-1)\pi^2}{4 \ln q}\right]\right\}^{1/m}$$

and as n increases the expression

$$\exp\left[\frac{(2n-1)\pi^2}{4 \ln q}\right]$$

decreases to zero, $\ln q$ being negative. Hence the early factors in η_2 will exceed the corresponding ones in η_1 but the situation will be reversed for later ones and the inequality $\eta_1 > \eta_2$ follows from the predominance of the later factors.

4

We now establish the following theorem.

Theorem 7.

$$\lim \eta_m = q.$$

Proof. We make use of the explicit values of the optimal parameters $\{r_j\}$ and the fact that $\prod(x - r_j)/(x + r_j)$ assumes its extremal value for $x = 1$. This gives

$$\eta_m = \left[\prod_{j=1}^{m} \frac{1 - \mathrm{dn}[(2j-1)K/2m]}{1 + \mathrm{dn}[(2j-1)K/2m]}\right]^{1/m}$$

so that

$$\ln \eta_m = m^{-1}\left[\sum_{j=1}^{m} \ln\left\{\frac{1 - \mathrm{dn}[(2j-1)K/2m]}{1 + \mathrm{dn}[(2j-1)K/2m]}\right\}\right]$$

which is an approximating sum for the (Cauchy–Riemann) integral

$$I = K^{-1}\int_0^K \ln\frac{1 - \mathrm{dn}\, x}{1 + \mathrm{dn}\, x}\, dx.$$

Now it is known (Dixon [4, p. 141]) that

$$\int_0^K \ln(1 + \mathrm{dn}\, x)\, dx = \tfrac{1}{4}\pi K' + \tfrac{1}{2}K \ln k$$

and from this and the facts that $(1 - \mathrm{dn}\, x)(1 + \mathrm{dn}\, x) = k^2 \,\mathrm{sn}^2\, x$ and

$$\int_0^K \ln \mathrm{sn}\, x\, dx = -\tfrac{1}{4}\pi K' - \tfrac{1}{2}K \ln k$$

(Dixon [4, p. 141]) we can obtain

$$\int_0^K \ln(1 - \mathrm{dn}\, x)\, dx = -\tfrac{3}{4}\pi K' + \tfrac{1}{2}K \ln k.$$

Hence

$$\int_0^K \ln \frac{1 - \mathrm{dn}\, x}{1 + \mathrm{dn}\, x}\, dx = -\pi K'$$

and so

$$I = -\pi K'/K.$$

Hence, using results of Ingham [6, 7],

$$\lim \eta_m = \exp(-\pi K'/K) = q.$$

In the special case discussed earlier (Todd [11]) when $k' \doteqdot \pi^2/4n^2$ we have

$$q \doteqdot 1 - \pi^2/(4 \ln n).$$

This result may be compared with those of De Boor and Rice [3].

Professor Carlson has provided another proof of Theorem 7. We have

$$\eta_m{}^m = \frac{\vartheta_2(0,\, q^{4m})}{\vartheta_3(0,\, q^{4m})} = \frac{2q^m + 2q^{9m} + 2q^{25m} + \cdots}{1 + 2q^{4m} + 2q^{16m} + \cdots}$$

so that

$$m \ln \eta_m = \ln 2 + m \ln q + \ln\left[\frac{1 + q^{8m} + q^{24m} + \cdots}{1 + 2q^{4m} + 2q^{16m} + \cdots}\right]$$

from which the result follows.

5

There are analogs of Theorems 6 and 7 for the Cauer situation. We confine our attention to the "even" case, i.e., Theorem 3.

We define

$$\mu_m = (k_{2m})^{1/2m}$$

and this can be interpreted as the "average attenuation per mesh."

Theorem 8.   *The sequence $\{\mu_{2m}\}$ is steadily decreasing.*

Proof.   As for Theorem 7.

As in the Jordan case the monotony of the sequence $\{\mu_m\}$ is plausible. As further evidence we give the following values of $-\ln \mu_m$, derived from the tables of Glowatzki [5]. These values correspond to $k = 1/\sqrt{2}$, $\theta = \arcsin k = 45°$.

$m =$	1	2	3	4	5	6
$-\log \mu_m =$	0.881	1.224	1.340	1.395	1.432	1.455

These results are consistent with the following theorem.

Theorem 9.

$$\lim \mu_m = \sqrt{q}.$$

Proof.   From Theorem 3, using the fact that the extreme value is attained with positive sign at $x = 0$, we have

$$\mu_m = \left\{\prod_{j=1}^{m} k \, \mathrm{sn}^2[(2j - 1)K/2m]\right\}^{1/m}.$$

Hence

$$\ln \mu_m = \ln k + 2K^{-1}(K/m) \sum_{j=1}^{m} \ln \{\mathrm{sn}[(2j - 1)K/2m]\}.$$

The sum on the right is an approximating sum for the (Cauchy–Riemann) integral

$$2K^{-1} \int_0^K \ln \mathrm{sn} \, x \, dx,$$

which can be evaluated (Dixon, [4, p. 141]) as

$$-\ln k - \tfrac{1}{2}\pi K'/K.$$

Hence, again appealing to the results of Ingham [6, 7], we have

$$\ln \mu_m \to -\tfrac{1}{2}\pi K'/K$$

which gives the result required.

In the tabulation above the theoretical limit is $\tfrac{1}{2}\pi$ since for $k = k' = 1/\sqrt{2}$, $K = K'$.

ACKNOWLEDGMENTS

I am indebted to my colleagues B. C. Carlson and A. M. Pfeffer for commenting on drafts of this paper.

REFERENCES

[1] Cauer, W., Bemerkung über eine Extremalaufgabe von E. Zolotareff, *Z. Angew. Math. Mech.* **20**, 358 (1940).

[2] Cauer, W., "Synthesis of Linear Communications Networks." McGraw-Hill, New York, 1958.

[3] De Boor, C., and Rice, J. R., Chebyshev approximation by $a \prod [(x - r_i)/(x + s_i)]$ and application to ADI iteration, *J. Soc. Indust. Appl. Math.* **11**, 159–169 (1963).

[4] Dixon, A. C., "The Elementary Properties of Elliptic Functions." Macmillan, London, 1894.

[5] Glowatzki, E., Sechstellige Tafel der Cauer-Parameter, *Abh. Bayer. Akad. Wiss. Math.-Nat. Kl.* **67**, 37 (1955).

[6] Ingham, A. E., Some Tauberian theorems connected with the prime number theorem, *J. London Math. Soc.* **20**, 171–180 (1965).

[7] Ingham, A. E., Improper integrals as limits of sums, *J. London Math. Soc.* **24**, 44–50 (1949).

[8] Jahnke, E., Emde, F., and Lösch, F., "Tables of Higher Functions." McGraw-Hill, New York, 1960.

[9] Oberhettinger, F., and Magnus, W., "Anwendung der elliptischen Funktionen in Physik und Technik." Springer, Berlin, 1949.

[10] Todd, J., "Introduction to the Constructive Theory of Functions." Academic Press, New York, 1963.

[11] Todd, J., Optimal ADI-parameters. *Proc. Conf. on Numerical Problems in Approximation Theory* (Internat. Ser. in Numerical Math., Vol. 6). Birkhäuser, Basel, 1967, to appear.

[12] Varga, R. S., "Matrix Iterative Analysis." Prentice Hall, Englewood Cliffs, New Jersey, 1962.

[13] Wachspress, E. L., Extended application of alternating direction implicit model problem theory, *J. Soc. Indust. Appl. Math.* **11**, 994–1016 (1963).

[14] Whittaker, E. T., and Watson, G. N., "Modern Analysis." Cambridge Univ. Press, London and New York, 1927.

[15] Zolotareff, E., Anwendung der elliptischen Functionen auf Probleme über Functionen die von Null am wenigsten oder am meisten abweichen, *Abh. St. Petersburg* **30**, (1877).

On the New Maximum–Minimum Theory of Eigenvalues*

ALEXANDER WEINSTEIN

Institute for Fluid Dynamics and Applied Mathematics
University of Maryland, College Park, Maryland

1. Introduction

The classical maximum–minimum theory of eigenvalues can be expressed in a fundamental inequality [see (5)]. Let A be a completely continuous (compact), negative-definite, symmetric operator on a real Hilbert space H with the scalar product (u, v). Denote by λ_k, $k = 1, 2, \ldots,$

$$\lambda_1 \leq \lambda_2 \leq \cdots$$

the eigenvalues, and by u_k the corresponding eigenfunctions (or eigenvectors) of the equation

$$Au = \lambda u; \qquad (u_i, u_k) = \delta_{ik}. \tag{1}$$

The assumption that A be negative-definite is made only for the convenience of ordering the eigenvalues in an increasing sequence. For the case of infinitely many eigenvalues we have $\lambda_k \to 0$. No other assumption such as the existence of Hellinger–Hahn finite invariants has to be made, as this would be a restriction on the operator A and would signify that the eigenvalues λ_k must converge sufficiently rapidly to zero. Let $n \geq 2$ and let $p_1, p_2, \ldots, p_{n-1}$ be any $n - 1$ elements in H. Denote by $R(u)$ the Rayleigh quotient $R(u) = (Au, u)/(u, u)$. Let us consider

$$\lambda(p_1, p_2, \ldots, p_{n-1}) = \min R(u) \tag{2}$$

under the $n - 1$ orthogonality conditions

$$(u, p_1) = (u, p_2) = \cdots = (u, p_{n-1}) = 0. \tag{3}$$

Obviously this minimum depends only on the subspace S generated by $p_1, p_2, \ldots, p_{n-1}$. Clearly

$$\lambda_1 \leq \lambda(p_1, p_2, \ldots, p_{n-1}). \tag{4}$$

* This work was supported in part by the Air Force Office of Scientific Research under Grant AFOSR 400-64.

On the other hand, we have the classical inequality

$$\lambda(p_1, p_2, \ldots, p_{n-1}) \leq \lambda_n \tag{5}$$

and, moreover, the equality

$$\lambda(u_1, u_2, \ldots, u_{n-1}) = \lambda_n. \tag{6}$$

Equation (6) states that the maximum of the minimum in (2) is attained for $p_k = u_k$, $k = 1, 2, \ldots, n-1$. Formulas (5) and (6) were derived by Weyl and have been used in his papers since 1911; see [12, p. 136]. Riesz and Nagy [11, p. 237] attribute the introduction of the maximum–minimum principle to E. Fischer, a statement confirmed in Courant–Hilbert [6, p. 47, fine print]. Recently Weinstein [14, 15] in an essentially new way derived a maximum–minimum theory which not only yields the old results (5) and (6), but also gives for the first time necessary and sufficient conditions for the equality

$$\lambda(p_1, p_2, \ldots, p_{n-1}) = \lambda_n. \tag{7}$$

The main purpose of the present paper is to give a new and more compact form for our previous results which may be considered as an improvement in some respects, especially as our criterion for (7) is presented in an invariant form depending only on the subspace S and not on any special basis $p_1, \ldots, p_{n-1}$.

The old theory uses a test function

$$u_0 = c_1 u_1 + c_2 u_2 + \cdots + c_n u_n \neq 0$$

which satisfies the $n - 1$ conditions (3) and the normalization $\sum_{k=1}^{n} c_k^2 = 1$. In this case

$$R(u_0) = \lambda_1 c_1^2 + \lambda_2 c_2^2 + \cdots + \lambda_n c_n^2 \leq \lambda_n.$$

Therefore

$$\lambda_1 \leq \lambda(p_1, p_2, \ldots, p_{n-1}) = \min_{\substack{(u, p_j) = 0 \\ 1 \leq j \leq n-1}} R(u) \leq R(u_0) \leq \lambda_n.$$

For $p_k = u_k$, $k = 1, 2, \ldots, n-1$, we obtain the equality (6). This result, which Weyl calls his fundamental lemma [12], only gives an estimate of $\lambda(p_1, p_2, \ldots, p_{n-1})$, and as we have previously shown $p_k = u_k$ only yields a sufficient condition for the equality (7).

2. The New Approach

A complete discussion of (7) cannot be obtained from Weyl's proof. Our new theory does not use a test function. Instead, we apply the methods of the theory of intermediate problems introduced by Weinstein. This approach is based on the observation that $\lambda(p_1, p_2, \ldots, p_{n-1})$ is the first or lowest eigenvalue of a new eigenvalue problem. (If A were positive, this would be the highest eigenvalue.) This remark in itself would be trivial were it not for the fact that the new eigenvalues can be computed from the eigenvalues and eigenfunctions of our problem (1).

This new problem is obtained by replacing Au by $Au - PAu$ where PAu is the projection of Au on S, where again S is the subspace generated by $p_1, p_2, \ldots, p_{n-1}$. We denote by r the dimension of S. Then we have $(Au, u) = (Au - PAu, u)$ for $u \in S$ so that $\lambda(p_1, p_2, \ldots, p_{n-1})$ is the first eigenvalue of the equation

$$Au - PAu = \lambda u; \qquad u \in S^{\perp}; \quad S \oplus S^{\perp} = H. \tag{8}$$

Since $PAu = \sum_{i=1}^{n-1} a_i p_i$ we can compute the coefficients a_i from the $n - 1$ equations

$$(Au, p_k) = \sum_{i=1}^{n-1} a_i(p_i, p_k) \qquad k = 1, 2, \ldots, n - 1.$$

Therefore, if $p_1, p_2, \ldots, p_r$ is a basis for S and $p_{r+1} = p_{r+2} = \cdots = p_{n-1} = 0$, we have

$$a_i = \sum_{k=1}^{r} b_{ik}(Au, p_k) \qquad i = 1, 2, \ldots, r$$

where $\{b_{ik}\}$ is the inverse of the Gram matrix $\{(p_i, p_k)\}$.

We denote by $\lambda_1^{n-1}, \lambda_2^{n-1}, \ldots,$ and $u_1^{n-1}, u_2^{n-1}, \ldots,$ the eigenvalues and eigenfunctions of Eq. (8). Therefore $\lambda(p_1, p_2, \ldots, p_{n-1}) = \lambda_1^{n-1}$. Sometimes we denote the eigenvalues and eigenfunctions of the original problem (1) by λ_k^0 and u_k^0 in place of λ_k and u_k. If we put $p_k = u_k$, $k = 1, 2, \ldots, n - 1$, into Eq. (8), we call the corresponding problem (8'). The eigenfunctions of (8') which can obviously be obtained by inspection are $u_n^0, u_{n+1}^0, \ldots,$ with the corresponding eigenvalues $\lambda_n^0, \lambda_{n+1}^0, \ldots.$ The connection of problem (8) with the theory of intermediate problems will become apparent from the following fact to be proved later. The eigenvalues λ_k^{n-1} of (8) are intermediate between the values $\lambda_k^0 (= \lambda_k)$ and the values λ_{n+k-1}^0 which are the eigenvalues of problem (8'). For this reason we may adopt the terminology of intermediate problems and call Eq. (1) the base problem. Then problem (8') would correspond to the given problem of the general theory and problem (8) would correspond to an intermediate problem. Actually we are interested here only in the properties of the eigenvalues of the base problem, and the intermediate problems are constructed for the purpose of studying these properties. To be more precise, we are only interested in the inequalities

$$\lambda_1^0 \leq \lambda_1^{n-1} \leq \lambda_n^0 \tag{9}$$

of which the nontrivial part is $\lambda_1^{n-1} \leq \lambda_n^0$.

3. The Main Theorem

Let us first prove

Lemma 1. *If $\lambda_1 = \lambda_2 = \cdots = \lambda_n$, then $\lambda(p_1, p_2, \ldots, p_{n-1}) = \lambda_n$ for any choice of $p_1, p_2, \ldots, p_{n-1}$.*

This follows immediately from the old maximum–minimum theory by putting $\lambda_1 = \lambda_n$ in (4) and (5). For the sake of completeness we give here a new proof independent of the old theory. In fact the multiplicity of $\lambda_1(=\lambda_n)$ is obviously $\geq n$. Let $u_1, u_2, \ldots, u_n$ be n orthonormal eigenfunctions belonging to λ_1. Let

$$u_0 = c_1 u_1 + c_2 u_2 + \cdots + c_n u_n$$

satisfy the $n-1$ conditions (3) and the condition $\sum_{i=1}^n c_i^2 = 1$. Then u_0 is an eigenfunction of (8) corresponding to the eigenvalue $\lambda_1 \ (=\lambda_n)$. In fact, in view of conditions (3),

$$A u_0 - \sum_{i,j=1}^{n-1} b_{ij}(A u_0, p_j) p_i = A u_0 - 0 = \lambda_1 u_0.$$

Since $\lambda_1 = \lambda_n$, λ_n is the lowest eigenvalue of (8) which means that $\lambda(p_1, p_2, \ldots, p_{n-1}) = \lambda_n$, independent of $p_1, p_2, \ldots, p_{n-1}$. Notice that we used Weyl's test function u_0 as a solution of (8) and not for estimating an upper bound to $R(u)$. From now on we assume that for a certain $m \geq 2$

$$\lambda_{m-1}^0 < \lambda_m^0 = \lambda_{m+1}^0 = \cdots = \lambda_n^0 = \lambda_{n+1}^0 = \cdots = \lambda_N^0 \tag{10}$$

where $m \leq n \leq N$, and where N is the number of eigenvalues which are less than or equal to λ_n^0.

In the determination of the eigenvalues of (8), especially λ_1^{n-1}, in terms of the eigenvalues and eigenfunctions of (1), the determinant

$$W(\lambda) = \det\left\{\frac{1}{\lambda}\left[\sum_{j=1}^\infty \frac{\lambda_j(p_i, u_j)(p_k, u_j)}{\lambda_j - \lambda} - (p_i, p_k)\right]\right\}, \quad i, k = 1, 2, \ldots, n-1, \tag{11}$$

which is usually called Weinstein's determinant, plays a decisive role. Since $\lambda \neq 0$ in the following considerations, we have included the factor $1/\lambda$ in order to be consistent with the usual notation. Using the fact that $(p_i, p_k) = \sum_{j=1}^\infty (p_i, u_j)(p_k, u_j)$, we can also write

$$W(\lambda) = \det\left\{\sum_{j=1}^\infty \frac{(p_i, u_j)(p_k, u_j)}{\lambda_j - \lambda}\right\}. \tag{12}$$

Its principal minors are denoted by

$$W_1, \quad W_2, \ldots, W_{n-1} \; (=W).$$

If r is less than $n-1$, we have

$$W_{r+1} = W_{r+2} = \cdots = W_{n-1} = 0.$$

Let us consider the open interval $\lambda_{m-1} < \lambda < \lambda_n$. In this interval the meromorphic functions W_1, W_2, $\ldots$, W_r may have a finite number of zeros. Let $\varepsilon > 0$ be such that $\lambda_{m-1} < \lambda_n - \varepsilon < \lambda_n$ and, moreover, if there are any zeros of the W_k, $\lambda_n - \varepsilon$ is greater than any of these zeros. These conditions are always satisfied for any $\varepsilon > 0$ sufficiently small, which explains the notation.

We now formulate our maximum–minimum-principle in a new way which may be considered a simplification of our previous results.

Theorem. *For any choice of p_1, p_2, $\ldots$, p_{n-1} we have the inequality*

$$\lambda(p_1, p_2, \ldots, p_{n-1}) = \lambda_1^{n-1} \leq \lambda_n^0. \tag{5}$$

A necessary condition for the equality

$$\lambda(p_1, p_2, \ldots, p_{n-1}) = \lambda_1^{n-1} = \lambda_n^0 \tag{7}$$

is that the dimension r of the subspace S generated by $p_1, p_2, \ldots, p_{n-1}$ satisfies the inequality

$$m - 1 \leq r \leq n - 1, \tag{13}$$

where m is defined by (10). Let $p_1, \ldots, p_r$ be a basis for S. Assuming that (13) holds we have the following necessary and sufficient condition for (7): The quadratic form with the symmetric matrix of the determinant $W_r(\lambda_n - \varepsilon)$ has in canonical coordinates $x_1, x_2, \ldots, x_r$ the form

$$-x_1^2 - x_2^2 - \cdots - x_{m-1}^2 + x_m^2 + x_{m+1}^2 + \cdots + x_r^2. \tag{14}$$

This is of course an invariant characterization of the subspace S. Let us emphasize that we do not have to assume that $p_1, \ldots, p_r$ are orthonormal. In fact, from the definition of W_r, a change of the basis of S is equivalent to a nonsingular change in the variables in the quadratic form (14).

The proof of (5) as well as the necessary condition (13) for equality (7) has been given in our previous paper [15] and will not be repeated here.

Our necessary and sufficient condition given here is equivalent to the one given in our previous papers, namely:

If $W_1(\lambda_n - \varepsilon) < 0$, the sequence

$$W_1, \quad W_2, \quad \ldots, \quad W_r \tag{15}$$

alternates in sign exactly $m - 2$ times. If $W_1(\lambda_n - \varepsilon) > 0$, the sequence (15) alternates in sign exactly $m - 1$ times.

4. Stenger's Counterexample

As mentioned in our previous papers, in the case $m = n$, the necessary and sufficient condition for (7) is that the quadratic form is negative-definite, that is

$$\lim_{\varepsilon \to 0} \operatorname{sgn} W_s(\lambda_n - \varepsilon) = (-1)^s \tag{16}$$

$$\varepsilon > 0; \qquad s = 1, 2, \ldots, m - 1.$$

In the case $m < n$, the condition (16) is sufficient for equality (7) for any choice of the vectors $p_m, p_{m+1}, \ldots, p_{n-1}$. This follows from the fact that we obviously have

$$\lambda_1^{m-1} = \lambda_2^{m-1} = \cdots = \lambda_{n-m+1}^{m-1} = \lambda_n^0 \tag{17}$$

so that the statement is a consequence of Lemma 1. However (16) is not a necessary condition for (7) as is shown by the following counterexample.

Stenger's Counterexample (communicated to the author).   Let $\lambda_1 < \lambda_2 = \lambda_3$ so that $m = 2$ and $n = 3$. Let $p_1 = u_2$ and $p_2 = u_1 + \alpha u_2$ where α is not zero but is otherwise arbitrary.
Using p_1 alone we obtain

$$W_1(\lambda_3 - \varepsilon) = \frac{1}{\lambda_2 - \lambda_3 + \varepsilon} = \frac{1}{\varepsilon} > 0$$

for any $\varepsilon > 0$. For a moment let us put $p_1' = p_2$. Then we have

$$W_1'(\lambda_3 - \varepsilon) = \frac{1}{\lambda_1 - \lambda_3 + \varepsilon} + \frac{\alpha^2}{\varepsilon} > 0$$

for $\varepsilon > 0$ and sufficiently small.
However,

$$W_2(\lambda_3 - \varepsilon) = \frac{1}{\varepsilon(\lambda_1 - \lambda_2 + \varepsilon)} < 0$$

for $\varepsilon > 0$ and sufficiently small. Therefore we see that $\lambda(p_1) < \lambda_2 (= \lambda_3)$ and $\lambda(p_2) < \lambda_2 (= \lambda_3)$, but $\lambda(p_1, p_2) = \lambda_3$. This shows that to obtain the equality (7) we need not satisfy (16). Let us also note that, depending on the choice of the $\{p_k\}$, the number r which appears in the criterion can be any value in the range (13).

5. An Application

We now give an application of the new maximum–minimum theory. Consider the classical Bernoulli eigenvalue problem

$$-u'' - \lambda u = 0; \qquad u(-\pi/2) = u(\pi/2) = 0 \qquad (18)$$

where

$$\lambda_k = k^2, \qquad u_k = \sqrt{2/\pi} \, \sin k(x + \pi/2), \qquad k = 1, 2, \ldots.$$

As the eigenvalues are increasing we can advantageously apply our theory without the introduction of the compact inverse operator in a Hilbert space, which would only complicate the discussion. The Rayleigh quotient in this case is

$$R(u) = \frac{\displaystyle\int_{-\pi/2}^{\pi/2} (u')^2 \, dx}{\displaystyle\int_{-\pi/2}^{\pi/2} u^2 \, dx}. \qquad (19)$$

Let us consider the minimum of $R(u)$ under the restriction that the mean value of u is zero, namely

$$\int_{-\pi/2}^{\pi/2} u \, dx = 0. \qquad (20)$$

We shall show that this minimum is equal to $\lambda_2 \,(=4)$. The condition (20) states that u is orthogonal to $p = 1$. Therefore, by the general theory, in order to find $W(\lambda)$ we must first solve the equation

$$-u'' - \lambda u = p = 1. \qquad (21)$$

Noting that the second derivative of 1 is zero, we find, as in [13],

$$u = R_\lambda p = \frac{1}{\lambda} \left(\frac{\cos (x\sqrt{\lambda})}{\cos (\pi/2\sqrt{\lambda})} - 1 \right), \qquad (22)$$

where R_λ is the resolvent. Then $W(\lambda)$, which is equal to $(R_\lambda p, p)$, is obtained by integrating (22) over the interval $[-\pi/2, \pi/2]$. In this way we have

$$W(\lambda) = \frac{1}{\lambda} \left(\frac{2}{\sqrt{\lambda}} \tan \left(\frac{\pi}{2} \sqrt{\lambda} \right) - \pi \right).$$

Let us apply our criterion by computing

$$W(\lambda_2) = W(4) = -\pi/4.$$

Hence, $W(\lambda_2 - \varepsilon) < 0$ so that our minimum is equal to $\lambda_2 = 4$. As can be seen *we have not used the formula* (12) *which represents* $W(\lambda)$ *as an infinite series.* For this reason, we would not have had any difficulty in determining numerically the eigenvalues of the first intermediate problem with $p = 1$. Let us note that by putting $p = 1$ we have in Weinstein's terminology a *distinguished choice* relative to the eigenfunction $u_1 = (\sqrt{2/\pi}) \cos x$, but *it is not a special distinguished choice* (or, for short, special choice) as sometimes used by Bazley [4] and Bazley and Fox [5], since p cannot be represented as a linear combination of a finite number of the eigenfunctions u_k.

6. The Connection with the General Theory of Intermediate Problems

Let us add a few words about the general theory of intermediate problems as they are related to our subject.

We consider the problem of the vibrating clamped plate [13]. In the language of Hilbert space [3] it can be stated as follows. Let D be the domain of the plate and let g be the Green's function for the Laplace equation in D. Denote by G the integral operator with the kernel g. G is positive-definite and completely continuous. Then the eigenvalues for the clamped plate are determined by the consideration of the Rayleigh quotient $R(u)$ where $A = -GG$ and u is restricted to the space orthogonal to the subspace of harmonic functions in $\mathscr{L}_2(D)$. If we drop this restriction and let u be any function in $\mathscr{L}_2(D)$, we obtain a base problem which is equivalent to the problem of the vibrating membrane for D and therefore can be solved explicitly for rectangular domains. This base problem gives lower bounds for the plate problem. Let $p_1, p_2, \ldots$ be a sequence of harmonic (or potential) functions in $\mathscr{L}_2(D)$. Then an intermediate problem of order s is formed by restricting u to the subspace orthogonal to $p_1, p_2, \ldots, p_s$. The eigenvalues of the intermediate problem give improved lower bounds for the eigenvalues of the plate problem. As we see, this is the same setup as is in the new maximum–minimum theory, with the difference that here the functions $p_1, p_2, \ldots$, are restricted to a subspace of the Hilbert space and that the purpose is to compute lower bounds for the unknown eigenvalues of the plate. The notation $\{p_k\}$ has been retained in the literature in all cases.

The general scheme of intermediate problems is the following.

(1) We have to introduce a solvable base problem which gives rough lower bounds to the eigenvalues of a given problem.
(2) We have to define intermediate problems depending on a finite number of functions $p_1, p_2, \ldots, p_s$ which give improved intermediate eigenvalues.
(3) We have to devise methods of solving the intermediate problems theoretically and numerically in terms of the base problem.

The oldest type of problems was first considered some 30 years ago by Weinstein. Such problems were sometimes called intermediate problems corresponding to a change in boundary conditions. The connection with the maximum–minimum theory shows that such a name is somewhat misleading and therefore we prefer to call these problems intermediate problems of the first kind. Later other types of problems, always following the same scheme (given problem, base problem, intermediate problems) were considered by several authors. In the very important problems of the second kind, introduced by Aronszajn [2], the given problem is obtained from the base problem $Au = \lambda u$ by adding to A a positive operator B. It has been shown by Kuroda [10] and later by Fichera [7] that under certain assumptions the first kind is reducible to the second kind. However, the first kind of problem appears in a natural way not only in the theory of plates but also in the fundamental maximum–minimum theory. Therefore a reduction to the second kind would rather obscure the issue and has not been investigated in the present paper.

In conclusion let us mention that if A were a positive operator, the quantity $\lambda(p_1, p_2, \ldots, p_{n-1})$ would be the highest eigenvalue of (8). *This remark was the starting point of our theory* and has been used later by Fichera [7] to derive another interesting criterion for the equality (7) under the restriction that the orthogonal invariants of A are finite. Let us emphasise that his operator is again an operator of the first kind as we have used throughout. More precisely, Fichera uses the operator $(I - P)A(I - P)$ which is Aronszajn's modification of Weinstein's operator $A - PA = (I - P)A$. Professor Fichera leaves the proof of his formula to the reader so that a complete discussion of his results must be postponed.

REFERENCES

[1] Aronszajn, N., The Rayleigh–Ritz and A. Weinstein methods for approximation of eigenvalues, I, II. *Proc. Nat. Acad. Sci. U.S.A.* **34**, 474–480, 594–601 (1948).

[2] Aronszajn, N., Approximation methods for eigenvalues of completely continuous symmetric operators, *Proc. Symp. on Spectral Theory and Differential Problems, Stillwater, Oklahoma*, 1951.

[3] Aronszajn, N., and Weinstein, A., Existence, convergence and equivalence in the unified theory of plates and membranes. *Proc. Nat. Acad. Sci. U.S.A.* **64**, 181–191 (1941); On the unified theory of eigenvalues of plates and membranes, *Amer. J. Math.* **64**, 623 (1942).

[4] Bazley, N. W., Lower bounds for eigenvalues. *J. Math. Mech.* **10**, 289–308 (1961).

[5] Bazley, N. W., and Fox, D. W., Truncations in the method of intermediate problems for lower bounds to eigenvalues, *J. Res. Nat. Bur. Standards* **65B**, 105–111 (1961).

[6] Courant, R., and Hilbert, D., "Methods of Mathematical Physics," Vol. I. Wiley (Interscience), New York, 1953.

[7] Fichera, G., "Linear Elliptic Differential Systems and Eigenvalue Problems" (Lecture Notes in Mathematics). Springer, New York, 1965.

[8] Fichera, G., Approximation and estimates for eigenvalues, "Numerical Solution of Partial Differential Equations" (J. Bramble, ed.) Academic Press, New York, 1966.

[9] Gould, S. H., "Variational Methods in Eigenvalue Problems," 2nd ed. Univ. of Toronto Press, Toronto, Canada, 1966.

[10] Kuroda, S. T., On a Generalization of the Weinstein–Aronszajn Formula and the Infinite Determinant, *Sci. Papers Coll. of Gen. Educ., Univ. of Tokyo,* **11,** No. 1 (1961).

[11] Riesz, F., and Sz-Nagy, B., "Functional Analysis." Ungar, New York, 1955.

[12] Weyl, H., Ramifications, old and new, of the eigenvalue problem, *Bull. Amer. Math. Soc.* **46,** 115–139 (1950).

[13] Weinstein, A., "Memorial des Sciences Mathematiques," fasc. 88. Gauthier-Villars, Paris, 1937.

[14] Weinstein, A., A necessary and sufficient condition in the maximum-minimum theory of eigenvalues, "Studies in Mathematical Analysis and Related Topics." Stanford Univ. Press, Stanford, California, 1962.

[15] Weinstein, A., Intermediate problems and the maximum–minimum theory of eigenvalues, *J. Math. Mech.* **12,** 235–246 (1963).

[16] Weinstein, A., "La Teoria di Massimo–Minimo." Seminari dell'Istituto Nazionale di Alta Matematica. Edizioni Cremonese, Rome, 1964.

Generalizations of Ostrowski's Inequality for Matrices with Dominant Principal Diagonal

Y. K. WONG
Department of Mathematics
State University of New York at Albany
Albany, New York

Introduction

Ostrowski [2] considered a matrix (a_{ij}), $i, j = 1, 2, \ldots, n$, with complex elements. Let $d = \det(a_{ij})$ and

$$s_i = \sum_{\substack{j=1 \\ j \neq i}}^{n} |a_{ij}| = \sigma_i |a_{ii}|. \tag{1}$$

By assuming all $\sigma_i < 1$ for $i = 1, \ldots, n$, Ostrowski established the existence of $(a_{ij})^{-1} = C = (c_{ij})$, and the inequality

$$|c_{ij}| \leq \sigma_i |c_{jj}| \qquad (i \neq j), \tag{2}$$

"a very remarkable inequality valid for the elements of the inverse matrix of A where $\sigma_i < 1$."

Our paper gives some inequalities related to (2) but without assuming all $\sigma_i < 1$. Since $c_{ij} = b_{ij}/\det(a_{ij})$, where $b_{ij} = \text{adj}(a_{ij})$, we may write (2) in the form

$$|b_{ij}| \leq \sigma_i |b_{jj}| \qquad (i \neq j). \tag{3}$$

We shall consider the column sums $|a_{ij}| + \cdots + |a_{nj}|$ for $j = 1, \ldots, n$, in place of row sums as indicated in (1).

Since we do not assume that all $\sigma_i < 1$, the determinant of (a_{ij}) may be zero. Secondly, if we let $b_{ij}^{(h)}$ be the adjoint elements of

$$\begin{pmatrix} a_{11} & a_{12} & \cdots & a_{1h} \\ \cdot & \cdot & \cdots & \cdot \\ a_{h1} & a_{h2} & \cdots & a_{hh} \end{pmatrix}, \qquad h = 2, 3, \ldots, n, \tag{4}$$

then

$$\sum_{j \neq n} a_{nj} b_{jk}^{(n-1)} = b_{nk}. \tag{5}$$

With obvious change of notation, we may obtain

$$b_{ik} = \sum_{j \neq i} a_{ij} b_{jk}^{(-i)} \tag{6}$$

where $b_{jk}^{(-i)}$ is the adjoint element at (j, k) of the $n - 1 \times n - 1$ submatrix of (a_{ij}), $i, j = 1, 2, \ldots, n$, with the ith row and ith column omitted. Thus we may just as well consider a matrix of the form

$$\begin{pmatrix} a_{11} & \cdots & a_{1m} \\ \cdot & \cdots & \cdot \\ a_{m1} & \cdots & a_{mm} \\ x_1 & \cdots & x_m \end{pmatrix}. \tag{7}$$

With $m = n - 1$, and $x_i = a_{ni}$ $(i = 1, \ldots, n - 1)$, we have the first $n - 1$ columns of A.

Without losing generality, we may assume that the principal diagonal elements $a_{11}, \ldots, a_{nn}$ have absolute values less than 1, for otherwise we simply multiply (a_{ij}) by a^{-1} with $a > \max(|a_{11}|, \ldots, |a_{nn}|)$. We may also write $a_{ii} = 1 - a'_{ii}$. Dropping the primes in a'_{ii}, relation (1) then becomes

$$s_i = \sum_{j \neq i} |a_{ij}| = \sigma_i |1 - a_{ii}|. \tag{1a}$$

In this paper we consider a matrix of the form

$$\begin{pmatrix} I - A \\ x' \end{pmatrix} \tag{8}$$

where $A = (a_{ij})$, $i, j = 1, \ldots, m$, and $x' = (x_1, \ldots, x_m)$. There is a certain advantage in considering matrices of the form $I - A$.

If $I - A$ is nonsingular, then Neumann's series $I + A + \cdots + A^n + \cdots$ exists and we may write $(I - A)(I + A_Q) = I$, where $A_Q = A + A^2 + \cdots$ is called the quasi inverse of A. If $x'A_Q$ is estimated, then $x'(I - A)^{-1} = x' + x'A_Q$ can be approximated. If we let $B = \mathrm{adj}(I - A)$ and $d = \det(I - A)$, then

$$x'B = (x' + x'A_Q) d. \tag{9}$$

In the remarks of this paragraph, we assume that a_{ij} are nonnegative.* As in (7), if $m = n - 1$ and $x' = (a_{n1}, \ldots, a_{n,n-1})$, then by virtue of (5), $x'B$ becomes $(b_{n1}, b_{n2}, \ldots, b_{n,n-1})$ and we have relations of the form

$$b_{nk} \leq c_k b_{nn},$$

where c_k is a constant to be estimated. If the $n - 1$ column sums $s_j = 1$ for all $j \neq i$, then $b_{ij} = b_{ii}$. Conversely, if $b_{ij} = b_{ii} \neq 0$, then $s_j = 1$ for all

---

* It is easy to extend the results to complex matrices. See Wong [4].

$j \neq i$. If $b_{ii} = 0$ for some i, then $b_{ij} = 0$ for all j and the determinant of $I - A$ is zero. If $b_{ii} \neq 0$ and if $s_k < 1$ for some $k \neq i$, then $b_{ii} > b_{ik}$ and furthermore, $b_{ik} < s_i b_{ii}$ or

$$b_{ik} < \frac{s_k - a_{kk}}{1 - a_{kk}} b_{kk}. \tag{10}$$

It is easy to see that

$$(s_k - a_{kk})/(1 - a_{kk}) < s_k$$

if $a_{kk} > 0$ and $s_k < 1$. To use our notation, Ostrowski's σ_i in (1) becomes $\sigma_i = (s_i - a_{ii})/(1 - a_{ii})$. We do not assume that

$$(s_i - a_{ii})/(1 - a_{ii}) < 1 \tag{11}$$

for all i. In the next two sections, we present some inequalities better than (10).

1. Nonnegative Matrices

We need the following:

Lemma. *If $A = (a_{ij})$, $i, j = 1, 2, \ldots, n$, satisfies*

$$0 \leq a_{ij}, \qquad a_{ii} < 1, \qquad s_j = \sum_{i=1}^{n} a_{ij} \leq 1 \tag{12}$$

for $i, j = 1, 2, \ldots, n$, then every adjoint element $b_{ij}^{(n)}$ of $I - A$ is nonnegative. Moreover, $b_{ij}^{(n)} \leq b_{ii}^{(n)}$ for $i \neq j$ and $0 \leq d_k \leq (1 - a_{kk}) d_{k-1}$ for $k = 2, \ldots, n$. If $d_n \neq 0$, then all the principal minors $d_k = \det(I - A_k)$ are greater than zero.

Proof. The lemma is valid for $n = 1, 2$. Assume the validity of the lemma for $k < n$. From the property of s_j, we have

$$a_{nj} \leq 1 - \sum_{i \neq n} a_{ij} = \sum_{i \neq n} (\delta_{ij} - a_{ij}).$$

The hypothesis of induction shows that the $b_{ij}^{(n-1)}$ are nonnegative. Multiplying both sides of the preceding inequality by $b_{jk}^{(n-1)}$ and summing for $j = 1, \ldots, n - 1$, we obtain

$$\sum_j a_{nj} b_{jk}^{(n-1)} \leq \sum_i \sum_j (\delta_{ij} - a_{ij}) b_{jk}^{(n-1)} = d_{n-1},$$

where the summations extend from 1 to $n - 1$. We can verify that

$$b_{nk}^{(n)} = \sum_j a_{nj} b_{jk}^{(n-1)}.$$

Since $d_{n-1} = b_{nn}^{(n)}$, we have $0 \le b_{nk}^{(n)} \le b_{nn}^{(n)}$. This proves that every adjoint element in the nth row is nonnegative. For general index i, we can either interchange the ith, nth rows and also the ith, nth columns or alter the notations slightly to suit our purpose in the above proof.

Let $A = (a_{ij})$, a square matrix of order m, and $x' = (x_1, \ldots, x_m)$ be nonnegative. Let $B = $ adjoint of $I - A$ so that $B - BA = B - AB = dI$, where $d = \det(I - A)$. We adopt the following notations:

$$u' = (1, 1, \ldots, 1), \qquad c' = (x_1, \ldots, x_m) + (s_1, \ldots, s_m)$$
$$= x' + u'A.$$

From the property of $B = \mathrm{adj}(I - A)$, we can verify

$$x'B = (c' - u'A)B = c'B - u'AB = c'(dI + B - dI) - u'(B - dI)$$
$$= c'd - (u' - c')(B - dI). \tag{13}$$

Now introduce a diagonal matrix D_h so that h_i is the ith element on the diagonal. Then

$$x'B = d[c' - (u' - c')D_h] - [u' - c'][B - d(I + D_h)].$$

Consequently $x'B \le d[c' - (u' - c')D_h]$ if and only if $[u' - c'][B - d(I + D_h)]$ is nonnegative. By choosing h_i properly, the preceding inequality gives a good estimate for the upper bound of $x'B$ or $x'A_Q$ with A_Q being the quasi inverse of A.

Theorem 1. Let $A = (a_{ij})$ be a square matrix of order m with nonnegative elements and $x' = (x_1, \ldots, x_m)$ with each component being nonnegative. Let

$$c_j = x_j + s_j^{(m)} = x_j + \sum_{i-1}^{m} a_{ij} = 1 \qquad (j = h+1, \ldots, m)$$
$$c_j < 1 \qquad\qquad\qquad\qquad (j = 1, 2, \ldots, h < m). \tag{14}$$

Assume the convergence of $A_Q = A + A^2 + \cdots$. Then

$$\sum_{j-1}^{m} x_j A_Q(j, k) \le (1 - \bar{c}_h)(s_k^{(m)} - s_k^{(h)}) + \left[\bar{c}_h - \frac{(1 - s_h)p}{1 - t}\right] s_k^{(m)}, \tag{15}$$

where

$$\bar{c}_h = \max(c_1, \ldots, c_h)$$
$$s_k^{(h)} = \sum_{j-1}^{h} a_{jk} \qquad (h < m; k = 1, 2, \ldots, m)$$
$$p = \min(s_1^{(h)}, \ldots, s_m^{(h)})$$
$$t = \min(s_1^{(m)}, \ldots, s_m^{(m)}).$$

Proof. We observe that $(I - A)(I + A_Q) = I$ and $(I - A)B = Id$. Hence $(I + A_Q) d = B$. Since $I + A_Q$ is the inverse of $I - A$, the determinant $d \neq 0$. By virtue of (13) we have

$$\sum_{j=1}^{m} x_j A_Q(j, k) \leq s_k^{(m)} - \sum_{j=1}^{m} (1 - c_j) A_Q(j, k).$$

For $j = 1, \ldots, h$, $c_j < 1$ implies $s_j < 1$, and hence $t < 1$. Since $c_j = 1$ for $j = h + 1, \ldots, m$, and $t < 1$, we have

$$\sum_{j=1}^{m} (1 - c_j) A_Q(j, k) = \sum_{j=1}^{h} (1 - c_j) A_Q(j, k) \geq (1 - \bar{c}_h) \sum_{j=1}^{h} A_Q(j, k),$$

$$\sum_{j=1}^{h} A_Q(j, k) = \sum_{j=1}^{h} (A + A^2 + \cdots)(j, k)$$

$$\geq s_k^{(h)} + p(1 + t + t^2 + \cdots) s_k^{(m)}$$

$$= s_k^{(h)} + p(1 - t)^{-1} \cdot s_k^{(m)}.$$

From the preceding inequalities, we have

$$\sum_{j=1}^{m} x_j A_Q(j, k) \leq s_k^{(m)} - (1 - \bar{c}_h) s_k^{(h)} - (1 - t)^{-1}(1 - \bar{c}_h) p \cdot s_k^{(m)},$$

which is the same as the inequality given in the theorem.

Remark 1. When $A_Q = A + A^2 + \cdots$ exists, then $I - A$ has an inverse, which is equal to $I + A_Q$. This does not imply that all the column sums of A are less than unity. The following proposition is a refinement of a related theorem of Minkowski. $A = (a_{ij})$ is assumed to have property (12).

Proposition. *The matrix $I - A$ has an inverse if and only if*

$$\sum_{i=1}^{j} a_{ij} < 1$$

for $j = 1, 2, \ldots, m$, subject to the permutation of rows and of the same columns.

Proof. From (13), we have

$$\sum_{j=1}^{m} a_{mj} b_{jk}^{(m-1)} \leq s_k^{(m)} d_m \leq d_m. \tag{16}$$

By Cauchy's expansion of determinant d_m,

$$d_m = (1 - a_{mm}) d_{m-1} - \sum_{i,j=1}^{m-1} a_{mi} b_{ij}^{(m-1)} a_{jm}. \tag{17}$$

It follows from (16) and (17) that

$$d_m \geq \left(1 - a_{mm} - \sum_{h=1}^{m-1} s_k^{(m)} a_{km}\right) d_{m-1} \geq \left(1 - \sum_{i=1}^{m} a_{im}\right) d_{m-1},$$

and hence

$$d_m \geq \left(1 - \sum_{i=1}^{m} a_{im}\right)\left(1 - \sum_{i=1}^{m-1} a_{i,m-1}\right) \cdots (1 - a_{22} - a_{12})(1 - a_{11}),$$

which proves the sufficiency of our proposition.

To prove the necessity, assume $d_m > 0$. If all the column sums $s_k^{(m)}$ are equal to 1, then $x_i = 1$ for all i would be a solution of the homogeneous equations $x_k - \sum_i x_i a_{ik} = 0$ for $k = 1, \ldots, m$. However, this is impossible, since by hypothesis, $d_m \neq 0$. There is at least one column sum, say $s_m^{(m)}$, being less than 1. Now by (17) and the fact that all $b_{jk}^{(m-1)}$ are nonnegative,

$$d_m \leq (1 - a_{mm}) d_{m-1}$$

and as $a_{mm} < 1$ by (12), $d_m > 0$ implies $d_{m-1} > 0, \ldots, d_k > 0$ for $k = 1, \ldots, m - 1$. Now applying the preceding argument to d_k, we have

$$\sum_{i=1}^{k} a_{ik} < 1 \qquad (k = 1, \ldots, m).$$

This completes the proof.*

* *Added in proof.* The preceding proposition has an important application.

Theorem 1a. *Let A and B be nonnegative square matrices of order m with property* (12). *If A and B have maximum proper value less than 1, then for $0 \leq h \leq 1$, the matrix $hA + (1 - h)B$ has maximum proper value less than 1.*

Proof. Let $C = hA + (1 - h)B$. One can verify that $C = (c_{ij})$ has property (12). A nonnegative square matrix A has a maximum proper value less than 1 if and only if $I - A$ has a nonnegative inverse (see [6], p. 896). The preceding proposition shows that

$$\sum_{i=1}^{j} a_{ij} < 1 \qquad \text{and} \qquad \sum_{i=1}^{j} b_{ij} < 1$$

for $j = 1, 2, \ldots, m$. In fact, the permutation of rows and of the same columns does not affect the proper values. Consequently the jth columns in A and B may be assumed to satisfy the same inequalities as given above. One can easily verify that

$$\sum_{i=1}^{j} c_{ij} = h \sum_{i=1}^{j} a_{ij} + (1 - h) \sum_{i=1}^{j} b_{ij} < 1 \qquad (j = 1, 2, \ldots, m).$$

This completes the proof.

If we let $C = (h_j A_j + (1 - h_j) B_j)$, where A_j and B_j denote the jth columns of A and B respectively, and $0 \leq h_j \leq 1$ for $j = 1, 2, \ldots, m$, the convexity property mentioned above still holds. Note that we do not assume the commutativity of A and B.

Remark 2.   If $c_j = x_j + s_j^{(m)} < 1$ for $j = 1, 2, \ldots, m$, then in Theorem 1, $h = m$ and $s_k^{(h)} = s_k^{(m)}$, $p = t$. Then inequality (15) becomes

$$\sum_{j=1}^{m} x_j A_Q(j, k) \le \frac{c - t}{1 - t} s_k^{(m)} \qquad (k = 1, 2, \ldots, m), \qquad (18)$$

where $c = \max(c_1, \ldots, c_m)$.

To state in terms of the adjoint elements b_{jk} of $I - A = (\delta_{ij} - a_{ij})$, for $i, j = 1, \ldots, n$, we set $m = n - 1$, and $x' = (a_{n1}, \ldots, a_{n,n-1})$. We then have

$$b_{nk} \le b_{nn}\left(a_{nk} + \frac{c - t}{1 - t} s_k^{(n-1)}\right) \qquad (k = 1, 2, \ldots, n - 1).$$

Thus even if we assume $c_i < 1$ for $i = 1, \ldots, n$, we have a sharper inequality than the one due to Ostrowski.

An unsolved problem.   Let $s = \max(s_1, \ldots, s_m)$ where $s_k = s_k^{(m)}$. Can we replace $(c - t)/(1 - t)$ in (18) by $(c - s)/(1 - s)$? The symbols c, s, and t have the following meanings: Let $c_j = x_i + s_i$ with s_i being the ith column sum. Define $c = \max(c_i)$, $x_0 = \max(x_i)$, $s = \max(s_i)$ and $t = \min(s_i)$. Then $c - s \le x_0 \le c - t$. There are instances with $c - s < x_0$ for which

$$\sum_{i=1}^{m} x_i A_Q(i, k) \le \frac{c - s}{1 - s} s_k \qquad (k = 1, 2, \ldots, m).$$

In the next section, we prove that

$$\sum_{i=1}^{m} x_i A_Q(i, k) \le \frac{x_0}{1 - s} s_k \qquad (k = 1, 2, \ldots, m).$$

2. Complex Matrices

For our purpose, we define the norm of a finite matrix A with complex elements to be a finite real-valued function $\|A\|$ satisfying the properties

(1) $\|sA\| = |s| \cdot \|A\|$ for every number s;

(2) $\|I\| = 1$, independent of the order of I;

(2a) For every submatrix E of I, $\|E\| \le \|I\|$;

(3) $\|AB\| \le \|A\| \cdot \|B\|$;

(4) $\|A + B\| \le \|A\| + \|B\|$;

(5)   For every pair of nonnegative A, B, $\|A + B\| \ge \max(\|A\|, \|B\|)$;

(6)   If $\lim A_k = A$, then $\lim_k \|A - A_k\| = 0$.

As examples, we mention the following instances:

$$\|A\| = \sup\left\{\sum_{i=1}^{m} |a_{ij}| \quad \text{for} \quad j = 1, 2, \ldots, n\right\},$$

and

$$\|A\| = \sup\{|x'Ay| \quad \text{for} \quad \sum x_i^2 = \sum y_i^2 = 1\}.$$

We now state the following

Theorem 2. *Let* $A = (a_{ij})$ *be an* $m \times m$ *matrix with real or complex elements such that* $\|A\| < 1$. *Let* $x' = (x_1, \ldots, x_m)$ *and* $A_Q = A + A^2 + \cdots$. *Then*

$$|x'A_Q(., k)| \leq \frac{\|x'\|}{1 - \|A\|} \|A(., k)\|, \tag{19}$$

where $A(., k)$ *denotes the kth column of* A.

Proof. Since $\|A\| < 1$, $A_Q = A + A^2 + \cdots$ exists so that $I + A_Q$ is the inverse of $I - A$.

$$|x'A_Q(., k)| = \left|\sum_i x_i(A + A^2 + \cdots)(i, k)\right|$$

$$\leq \|x'\| \sum_{p=1}^{\infty} \|A^p(., k)\|$$

$$\leq \|x'\| \sum \|A\|^p \|A(., k)\|$$

$$\leq \frac{\|x'\|}{1 - \|A\|} \|A(., k)\|,$$

which proves our assertion.

Remark 3. Let B be the adjoint of $I - A$. Then $(I + A_Q)\,d = B$ with d being the determinant of $I - A$. Thus we have

$$|x'B(., k)| \leq |d|\left[|x_k| + \frac{\|x'\|}{1 - \|A\|} \|A(., k)\|\right]. \tag{20}$$

To simplify inequality (20), we observe that

$$|x_k| \leq \|x'\|, \qquad \|A\| \geq \|A(., k)\|.$$

Then inequality (20) may be weakened and simplified as follows:

$$|x'B(., k)| \leq |d| \frac{\|x'\|}{1 - \|A\|}, \tag{21}$$

for the right-hand side of (20) is less than or equal to

$$|d| \cdot \|x'\| \frac{1 - [\|A\| - \|A(., k)\|]}{1 - \|A\|} \leq |d| \frac{\|x'\|}{1 - \|A\|},$$

which gives (21).

A special case. Let $A = (a_{ij})$ be a square matrix of order n with real or complex elements. Let $B = \text{adj}\,(I - A)$. Assume

$$\max_{k \neq i} \sum_{j \neq i} |a_{jk}| < 1$$

for all $i, k = 1, \ldots, n$. Then

$$|b_{ik}| \leq |b_{ii}| \left(|a_{ik}| + \frac{a^{(-i)}}{1 - \max_{k \neq i} \sum_{j \neq i} |a_{jk}|} \sum_{j \neq i} |a_{jk}| \right), \tag{22}$$

where

$$a^{(-i)} = \max |a_{ik}| \quad (\text{for } k \neq i, \quad k = 1, \ldots, n).$$

Inequality (22) can be established as a special case of (20). To this end, we define

$$\|A^{(-i)}(., k)\| = \sum_{j \neq i} |a_{jk}|$$

$$\|A^{(-i)}\| = \max_{k \neq i} \sum_{j \neq i} |a_{jk}|.$$

By hypothesis, $\|A^{(-i)}\| < 1$ for $i = 1, 2, \ldots, n$. The verification is simple and hence is omitted.

Applications of our results will be presented in a later paper.

Appendix. Inequalities Related to the Maximum Proper Value of a Nonnegative Matrix

Let A be a square matrix with nonnegative elements. Frobenius proved that A has a positive maximum proper value. This paper gives an elementary proof for an equivalent condition in order that such a maximum proper value be less than t. By dividing A by t, the resulting matrix will have a proper value less than unity. We reduce $I - A$ by elementary transformations to a triangular form where the elements below the principal diagonal vanish, and the elements on the principal diagonal are of the form $1 - f_1, 1 - f_2, \ldots, 1 - f_n$. A necessary and sufficient condition for A to have a maximum proper value less than unity is that all $1 - f_i$, for $i = 1, 2, \ldots, n$, are positive. In particular, all the elements $a_{11}, a_{22}, \ldots, a_{nn}$

are necessarily less than 1. Thus our first approximation is to choose t_1 greater than the maximum of $a_{11}, a_{22}, \ldots, a_{nn}$. Then our theorem shows that $1 - A/t_1$ has maximum proper value less than 1 if and only if all the values $1 - f_i$, which are dependent on t_1, are positive. Since the maximum proper value of A is bounded by $\|A\|$, it is only natural to choose $t_1 < \|A\|$. The last proposition gives a practical method for determining an upper bound t of a maximum proper value of a nonnegative matrix A.

1

The following theorem is fundamental in this paper. Frobenius [1] proved that A has a positive maximum proper value less than 1 if and only if $I - A$ has a nonnegative inverse. This fact will be used in our discussion.

Theorem 1. *The matrix $I - A$ has a nonnegative inverse if and only if for $k = 1, 2, \ldots, n$*

$$a_{kk} + c_k < 1, \tag{A1}$$

where

$$c_1 = 0, \qquad c_k = \sum_{\gamma, s=1}^{k-1} a_{kr}(I - A_{k-1})^{-1}(r, s)a_{sk}, \qquad k = 2, \ldots, n, \tag{A2}$$

and A_k is the principal submatrix consisting of the elements in the first k rows and k columns.

Proof. We first prove that if (A1) is satisfied, then all the principal submatrices $I - A_k$ for $k = 1, 2, \ldots, n$ have nonnegative inverse. This is obvious for $k = 1$. Assume that $I - A_{k-1}$ has a nonnegative inverse. Then in (A2) the determinant of $I - A_{k-1}$ is not zero and c_k is well defined. By Cauchy's expansion for determinants, we can verify that

$$d_k = d_{k-1}(1 - a_{kk} - c_k). \tag{A3}$$

Let $e_k = 1 - a_{kk} - c_k$. Then

$$I - A_k = \begin{pmatrix} I & 1 \\ -\alpha' L_{k-1}^{-1} & 0 \end{pmatrix} \begin{pmatrix} L_{k-1} & 0 \\ 0 & e_k \end{pmatrix} \begin{pmatrix} I & -L_{k-1}^{-1}\beta \\ 0 & 1 \end{pmatrix}$$

where $L_k = I - A_k$, $\alpha' = (a_{k,1}, \ldots, a_{k,k-1})$, and $\beta = \mathrm{col}(a_{1,k}, \ldots, a_{k-1,k})$. Hence

$$(I - A_k)^{-1} = \begin{pmatrix} I & L_{k-1}^{-1}\beta \\ 0 & 1 \end{pmatrix} \begin{pmatrix} L_{k-1}^{-1} & 0 \\ 0 & e_k^{-1} \end{pmatrix} \begin{pmatrix} I & 1 \\ \alpha' L_{k-1}^{-1} & 0 \end{pmatrix}.$$

This shows that $L_k = I - A_k$ has a nonnegative inverse if $L_{k-1} = I - A_{k-1}$ has a nonnegative inverse. This completes the induction proof.

For the demonstration of the converse, we shall use the following

Lemma 1. *If $x - Ax = h$, where $A \geq 0$, has a unique nonnegative solution for every nonnegative $h \neq 0$, then $1 - a_{ii} > 0$ and the diagonal elements of the inverse of $I - A$ are at least unity.*

Proof. Express (by Cramer's rule) the solution of the linear equations in the form $0 \leq x_i = \sum_j c_{ij} h_j$. By setting h to be the kth column of the identity matrix of order n, we have $0 \leq \sum c_{ij} \delta_{jk} = c_{ik}$. Since $C = (c_{ij})$ is the inverse of $I - A$, then

$$1 = \sum c_{ij}(\delta_{ji} - a_{ji}), \qquad 1 = c_{ii}(1 - a_{ii}) - \sum_{j \neq i} c_{ij} a_{ji}.$$

The last equality shows that $c_{ii}(1 - a_{ii}) \geq 1$. Since c_{ik} and a_{ik} are nonnegative for all i, k, both c_{ii} and $1 - a_{ii}$ must be positive. From $1 - a_{ii} \leq 1$ it follows that c_{ii} must be equal to or greater than unity.

Evidently, $I - A$ has a nonnegative inverse if and only if $x - Ax = h$ has a unique nonnegative solution for every nonnegative $h \neq 0$.

To prove the "necessary" part of Theorem 1, let $a_{ij}^{(0)} = a_{ij}$ and $h_i^{(0)} = h_i$. For $p \geq 1$, assume that $e_p = 1 - a_{pp}^{(p-1)} > 0$, $h_i^{(p-1)} \geq 0$ and $a_{ij}^{(p-1)} \geq 0$ for $i, j = p, p+1, \ldots, n$, where

$$a_{ij}^{(p)} = a_{ij}^{(p-1)} + a_{ip}^{(p-1)} e_p^{-1} a_{pj}^{(p-1)} \geq 0, \qquad i, j = p+1, \ldots, n, \tag{A4a}$$

$$h_i^{(p)} = h_i^{(p-1)} + a_{ip}^{(p-1)} e_p^{-1} h_p^{(p-1)} \geq 0, \qquad i, j = p+1, \ldots, n. \tag{A4b}$$

From the pth step of the elimination process (by elementary transformations), we have

$$\sum_{j=p+1}^{n} (\delta_{ij} - a_{ij}^{(p)}) x_j = h_i^{(p)}, \qquad i = p+1, \ldots, n. \tag{A4}$$

Evidently (A4) has a unique nonnegative solution for $x_{p+1}, \ldots, x_n$, which are the same as those in the original equation $x - Ax = h$. Applying Lemma 1, we have

$$1 - a_{kk}^{(p)} > 0, \qquad k = p+1, \ldots, n.$$

It remains to show that $a_{pp}^{(p-1)} = a_{pp} + c_p$, where c_p is defined by (A2). This is true for $p = 1$. Assume that it is true for $p = k - 1$, with $k > 1$; then the elementary elimination process shows that $d_k = d_{k-1}(1 - a_{kk}^{(p-1)})$, where d_k is the determinant of $I - A_k$. In comparison with (A3), we have the desired result, since d_{k-1} and d_k are positive.

Actually, we have proved a stronger necessary condition.

Corollary. *The matrix A has its maximum proper value less than 1 if and only if the property given by* (A1) *and* (A2) *is satisfied.*

Theorem 1 or its corollary gives us a practical method for testing whether the maximum proper value of a nonnegative matrix A is less than unity.

Let $A = (a_{ij})$ be a square matrix of order n with nonnegative elements. By elementary transformations, we reduce $I - A$ into a triangular form

$$\begin{pmatrix}
e_1 & -a_{12} & -a_{13} & \cdots & \cdot & -a_{1n} \\
0 & e_2 & -a_{23}^{(1)} & \cdots & \cdot & -a_{2n}^{(1)} \\
0 & 0 & e_3 & \cdots & \cdot & -a_{3n}^{(2)} \\
\cdot & \cdot & \cdot & \cdots & \cdot & \cdot \\
0 & 0 & 0 & \cdots & e_{n-1} & -a_{n-1,n}^{(n-2)} \\
0 & 0 & 0 & \cdots & \cdot & e_n
\end{pmatrix} \qquad (A5)$$

where $a_{ij}^{(p)}$ are nonnegative for $i, j = p + 1, \ldots, n$.

Theorem 2. *A necessary and sufficient condition for the maximum proper value of A to be less than 1 is that all the elements $e_1, e_2, \ldots, e_n$ on the principal diagonal are positive.*

Since the results of this paper will be useful for practical computation, it is desirable to give some detail for the elementary transformations. Then our proof of Theorem 2 will be simple and evident.

At the start, we let $p = 0$, and define $e_1 = 1 - a_{11}^{(0)} = 1 - a_{11}$, and $a_{ik}^{(0)} = a_{ik}$ for $i, k = 1, 2, \ldots, n$. Let $p = 1, 2, \ldots, n - 1$. After applying the elementary transformations to the first p rows and p columns of $I - A$, we have

$$I - A = (I - R^{(p)}) \begin{pmatrix} E_p & 0 \\ 0 & I - A^{(p)} \end{pmatrix} (I - S^{(p)}), \qquad (A6)$$

where E_p is a diagonal matrix with $e_1, \ldots, e_p$ on the diagonal. $A^{(p)} = (a_{ij}^{(p)})$, $i, j = p + 1, \ldots, n$, are defined by

$$a_{ij}^{(0)} = a_{ij}, \qquad a_{ij}^{(p)} = a_{ij}^{(p-1)} + a_{ip}^{(p-1)} e_p^{-1} a_{pj}^{(p-1)} \qquad \text{if} \quad e_p = 1 - a_{pp}^{(p-1)} \neq 0,$$
$$= a_{ij}^{(p-1)} \qquad \qquad \text{if} \quad e_p = 0,$$
$$\qquad (A7)$$

and for i, j ranging from 1 to n,

$$R^{(p)}(i, j) = a_{ij}^{(j-1)} e_j^{-1} \qquad (j = 1, 2, \ldots, p; \quad i = j + 1, \ldots, n) \quad \text{and } e_j \neq 0$$
$$= 0 \qquad \qquad (i \leq j; \quad \text{or } j > p) \quad \text{and} \quad e_j = 0;$$
$$\qquad (A8)$$

$$S^{(p)}(k, m) = e_k^{-1} a_{km}^{(k-1)} \quad (k = 1, 2, \ldots, p; \quad m = k+1, \ldots, n) \quad \text{and} \quad e_k \neq 0$$
$$= 0 \quad (k \geq m, \text{ or } k > p) \quad \text{and} \quad e_k = 0.$$

$$\text{(A9)}$$

We shall adopt the notations

$$\prod_{i=123} A_i = A_1 A_2 A_3, \qquad \prod_{i=321} A_i = A_3 A_2 A_1.$$

With these notations, it is advantageous to write $I - R^{(p)}$ and $I - S^{(p)}$ in the following forms:

$$I - R^{(p)} = \prod_{j=1\cdots p} \left(1 - \sum_{i=j+1}^{n} \delta_i a_{ij}^{(j-1)} e_j^{-1} \delta_j' \right) = I - \sum_{j=1}^{p} \sum_{i=j+1}^{n} \delta_i a_{ij}^{(j-1)} e_j^{-1} \delta_j',$$

$$\text{(A10)}$$

where δ_i, δ_j' are the ith column and the jth row, respectively, of the identity matrix of order n. Thus $\delta_i a_{ij}^{(j-1)} e_j^{-1} \delta_j'$ is a square matrix of order n such that its element in the ith row and jth column is $a_{ij}^{(j-1)} e_j^{-1}$. The square matrix $\sum_{i=j+1}^{n} \delta_i a_{ij}^{(j-1)} e_j^{-1} \delta_j'$ contains *nonnegative elements* only in the jth column and $(j+1)$th, $(j+2)$th, $\ldots$, nth rows, and zeros elsewhere. Similarly

$$I - S^{(p)} = \prod_{k=p\cdots 21} \left(I - \sum_{m=k+1}^{n} \delta_k e_k^{-1} a_{km}^{(k-1)} \delta_m' \right)$$

$$= I - \sum_{k=1}^{n} \sum_{m=k+1}^{n} \delta_k e_k^{-1} a_{km}^{(k-1)} \delta_m'. \qquad \text{(A11)}$$

The inverses of $I - R^{(p)}$ and $I - S^{(p)}$ consist of only nonnegative elements, and are of the forms

$$(I - R^{(p)})^{-1} = \prod_{j=p\cdots 21} \left(I + \sum_{i=j+1}^{n} \delta_i a_{ij}^{(j-1)} e_j^{-1} \delta_j' \right) \qquad \text{(A12)}$$

$$(I - S^{(p)})^{-1} = \prod_{k=12\cdots p} \left(I + \sum_{m=k+1}^{n} \delta_k e_k^{-1} a_{km}^{(k-1)} \delta_m' \right). \qquad \text{(A13)}$$

Proof of Theorem 2. Let $p = n - 1$; if all $e_i > 0$, then

$$(I - A)^{-1} = (I - S^{(n-1)})^{-1} E_n^{-1} (I - R^{(n-1)})^{-1},$$

where E_n^{-1} is a diagonal matrix with $e_1^{-1}, \ldots, e_n^{-1}$ in its diagonal. We see that $(I - A)^{-1}$ consists of nonnegative elements, or equivalently speaking, A has a maximum proper value less than 1.

The proof of the converse is similar to that given in the demonstration of Theorem 1. Another proof is given in the demonstration of Lemma 2.

The following proof of the necessary condition in Theorem 1 or 2 is very simple and requires the convergence of Neumann's series. If $(I - A)$ has an inverse, then

$$(I - A)^{-1} = I + A^- \tag{A14}$$

$$A^- = A + A^2 + \cdots + A^k + \cdots, \tag{A15}$$

where A^- is the quasi inverse of A. If $I - A$ has an inverse, then every principal submatrix $I - B$ of $I - A$ has an inverse.

Lemma 2. *Let $I - A_k$ be the principal submatrix consisting of the first k rows and columns of $I - A$. Let d_k be the determinant of $I - A_k$. If $(I - A)^{-1}$ exists, then*

$$0 < d_n \le d_{n-1} \le \cdots \le d_1 = 1 - a_{11}.$$

If $a_{ii} > 0$, then $d_i < d_{i-1}$ for $i = 2, \ldots, n$.

Proof. The lemma holds for $n = 2$. In fact, as d_1/d_2 is the element in the 2nd row and 2nd column of $(I - A_2)^{-1}$, we have by (A14)

$$d_1/d_2 = 1 + A_2(2, 2) + \cdots \ge 1,$$

which shows that $0 < d_2 \le d_1$. Similarly, d_{h-1}/d_h is the element in the hth row and hth column of $(I - A_h)^{-1}$. By virtue of (A14),

$$d_{h-1}/d_h = 1 + A_h(h, h) + \cdots \ge 1.$$

By induction, if the lemma holds for $n = h - 1$, then the preceding expression shows that $0 < d_h \le d_{h-1}$. If $A(h, h) = a_{hh} > 0$, then $d_h < d_{h-1}$, completing the proof.

Interchanging 1 with $i = 2, \ldots, n$, we see that $1 - a_{ii} \ge d_n > 0$ for all i.

2

The following proposition is very practical in determining an upper bound t of a maximum proper value of a nonnegative matrix A.

Proposition.. *Assume that the nonnegative matrix A has the following properties:*

$$a_{jj} < t, \qquad s_j = \sum_{i=1}^{n} a_{ij} \le t \qquad (j = 1, 2, \ldots, n) \tag{A16}$$

$$\sum_{i=1}^{n} S' A^k(i, j) \le e < 1 \qquad (j = 1, 2, \ldots, n) \tag{A17}$$

for some k and $e > 0$, where $S' = (s_1, \ldots, s_n)$. Then the maximum proper value of A is less than t.

In the proof, we let $\|A\| = \max(s_1, \ldots, s_n)$. Then (A17) can be written in the form $\|S'A^k\| \leq e < t$ for some k. The conclusion of the proposition will be proved if we show that $\lim \sup_q \|A^q\|^{1/q} < t$.

Consider $t = 1$. Set $e_0 = e^{1/(k+1)}$, where k and e are given in the hypothesis. Then $e_0 < 1$. For any integer $q \geq k+1$ we can set $q+1 = h(k+1) + r$, where $h > 0$ and $0 \leq r < k+1$. Property (A16) shows that $\|A^r\| \leq 1$ for $r = 0, 1, \ldots$. Since $e < 1$ and $r < k+1$, we have $1/e > 1$ and hence

$$(1/e)^{r/(k+1)} < 1/e. \tag{A18}$$

As $q > k$, and $0 < e < 1$, we have $e^{q+1} < e^{k+1}$, and hence

$$e_0^{q+1} < e. \tag{A19}$$

By hypothesis, we have

$$\|A^{q+1}\| = \|A^{h(k+1)+r}\| \leq \|A^{h(k+1)}\| \cdot \|A^r\| \leq \|A^{k+1}\|^h = \|S'A^k\|^h < e^h$$

and

$$e^h = e^{(q+1-r)/(k+1)} = e^{(q+1)/(k+1)}(1/e)^{r/(k+1)} < e_0^{q+1}(1/e) < 1.$$

The last two inequalities follow from (A18) and (A19). Thus, we have shown that for every $q > k$,

$$\|A^{q+1}\|^{1/(q+1)} < e_0(1/e)^{1/(q+1)}$$

and it follows that

$$\lim \sup \|A^q\|^{1/q} \leq e_0[\lim(1/e)^{1/q}] \leq e_0 < 1,$$

as we wish to prove.

REFERENCES

[1] Frobenius, G., Über Matrizen aus nicht-negativen Elementen, *Sitzber. Konig. Preuss. Akad. Wiss. Berlin*, 456–477 (1912).

[2] Ostrowski, A., Note on bounds for determinants with dominant principal diagonal, *Proc. Amer. Math. Soc.* **3**, 26–30 (1952).

[3] Wielandt, R., Unzerlegbare nicht-negative Matrizen, *Math. Z.* **52**, 642–648 (1950).

[4] Wong, Y. K., An inequality for Minkowski matrices, *Proc. Amer. Math. Soc.* **4**, 137–141 (1953).

[5] Wong, Y. K., On nonnegative-valued matrices, *Proc. Nat. Acad. Sci. U.S.A.* **40**, 121–124 (1954).

[6] Wong, Y. K., Some properties of proper values of a matrix, *Proc. Amer. Math. Soc.* **6**, 891–899 (1955).

Index

355